ORIFLAMME

Other Books
by Margaret Trouncer:

Novels

GO LOVELY ROSE
THE SMILING MADONNA
WHY SO PALE?

Biography

COURTESAN OF PARADISE (*Book Guild Recommendation*)
THE POMPADOUR

MARGARET TROUNCER

ORIFLAMME

BEING THE TRUE STORY OF

MADAME DE SABRAN AND HER LOVER

THE CHEVALIER DE BOUFFLERS

DURING THE TIMES OF MARIE-ANTOINETTE AND THE REVOLUTION

"... one thing is sure: griefs of the heart can poison a whole life."

Madame de Pompadour to the Duc de Chaulnes, January 26, 1760

"I bask in being loved by you; . . . it is by this means that I lay hold on perfection; for I am a little like the ancients who clothed all intellectual ideas in human form, and I adore virtue in your person."

Letter of the Chevalier to Madame de Sabran

MACDONALD & CO. (Publishers) LTD.
19 LUDGATE HILL :: LONDON, E.C.4

TO
A. E.

This book is produced
in complete conformity
with the War Economy Agreement

MADE AND PRINTED IN GREAT BRITAIN BY PURNELL AND SONS, LTD.
PAULTON (SOMERSET) AND LONDON

INTRODUCTION

Anatole France described the Comtesse de Sabran and the Chevalier de Boufflers as "these proud and charming beings who could be born nowhere else but in eighteenth-century France".

I introduce them now, in the background of their enchanting century, to all those who have a nostalgia for an age of leisure and beauty in this era of transition. Strangely enough, many of their social problems are akin to our own.

First among the kind friends who helped me, I must warmly thank Miss Catherine Barne, who took down my notes one winter, and who gave such helpful suggestions in the translations of the letters. We both fell under the spell of the fascinating Chevalier, and we vowed that his wit redeemed his blasphemies. In the Bodleian, as I was translating his works, I decided, very reluctantly, that most of his little verses were quite unsuitable for publication in England. I thank many other friends for their assistance in sorting the vast mass of material on clothes, gardens, houses and street-life, the librarian of St. Hilda's College, Oxford, for inviting me to use a collection of books on Marie-Antoinette, the staff of the London Library, and of the Art Library in the Victoria and Albert Museum, for their helpfulness and courtesy. And above all, I want to thank Mrs. Nesta Webster for so kindly allowing me to quote various illuminating sentences from her scholarly work on the Chevalier de Boufflers (John Murray, 1916), and for giving me permission to use the unpublished proposal of marriage and various letters written in exile. I have not described the adventures of Delphine de Custine during the Terror, for Mrs. Webster has already done it so admirably. I wish to thank Mr. R. C. Maasz, of the Taylorian Library, Oxford, for so kindly revising the proofs.

Had it not been for the war, I would, no doubt, have found at the Bibliothèque de Versailles many documents and pamphlets not available in England. It may be as well that this additional storehouse of information was temporarily closed to me, for this book might have been more of a mosaic pattern of historical reconstruction than it is already: the damask of the fabric would be too stiffly encrusted with jewels, thus concealing the living movement of the human figures in this wonderful love-story. There was *embarras de richesses* in the many contemporary memoirs and letters in which the Comtesse and the Chevalier are mentioned, not to speak of their own love-letters and journals edited by Magnieu et Prat (an incomplete collection), and the collected works of the Chevalier, published in 1792. For English readers Eric Sutton has translated the lively stories "Ah, if only", and "Aline", in *The Queen of Golconda and Other Tales* (Chapman & Hall, 1926). There is also an English translation of M. Gaston Maugras' book on the Marquise de Custine, in which he includes several letters not found in the Magnieu et Prat edition. The translations of the poems are my own.

I have written nothing but historical truth. Even the imaginary episodes such as the Ball, the Coach Drive, the Supper-Party, the Picnic, are in their authentic settings. I wish to take the opportunity of saying that the account of convent education in the eighteenth century does not prove that all nuns were bad, either then or now. Here I used what Elzéar de Sabran wrote, because I feel that Catholic historians should tell the whole truth, even at the risk of scandalizing Protestants. This impartiality applies to the great moral of the story, hidden behind all the scandal.

Now they must be allowed to tell their own story, these great lovers whose youth was spent in the happy times of Louis XV and Louis XVI, who were exiled during the Revolution, and whose love survived through the Napoleonic and Restoration eras, as fresh and ardent as ever.

October, 1944.

CONTENTS

Part I

ELÉONORE

Part II

STANISLAS

Part III

THE PURSUIT

Part IV

THE CAPTURE

PART V

TILL DEATH

Part I

ELÉONORE

CHAPTER I

AN UNHAPPY CHILDHOOD

In March, 1749, Madame de Jean de Manville lay in her great bed after giving birth to her second daughter, Eléonore. She was alone in the cold Spring twilight. Capricious gusts of wind rattled the high, folding doors and blew the disconsolate ostrich plumes at the four corners of her bed. Her first child, a daughter of great beauty, born a year or two before, had nearly broken her heart, for she was defective in intelligence. This second baby showed promise of even greater beauty than the first. But before her mother, exhausted by the tortures of a severe confinement, could gaze at the blue eyes and try to fathom whether this child, too, had been deprived of the gift of reason, the attendants had sent the baby away to the country to a wet-nurse.

"I am alone," thought Madame de Manville. "Alone! Alone!" She recalled how her husband had said in the next room: "What, another girl?" He had not come in to see her, she had no one to turn to. After the ordeal, husband and wife did not gaze together at their new baby, for that was not in the tradition of the century. It would be useless to implore him to let her keep the child for a little while, before it was taken away for two years, for he was a complete egoist. The realization of this finally broke her spirit.

"I am alone. If my babe were here, I could not raise my lids to look at her for the last time. Why does no one come? I cannot lift my hand to the bell-cord. Will they leave me to die untended, without shrift? How cold it is. . . . Ah, good Jesus, let me live for this child! Who will love her if You take me away?"

She made a great effort to cry out, but no sound came from her lips. She was sinking right into the bowels of the voluminous bed. Darkness. . . .

The capricious gusts of wind rattled the high, folding doors and blew the disconsolate ostrich plumes at the four corners of her bed.

As she lost consciousness, Madame de Manville again cried brokenly to God: "Who will love her, if not I?"

And the Spirit who had ordained the birth of the waif and permitted the death of her mother, the Spirit who numbers each hair of the orphan's head, echoed: "Who will love her, if not I?"

An unhappy childhood cripples the rest of life. Children can survive without creature comforts, but they wilt if deprived of love; for the whole of their lives they may seek to assuage the hunger of their hearts.

Monsieur de Jean de Manville married again. His new wife, a young woman with an iron will and a nature even harder than his own, promptly became complete mistress of the house and servants, ruled her husband, and made use of his vast fortune in a way that the first wife had never dared to do. Moreover, she took an instant dislike to her two defenceless stepdaughters.

The attitude of servants to guests and children being determined by the mistress of the house, Eléonore and her sister suffered at the hands of the maids to whom they were relegated. In this rich house, packed with lackeys, where there was plenty of food and warmth for everyone else, the two little girls were stuffed away in the attics, left entirely alone, sometimes for three days at a time. Occasionally Eléonore would creep downstairs, when there was no fear of meeting her stepmother, fetch something to eat from the dining-room, hide it in her panniers, and steal upstairs to feed her imbecile sister. There was no question of walking in the garden, and the company of other children was unknown to them. The winters were terrible, as the footmen often neglected to bring sufficient wood for the fire. The girls' clothes resembled those of poor relations, for their maid, Barbe, spent on herself almost all the meagre sums which she extorted from Monsieur de Manville for their wardrobe. Barbe's main object in life was to make herself attractive to the men. She had just jilted a former lover, and there had been rowdy scenes below stairs. The children were simply a nuisance. For the rest of her life, as a result of early neglect, Eléonore was delicate, and she ended her days crippled by rheumatism.

One day in February, when Eléonore was five years old, she was sitting huddled up with her older sister in the window seat of their attic. Both little girls were golden-haired, with that rare beauty of dark brows and lashes. They were dressed in faded brown taffeta skirts edged with rows of pink ribbon, very frayed. They wore bonnets tied under their chins, also little toques which had pom-poms perched on top. There were no toys on the ill-swept floor—none of those heavily-rouged dolls, tricked out in full Court dress, which little girls used to play with, no imitation coach and horse, no lamb drawn on wheels; not a plaything anywhere.

Eléonore, though the younger of the two, adopted a protective attitude to her sister. She held her head firmly against her tiny chest, and said:

"I like looking out on to the street; there are always such a lot of exciting things happening outside."

"I'm hungry," wailed the other girl. "I wish the chestnut woman would throw us up some nuts again."

In the angle of the street, out of the way of the mud and the carriages, stood a kindly-looking woman presiding over a large iron cauldron. Various street urchins around it were staring at the chestnuts rather avidly, their faces aglow in the heat of the coals. They were on their way home from school, and some of their friends were playing leap-frog and marbles.

In the opposite corner of the roadway a religious street-singer had unfolded his great portable canvas depicting scenes from Christ's Passion; he was pointing with a stick to each individual scene and singing about it. A girl selling small windmills was looking up in great awe. Trudging along with his head down, an old charcoal-seller passed by, bringing some braziers in a hand-cart to the house of the Duc de Nivernais; during the winter he always had these great braziers lit for the poor in his courtyard, and gave them soup and bread.

Eléonore said: "Do you think if we let down our basket the chestnut woman would give me some more? She must be feeling kind if she is listening to the street-singer."

"Supposing Barbe saw us?"

"She wouldn't bother to climb up four flights to smack us. Come, we'll risk it. I'll put a handkerchief inside the basket for payment. I can spare one."

Cautiously they let their basket down and made noises to the woman. She looked up and smiled at them. She had heard rumours in the adjoining street about the cruel stepmother and these neglected little girls, and, because she had children of her own, she took pity on these two. She told one of the urchins to steal across quickly with some of her biggest chestnuts and slip them into the basket, also a piece of a golden-brown *galette* which she had saved for them. She refused to take the handkerchief for payment, in spite of all manner of miming and expostulation from the window.

At length the children had drawn the basket up and were eating avidly. Soon there was nothing left.

"I'm still hungry," whimpered the poor imbecile.

Outside in the street, the singer pointed to a crude picture of Christ meeting His Mother on the way to Calvary. He sang:

"Behold the Mother
Of all the world.
Shall a Mother forget her child?"

Words of heart's-ease falling on the ears of two hungry children whose mother was dead. Two little girls receiving comfort from the streets, from that populace which later on acquired such an unfounded reputation for wolf-heartedness. Even the jailers of Marie-Antoinette sought to lighten her captivity by little gifts of flowers and melons, carefully chosen in the market. Those good people of Paris! What a fund of courtesy and kind-heartedness was to be found among them in the days when the cabbies were polite to one another.

"I like looking at the clouds," said Eléonore. "We can see them better up here than if we lived downstairs."

It was one of those cloud-driven, wistfully changeful afternoons which lend Paris such individual charm: the atmosphere is rarely clear and sharp, for there are drifting clouds against the horizon, dappled in the grey and light azures of Moreau's canvases.[1]

"Will it soon be Spring?" asked the sister, staring vacantly.

"Yes, and then all the little buds will come out, the leaves will burst out of them, so our far-away trees will have dresses again."

Ah! those beloved Parisian horizons, those light transparencies of leaves against the blue distance, those deep alleys of trees with their infinite variety of green tones. Alas for the vanished city of Eléonore's day, a Paris with the country lapping it round, the green tints rushing in to the very doorsteps of these city-dwellers.

After a quiet interim for the dinner hour, the street became noisier. Carriages and horses on the cobbles, coachmen and waggoners shouting—soon there was such a din that it became almost impossible to hear oneself speak. Then there were church and convent bells ringing for Vespers; hundreds of beggars crying in whining voices, or else assembling in droves outside the nearby monastery gates and clamouring for food; the shouts of the official hawkers of vegetables, milk, fruit, rags, sand, brooms; not to speak of the drone of the many water-carriers. The pandemonium was further increased by that legacy of the Middle Ages—the small hucksters, who had preserved terrible, discordant street-cries in their integrity—just incomprehensible guttural sounds. In those merry times the people were witty even in crying their wares: "Baked potatoes, piping hot", really meant "Stone-cold cakes", while "Pleasure for the ladies, pleasure for the ladies", meant "gingerbread". The men huck-

[1] The brother of Moreau le Jeune, a delightful landscape painter.

sters cried like women; the women like men. Later in the night there would be the screeches of the lantern-bearers, escorting people to their homes.

Very soon the street got so crowded that the chestnut woman moved away. The footmen of great Court coaches jeered loudly at the foot-passengers in trouble. Fortunately the day was dry, for on wet days street-walkers who did not leap out of the way in time and flatten themselves against the wall, got covered from head to foot in mud and liquid dung. The middle of the street was simply a stagnant drain of refuse; people either had to be carried across or pay to go over the movable bridge. Indeed, it was safer to view everything from a height, like these two little sparrows under the eaves.

Just then a most unfortunate thing happened; a fine coach drew up at the entrance of the house; two footmen jumped out to let down the footboard and open the carriage door to a commanding old lady with a face like a vulture's. She wore a three-tiered black mantle, and an enormous feathered hat of the kind which had been fashionable during the last century.

"It's grandmother!" cried Eléonore. And they both started to tremble. They were too paralysed with fear even to clear up the tell-tale litter of chestnut husks in the room. They peeped behind the curtain.

Madame de Montigny was their maternal grandmother. She held firmly that fear should be the foundation of all education. She detested her son-in-law and his second wife, and, more to annoy them than from any sense of duty, she made a weekly visitation to her grandchildren on a fixed day at a fixed hour. Barbe the maid could then wash and dress them properly, and bring them down to the library. But this afternoon her visit was quite unexpected. What could she want?

As luck would have it, at that precise minute an old orange-vendor, who was a favourite of the girls, came trundling down the street, bag on back, crying: "Portugal, Portugal." He stopped at the corner. Oblivious of the coach and the terrifying grandmother, he took his best orange out of his bag and aimed it at the attic window, as he had always done. Unfortunately, this time he missed, and the orange came bounding down again, plomp! right on to Madame de Montigny's hat.

The vendor gave a yell, took to his heels, and ran up a side alley as fast as his legs would carry him. "I don't want any lackeys with sticks after me," he thought, "although, if matters came to a head, I could always pelt them with my bad oranges."

Barbe came rushing upstairs ahead of the infuriated granddame, hoping to snatch one moment to set things right. Why had the old lady come on her unawares like this? The attic fire was probably out, and she was an hour or two late with the children's dinner. She'd been at the fair of *Saint-Ovide*, and forgotten the time. She hoped, furiously, that the little wretches would not betray her; she must pinch them into submission. Bother; no time. The cormorant was swift on her heels, grasping an orange in her claws. She pushed Barbe aside and came into the room. There was a dead silence. Eléonore curtsied.

Said Madame de Montigny—viewing the desolate scene with eyes which took in every detail of dirt and neglect: "Are passing hucksters in the habit of throwing oranges up to your window?"

"*Madame*, I must explain," said Barbe very agitatedly, with an artificial smile on her face.

"Hold your tongue, baggage. Answer me, children."

The imbecile child stammered: "Yes, we get lots of food thrown in at the window. People are very kind to us."

"*Madame*," laughed Barbe in a forced manner, "one would think, to hear them speak, that they were starving."

"We are," said Eléonore, very quietly. "We have eaten nothing but chestnuts and a piece of cake since yesterday."

Her sister laughed, a high, nervous laugh, and started babbling: "Yes, nothing but chestnuts, nothing but chestnuts. Hee! Hee!"

There was another terrible silence in the room. The two elders were white with rage, the two children white with fear.

At last, very suddenly, Madame de Montigny turned on Barbe, and before she could escape, had given her two resounding smacks on the face. Her hands were horny with age, the hands of a terrible old woman.

"I'll have you sent to the Salpêtrière for this. My under-footman told me he found you selling the children's trinkets at the fair this morning. I'd always had my suspicions that you were a piece of garbage. But I'll see to it that you rue the day you first applied for service in this house."

(The under-footman was Barbe's rejected lover.)

Madame de Montigny rang the bell violently, nearly pulling the bell-rope down. To the footman who came she said: "Call the sergeant."

When the shrieking Barbe had been disposed of, the grandmother wrapped the two shivering girls in rugs—she could find no cloaks—and bundled them into her coach. None of the other servants dared say or do anything. The master and mistress were out. Madame de Montigny was still holding the fatal orange as they drove away towards her own house in the Rue des Vieilles-Audriettes, near the Temple.

"Sit up straight," she snapped at the little girls. "I see that you need lessons in deportment, as well as food and clothing."

"What a pity," she thought, "that this abduction would suit their stepmother so well." However, Madame de Montigny laughed with sinister pleasure at the prospect of her son-in-law's discomfiture on his return that evening. Outwitted at last! Perhaps some of the shame would, in time, be felt by his wife. After all, it did them no credit, and people would talk.

And all because of an orange. . . .

CHAPTER II

THE CONVENT

NINE years later, 1763, the year before the death of the Marquise de Pompadour, Eléonore was fourteen years of age, and growing daily more lovely. Her golden hair was so abundant that it was very difficult to keep up; it had a way of falling down suddenly, mantling her in a shower of gold. "*Mademoiselle*, go upstairs immediately and attend to your hair." The child would curtsey to her grandmother and leave the room. Both girls were properly fed and clothed, and they were taught dancing and music, to their great delight. Eléonore danced beautifully, in stately-delicate wise. She was small in stature, with tiny feet, light as a fairy. Her master would say: "*Mademoiselle* will have a great success when she goes to Court. La Poisson will have to look to her laurels, or you will be stealing somebody's heart away." (La Poisson was the popular name for the Marquise de Pompadour.) "Who is La Poisson?" asked Eléonore, looking up at him. "You will find out soon enough. I must not tell you frivolous stories." "Oh, please, tell us Court stories," pleaded the younger girl. "Tell us about His Majesty's daughters when you taught them to dance at the Abbey of Fontevrault. Was Madame Louise a good dancer?"

"She was a very capricious little princess. One day I was trying to teach her a *menuet rose*, when she suddenly sat down on the floor and refused to go on with her lesson unless I called it a blue minuet; I kept saying 'rose', the princess, stamping her feet, yelled 'blue'. The whole business threatened to take a very serious turn. I assembled the entire community of nuns and asked their opinion. They voted unanimously that the minuet must be blue. Now I must gossip no longer. Come along, *Mesdemoiselles*; one, two, three, head straight, more boldness in the glance. Turn now! Glide smoothly; one, two, three. Pom. Pom. Pom."

At fourteen Eléonore was dressed like a grown-up woman in the fashion of her day—tightly-laced whalebone bodice, huge panniers, high heels, rouged cheeks. Everything had been done to discipline her body, and to constrict all the natural impetuosities of childhood. Even if she were taken for an airing in the fashionable Tuileries gardens, she must walk gravely like a Spanish Infanta. It was forbidden to run and chase butterflies. This Spartan education apparently did the little girls of that day no harm. It is a mistake to visualize eighteenth-century woman as a frail being, languishing helplessly in silken skirts: very often she was a creature of iron. For example, the Marquise de la Tour du Pin, who was forbidden by her grandmother to lean back during those day-long coach journeys on a hard narrow bench, grew up to be so steeled to fatigue that she surmounted years of child-bearing, followed by more strenuous years of dairy-farming in exile, without flinching. This aristocratic training produced women who could go to the guillotine as calmly as to a Court ball. Reading the memoirs of the time, one feels that it was the age of stern grandmothers. Eléonore's grandmother, perhaps, went too far. She clung to her principle that fear should be the basis of all education; she never kissed her once, all the time that she was living in her house. Both the girls were seized with attacks of trembling when they saw her—that historic trembling of little girls in the presence of their elders, before Rousseau had upset the social apple-cart by making family affection modish.

The girls were allowed to visit their father once a week. When they returned, Madame de Montigny always subjected them to a rigorous cross-examination. "Did your father say anything about me?" Eléonore tactfully glossed over his many sarcastic comments, but her sister, with her weak intellect, would speak the truth. "He said 'How's the aged harridan?'" A terrible scene always followed, as on the day when they brought back some sugared pastilles which their stepmother had given them. Madame de Montigny seized them and threw them into the fire. "They're poisoned, you little geese. Never accept anything from her again. They're poisoned. Have you tasted one?"

Madame de Montigny believed in breaking the spirit of the young. She was furiously jealous of Eléonore's staunch affection for her father, and was always doing her best to destroy it. Coming suddenly into the child's bedroom one day, she found her putting the finishing touches to some drawings she had been secretly preparing for his birthday during the last two months. Without a word, Madame de Montigny seized them and threw the lot into the fire. Then she left the room, without even glancing at the child. In the drawing-room, afterwards, she boasted of this to her friends, and when they reproached her, she replied: "I did not do this because I was in a bad mood, but on principle, and to form the character of my little girl."

One day, both girls were again pursuing their favourite occupation—looking out of their window. Their grandmother's house in the Rue des Vieilles-Audriettes was in the north-east of Paris. It was near the Temple, which was to be the prison of the royal family, one far-off day. Towards the west were the Comédie Italienne and all the theatres, also the ancient Church of Saint-Sévérin. From the window could be heard the bells of Notre-Dame, and those of the enclosed Carmelite nuns whose convent, in its large garden, was only a stone's-throw away. One could watch splendid coaches bringing magnificent guests to receptions and balls at the palatial houses of Soubise and Beauvau nearby.

"Do you remember the day we got caught by grandmother when the orange-man missed his throw? But for that orange I suppose we wouldn't be here now."

Matured by her sufferings, at fourteen Eléonore was as tender-hearted as a mother. She was devoted to her father, but since both her grandmother and her stepmother did everything they could to thwart her affection, all the loving-kindness of her nature, which craved to spend itself on others, was lavished on her unfortunate sister. In after life, the Prince de Ligne said of her, in his memoirs: "The secret of her charm lies in this: she knows how to love." She had learnt selflessness very young.

Just then there was a scratch on the door, and their uncle came in. Monsieur de Montigny was a fairy godfather to the girls, though, being of a timid nature, and financially dependent on his mother, he could not assert himself, and was forced to do good to his nieces by stealth. He was plump, middle-aged, and smiled diffidently, as if he were always apologizing for his existence. He never took snuff, because his mother detested it. Had he been a more virile character, he would have broken loose from the maternal tyranny long ago, but unfortunately, like a domestic cat, he liked his comforts too much.

Perhaps the fastidiousness of his tabby-hood was his principal charm, for he was one of those amiable, apparently useless, creatures who have a perfect genius for the art of living, and for taking pleasure in little things—the colour of a piece of flame-coloured brocade; the purchase of a new cockatoo with emerald-green plumage; a rare binding; a cornucopia of moss-roses; in fact he cultivated all the more feminine arts in which men take refuge when their natural propensities to soldiering, sport, and the society of other men have been stifled. He loved his nieces because they were so appreciative of any small service he did them. And they were women in miniature.

He carried a mysterious bundle under his coat; moving stealthily, as he always did when he gave them a surprise, he said in a whisper: "Look! I have got here a small somebody whom Eléonore will look after, and who will console her when Someone scolds very hard. Her name is Zina." And he revealed a little grey poodle, trembling nervously, beautifully clipped and trimmed, with a wet nose and eyes which said: "Don't hurt me."

Eléonore gave a cry, seized Zina from her hiding-place, and held her up against her cheek. The puppy looked at her, ceased trembling, and then gave the end of her nose a timid lick. The child was too excited to say "Thank you".

The uncle continued: "Zina will console you when . . . hm . . . hm . . . when anybody else scolds . . . when . . . hm . . . you go away to school next week."

And that was how he broke the news to them that they were to go for three years to the very strict convent school of the Conception in the Rue Saint Honoré, number 354.

It was a convent according to Madame de Montigny's own heart, for the nuns were severe, unbending women. They would have thrown up their hands in horror at the tantrums of Madame Louise about her blue minuet, or at Hélène de Ligne in the Abbaye-aux-Bois putting empty walnut shells on her cat's paws, and allowing it to scamper about the corridors. In a way, the Conception was outside the general eighteenth-century trend of education, the great tradition, started at the fountain-head of Saint-Cyr, that the convent should prepare a girl for life as a woman of the world, both in the home and in society. The Conception was extremely quiet and strict. What a contrast to the more expensive, more fashionable convents! At the Abbaye-aux-Bois, for instance, there was very little conventual calm, and the courtyard was always filled with coaches bringing noble mamas, all rouge and diamonds, to visit their daughters, or carrying the same daughters away for a night to a ball. One even saw the suitors of these young ladies coming to visit them in the convent parlour for an hour or two, in order to be better acquainted with them before marriage. As the de Goncourts have said, it was ordinarily "an education which went from God to the master of deportment, from a meditation to a lesson in court-curtseys".

But at the Conception it was all work and discipline, religion and morals, punishment and repression. However, even that programme was a relief from the terrible rages of grandmama.

Sister Agatha, a dyspeptic nun of thirty, whose matrimonial future had been blighted at fourteen by small-pox—that scourge afflicting a quarter of all Frenchwomen—paced the private enclosure, trying to say her Office. Her eyes were the colour of a cod's belly, and she had never been known to smile. Her manners were devastatingly genteel. She rested assured that her life rose up to the Lord as a pleasant odour of incense. It was difficult to say Office at that hour, for she could hear the pupils at recreation in their part of the garden. Moreover, she had distractions. She was again suffering from a bad attack of suppressed envy about Eléonore de Manville's flawless complexion. The Pompadour said that beauty was a curse to women, for it made all other women her enemies. Everything about the girl annoyed her: the heavy, golden hair, which certainly needed cutting or stuffing under a bonnet, the long, dark lashes which formed such a ridiculous contrast with the hair, the protective air she adopted towards that imbecile sister, and, above all, her dog Zina, into whose ears she was always whispering secrets. (Eléonore wrote, long afterwards, about her dog: "I told her quite quietly all my troubles when my heart was full. . . . Zina seemed to understand her mistress's grief, and licked my hands when she saw me crying.")

Sister Agatha did nothing to protect the poor, backward sister, when the pupils turned on her because of her helplessness, and made her the butt of their laughter and the victim of their practical jokes. Sister Agatha left the protecting to the precious Eléonore; it was she, fighting like a little tiger, who defended her sister against the bullies. It afforded the nun sinister pleasure to see her face covered in bruises, and her hair torn out in handfuls, after some particularly savage encounter with a great, tall *pensionnaire* who would fight shamelessly, with feet and nails. Then Agatha would go up to Eléonore, mock her dishevelled appearance, and punish her by confiscating Zina for the day. Reverend Mother, on the other hand, had a weak spot for this pretty, charming girl, so spirited and warm-hearted. She was one of those old ladies who have been so beautiful themselves, and so much admired in their young days, that they are strangers to jealousy.

Reverend Mother thought Sister Agatha was too hard on the child, and would mitigate her punishments by giving Eléonore pieces of candied citron, specially confectioned at the Convent. This only made it harder for Eléonore in the long run, for the other girls then thought Reverend Mother was making a favourite of her, and began feeling envious.

They planned their revenge. One day, they got hold of Reverend Mother's cat—a temperamental creature called La Grise, disliked by everybody but her mistress—and tied a pewter cup to its tail. The cup was Eléonore's, and had her initials engraved upon it: "E de M." La Grise ran down the cloister shrieking and miaowing with fear, the cup making a hideous din behind her. She was rescued by Reverend Mother. She saw the initials on the pewter. Eléonore—who could not be induced to name the culprits, even in her own defence—was sent to her bedroom, there to await her sentence.

After a while Sister Agatha came to the door and said, without even looking at her: "Reverend Mother sends me to say that she is very surprised at the ungrateful way you repay her kindness. You are to forfeit Zina for a week. The gardener will take her."

"But, Sister, I know nothing about this joke. Allow me to go down and assure Reverend Mother, for a second time, that I am speaking the truth."

"That is enough. You heard what I said. Give me your dog, or the punishment will be made more severe."

Trembling with dismay, Eléonore whispered a last word into Zina's ear and gave her up to the nun, for fear of anything worse.

As if aware that something dreadful was happening, Zina looked round beseechingly at her mistress, and started crying like a baby. When Eléonore was left alone, she could hear that whimpering all the way down the corridor. Then it ceased altogether. . . .

She spent a sleepless night, in floods of tears, wondering whether the gardener would remember to give Zina her supper and a warm box to sleep in. How the sensitive little dog would be fretting! The first thing next morning, before the bell rang for prayers, she slipped out into the garden without asking for permission, and, feeling very apprehensive, she bravely went up to the gardener, who was wheeling a barrow of faggots. He squinted, and had red hair, and large, butcher's hands. Timidly, Eléonore looked up at him and asked, in a tenuous, plaintive voice: "Please, how is my Zina?" "Who's Zina?" "Oh, but surely you must know, she's my little dog. You are looking after her." The man broke into a loud, coarse laugh. "Yes; we looked after her all right. We put her on the spit last night and roasted her for our supper. She was very . . . Hi, there, what's the matter?"

Eléonore had collapsed at his feet in a dead faint.

Eléonore fell seriously ill. Some spring of resilience had snapped within her that morning. For several days she lay in her bed, distracted with grief, refusing food and comfort.

A just fate ordained that retribution should fall heaviest on Sister Agatha, for it was she who had persuaded the Superior to take away the dog. It was her turn that week to answer the visitors' bell at the convent door. She never had a moment's peace: the story had leaked out somehow, through one of the extern Sisters, and now all Paris knew about the tragedy of poor little Zina. Aristocratic parents poured in with dogs, both great and small, poodles, pugs, greyhounds, sheep-dogs, spaniels, even some adorable mongrels, as gifts to replace the late-lamented. The dogs made a great commotion, and showed an unfortunate liking for chasing La Grise. In order to re-establish the good name of the convent, the exasperated Reverend Mother was obliged to dismiss the wicked gardener. She relieved her feelings by imposing a penance on Sister Agatha for her share in the disaster. But it was punishment enough to the Sister to answer the bell, for now everyone knew who she was; she received not only a great many veiled snubs, but even some open reproofs. Above all, she was teased and mauled and worried to death by the endless streams of dogs, both great and small, which kept escaping from their owners, biting her ankles, tearing her habit and veil, knocking off vases from tables, soiling curtains, barking, yapping, snapping, scratching, yowling, howling, jumping up and dancing round in circles, chasing stray pupils, leaping into classrooms . . .

Worst of all, Sister Agatha was obliged to bring each of these demons in turn to Eléonore's bedside, and ask her whether she would consider accepting it as a gift to take the place of Zina.

"Never," sobbed the unhappy child, and buried her face in her pillow.

When she had recovered, Eléonore had to pay for all the publicity she had excited. She grew more unpopular than ever with Sister Agatha, who devised a new way of breaking her spirit. Knowing that she could not punish her through hurting her sister, for then she would have driven her into a frenzy of rage, a dangerous windmill of fists and feet, she found out that she was devoted to her father, and acted accordingly. On Sundays, when Sister Agatha distributed the model letters which all the pupils copied to send home to their parents, she deliberately omitted to give one to Eléonore, hoping that she would then be at a loss and unable to write home to her father.

Eléonore wandered about in the Library, feeling rather wan. "Perhaps I can find a model letter somewhere." She pulled out a volume of the letters of Madame Sévigné and started reading. After a while she said to herself: "Why, the way to compose a good letter is simply to write as you speak, quite naturally."

That week Eléonore wrote to her father out of her own head. At once he wrote back to say that never before had he been so pleased with her style, and begged her to continue in the same vein.

Thus it was that she, who was to write some of the most entrancing love-letters of the century, began her apprenticeship in this "gentlest art" as the result of a nun's punishment.

Sister Agatha was very displeased. More so when she found that a passion for letter-writing was now absorbing Eléonore, and that she spent every available minute writing letters to her school friend, little Marie de Bavière, who later became Marquise de Hautefort. It was her only outlet in life. At last, infuriated beyond endurance, Sister Agatha searched the desks of the two girls and fished out bundles of letters. She wanted to read them aloud in class in such a way as to make them seem ridiculous, but just at that moment, the drawing masters came, so she rolled the letters into long donkeys' ears and jabbed them on to the girls' heads. Then she ordered them to stand in the corner, in front of the whole class, while the two drawing masters gave their lesson. Eléonore hated missing this class. Sister Agatha retired to the bottom of the room to chaperone the manners of the pupils.

Just then Eléonore's hair, as usual, fell down, and with it her donkeys' ears! Monsieur Périmet, who secretly admired her, and detested Sister Agatha, picked up the ears, and, seeing that they were letters, he started to unfold them and to read them. After a while, finding them to his liking, he took the ears from Eléonore's friend and read these also. His shoulders shook with suppressed laughter. Then he showed them to his assistant, and they both smiled and rubbed their hands. Eléonore was covered in confusion.

"*Mademoiselle,*" said Monsieur Périmet, "are these your letters?"

"Yes, Monsieur Périmet."

"Allow me to congratulate you on being our second Madame de Sévigné. Your style is completely charming—so artless, and yet so piquant. You must let me keep these letters, I have enjoyed their wit very much."

Instinctively, as if swayed by an ill wind, all the other girls turned their heads and eyed Sister Agatha surreptitiously.

She was saying her Rosary.

Towards the end of her time, Marie de Bavière interrupted her letter-writing and left the convent to get married. She returned to visit her friends at the Conception when she had become the Marquise de Hautefort. They all clustered round her, hardly able to believe that this very young girl, this child almost, was now a *femme du monde*, with a household of her own, going to Court for her presentation and her balls, attending the Opera on Fridays—the official night for brides to make their first appearance—receiving her friends at her *toilette*, riding in the Cours-la-Reine. They asked her a hundred questions. "Tell us about the King and Queen. Have you seen them lately?"

The little Marquise de Hautefort, in her brand-new plumage, bustled with self-importance. What fun it was to initiate her former school-fellows into the mysteries of grown-up life. She unfurled her fan and adopted an air of nonchalance. "I saw them both driving in the Park of Versailles only this morning. Her Majesty looked sad, as she has just lost her father. He was burnt to death, you know, in a wadded dressing-gown she had given him."

"How awful!"

"He was too fat to save himself, and when at last an old servant-woman heard him and caught fire herself trying to rescue him, he was witty to the end, and said: 'Who'd have thought, *Madame*, that you and I would burn with the same flame?'"

The girls tittered. One of them said: "Poor King Stanislas. Is the Queen as witty as her father?"

"No, she does not know how to amuse the King. They tell me that he sought diversion elsewhere when she assumed prudish and disdainful airs in the evenings. She put him off by chatting and playing cards in her drawing-room, because she'd heard it was the fashion in France to be coquettish with your husband; the King killed flies on the window pane, out of sheer ennui."

"What was he like in the carriage this morning?"

"Full of grandeur and gentle majesty. He still has a fine face, and large blue eyes, with an expressive glance. He's got an aquiline nose and a regal way of carrying his head. When I was presented to him I thought his attitude very dignified, though not at all stiff. His manners were elegant and simple, and he had a penetrating tone of voice."

When Eléonore was left alone with Marie, the conversation turned on Rousseau, who was beginning to addle all feminine heads. The boarders, however, were forbidden to read the *Nouvelle Héloïse,* which had appeared two years previously. Marie talked of it with enthusiasm.

"I can lend you a copy now," she said, "but, of course, you mustn't let Agatha find you out, or she'll tell my mother-in-law, and we'll both get into trouble." (The mother-in-law in France was the guardian of the naughty young brides of the century.)

Eléonore took the volume and hid it in a fold of her pannier. When she got to her room she opened it. She began with these words in the preface: "*A young girl who wishes to read this novel is already lost.*"

Terrified, she closed it quickly. Then she wrapped it in many layers of paper and hid it in a remote drawer, lest its very exhalations should harm her. "Oh, I hope Marie comes back soon, so that I can return it to her. Am I already lost?"

CHAPTER III

MARRIAGE

1767. Three years later.

Eléonore at eighteen had left the Convent of the Conception, and returned with her sister to their grandmother of the Rue des Vieilles-Audriettes.

1769. Two years later, the year before the little Austrian Princess Marie-Antoinette came to France to marry the Dauphin. Eléonore, now twenty years of age, was sitting all alone in her bedroom, one morning in June. She was weeping. The last two years since her return from the Convent had been filled with unhappiness, and now things had become so intolerable that she felt she could bear life no longer. "Shall I go down to her and say I'm taking the veil, and then I will be left in peace?"

The scent of lime flowers was wafted into her window by the breezes of Summer. Breathing it in, this girl, who always loved trees so passionately,—in spite of not reading Rousseau—felt she could not so easily relinquish her hold on life. "No, I must fight a little longer." She recalled the events of the past two years.

Overshadowing everything, there had been the daily tyranny of *grand'mère*, the hourly supervision, the complete lack of privacy, the deliberate thwarting of personal tastes and preferences. For example, one day her kind uncle had given her a long-coveted modish posy of artificial flowers, each blossom scented with its own individual perfume. She was delighted, and unwisely brought it with her on a coach drive with her grandmother.

"Sit up straight," rapped out the old lady, as she took a pinch of snuff. Quietly and unobtrusively, Eléonore slipped her treasure from under her mantle and fondled it. Here were branches of honeysuckle, red and yellow, with perfect feathery pistils, columbines with mauve corollas and yellow trumpets, frilled and streaked carnations, drowsily perfumed tuberoses, and dark red rose-buds; the whole nosegay was surrounded by a frill of silver lace, the stem tightly twined with blue velvet ribbons. Eléonore planned to put this bouquet away in a box and take it out at bed-time; that would be something to look forward to all day. She might even try painting it—for she was never given real flowers.

"*Mademoiselle*, how *dare* you bring flowers into the carriage, when you know very well they give me a headache!"

"They are not real, *Madame*, I assure you; please look."

"Don't argue with me. Throw them out of the window at once. Oppressive smell."

"Oh, *Madame*, please, please . . ."

Without a word, Madame de Montigny snatched the flowers roughly from Eléonore's hands and threw them out of the window. They were crushed in the mud by a carriage behind them. A girl's first bouquet lay trampled in the road. . . .

Eléonore went to see her father once a week. Many years later, she said: "I only had him to love, and I sought in him a little of that tenderness of which I was deprived, and which I would have found so sweet."

But, alas, the stepmother, who now completely dominated the old man of enfeebled brain, persuaded him that his daughter did not really love him.

She used to say to him, over and over again: "She only comes here because she's frightened that you'll disinherit her. She doesn't care for you. All those affectionate glances and loving gestures—simply play-acting. She's a perfect little hypocrite. Don't be weak. Don't be so easily taken in by those innocent blue eyes of hers. Believe me, her grandmother has made her share her views. Refuse to see her. Give orders that she must not be admitted."

The result was that, one day, when Eléonore called at her usual time, she was told by the footman that her father was out.

"But surely *Monsieur* knew that I was coming to-day?"

The footman looked embarrassed: "I am sorry, *Mademoiselle*, I have orders to say that *Monsieur* your father is out."

"Will you go and fetch *Monsieur l'Abbé*, then? I wish to speak to him." (This was one of those tame abbés who were often fashionable appendages to the households of the day.)

The abbé wrote his own account of what happened. Eléonore pleaded with him to fetch her father. "'He is all I have left in the world.' Her tears covered her lovely face; she hid her head in her hands, and in her agitation the comb that with difficulty held up her wealth of hair, fell out, and a forest of fair hair, forming a unique contrast to her brown eyebrows and long, black lashes, covered her from head to foot like a thick mantle."

During those months one trouble had followed another; first grandmother, then her stepmother, her father, and lastly the Chevalier. A certain Chevalier, an adventurer and a rank outsider, whose name Eléonore always refused to reveal, coveting a large fortune, persuaded Monsieur de Manville to let him marry the imbecile daughter.

Eléonore was in despair. Everything had been arranged, the bridal dress made, the contract drawn up, the guests invited. However, the night before the wedding, Providence, which knows when a sparrow falls, delivered the girl from so great an evil. She was suddenly seized with a violent fever, and put to bed. After some time she called Eléonore; she threw her arms around her, and cried: "Good little sister, alas, now you will be all alone." Then, looking up at her with eyes of measureless gratitude, she died. Eléonore was alone.

The body was hardly out of the house, and the black draperies still hanging everywhere, when the Chevalier was announced. Eléonore, dressed in deep mourning, was called down to the drawing-room to speak to him. No doubt, feeling somewhat ashamed, he had come to offer his sympathy, for he knew how much Eléonore had loved her sister. They sat down in chairs opposite each other; tall and thin, with a long, narrow, wolf-face and pointed chin, this powdered exquisite, with a reputation for twisted, unnatural ways, preyed on the lives of others. He carried a lorgnette, a dressed-up monkey, a muff and a pomander. There was a perpetual terrifying smile on his face. Eléonore tried not to shiver as she glanced at him.

"*Mademoiselle*," he said, in high, mincing tones, "I came to offer you consolation in your great loss, and to unite my grief with yours."

"*Monsieur* is all courtesy; I am deeply indebted to you for your remembrance of my beloved sister."

There was an uncomfortable pause. He had been thrown off his balance by her perfect poise. Then he cleared his throat.

"We must leave the dead to bury the dead, *Mademoiselle*; you are too young to blight your beauty in useless repining. In your present loneliness you should turn your thoughts in the direction of those best fitted to console you."

(What did this mean? Eléonore sensed danger, so she remained silent.)

He gave a discreet little cough, slapped his monkey, who had just bitten his finger, then went on: "I have your father's permission and approval to come and lay my heart at your feet."

Eléonore jumped up. For the first time since she had fought the big girls at school, she forgot that she was frail and small, and she lost her temper completely and outrageously. Trembling with rage, she lashed him contemptuously with her tongue.

"Carrion crow! Drone! Mass of corruption! My poor sister is hardly cold in her tomb, and you come and lay your so-called heart at my feet! Faugh! Pouah! You found it difficult to bear, didn't you, this sudden loss of so great a fortune? You'd made such plans, hadn't you? Counting on my sister's docility and weak state of health, you would have grabbed every *sou* and started again on your career of self-indulgence. You'd have built a house in the Rue Saint-Honoré, a pleasance near the Bois de Boulogne, ordered coaches from Francine, waistcoats from Pagelle, enough scents and unguents to fumigate a pest house, rings for your useless fingers. Bah! you think you can drag *me* to the altar and make *me* comply with your wishes. Look, *Monsieur* . . ." she lifted the lace frill from her arm—"you see this red mark here? A big girl at my school bit me one day when I was defending my sister. She kept her teeth well in because I would not let go of her hair, and these marks will remain till the day of Judgement. Well, I'm even stronger now than I was then. I warn you that if you force this marriage upon me, they will have to drag me, bound hand and foot, to the altar, biting and screaming; and when the priest asks me whether I am willing to take you as my husband, I will shriek out, 'No! No! No!' until the walls of the church echo with my cries. After that I will start *Biting*. Do you hear? Do you hear? Do you hear? Or do you want me to bite your face now?"

The monkey chattered with fear, and ran up a curtain; the Chevalier dropped his muff and fled. For once he had met his match.

Little by little, a great portion of Monsieur de Manville's fortune found its way into the Chevalier's pockets. Soon there would be none left for Eléonore. The grandmother said that the only way to insure against her ultimate financial ruin was to marry someone else, for then she could claim some money for her marriage settlement. There was no lack of suitors. But whenever a name was suggested by Monsieur de Manville, Madame de Montigny turned it down, for she swore that it was one of the Chevalier's minions; and every time Madame de Montigny suggested someone, the Chevalier saw to it that Monsieur de Manville turned it down. There was a deadlock, and Eléonore could see no way out.

Then came a horrible interim when Monsieur de Manville was stricken with by paralysis. When he was convalescing the doctors advised him to take the waters at Bourbon l'Archambault. Eléonore firmly announced her decision of going with him. It was her only chance to re-establish herself in his favour, and get him away from the Chevalier.

"I forbid it," said Madame de Montigny. "If you go I will never open my doors to you again." She came a little closer to the girl and whispered menacingly: "*Then* what will you do, all alone in the house, with your stepmother and the Chevalier dividing the spoils behind your senile father's back?"

"I am in the hands of God," replied Eléonore simply.

This was outside Madame de Montigny's province; she did not account for the interventions of the Almighty. She went on:

"What will you do if your father dies while he is taking the waters? No house will be open to you then."

"I will become a nun."

The visit to the watering-place was a great success. The old man got better. Everyone admired Eléonore's beauty and her devoted tenderness to her old father. At last she brought him back to Paris in fairly good health. Seeing that she could gain nothing by threats, Madame de Montigny took her back after all.

All these events Eléonore recalled on this June morning of 1769. As she sat by her window and tried to form a plan of action for the future, she realized more forcibly than ever that in marriage lay her only hope of escape; and time was passing, passing. Here she was, twenty years of age, and many of her friends had been married at fourteen; in fact some of them had been betrothed in the cradle. But she mistrusted so many of the young men who had been chosen for them. From her school friends she had so often gleaned tragic stories. The girl-bride, with her imagination on fire from reading novels, had timidly opened her heart to her husband during the honeymoon. At first he had been a little touched, a little flattered, and then, on returning to Paris, his old bachelor habits seized hold of him again, and he would go to supper parties with actresses, creeping back to his own suite at dawn. Tears and recriminations would be met by delicate mockery. After six months, the bride in high society would too often be left to lead her own life, open to all the temptations of taking a lover, and, as long as she was discreet, society did not condemn her for this. No, that was not Eléonore's idea of happiness. She wanted to marry someone who would be devoted to her always, a man old enough to be immune to the temptations of a wild life.

Suddenly, her thoughts turned to one, the Comte Elzéar Joseph de Sabran-Grammont, Seigneur de Beaudinar, a frequent guest in her mother's drawing-room. He did not look as if he were nearly seventy, for he had been a sailor all his days, and had lived a man's life. He had a great air about him; tall and imposing, young in his movements, he had a grave face, with regular features; a tender smile softened his severe expression when he looked down at Eléonore. Her uncle used to tease her about the change she wrought in him, for the Comte de Sabran, who had rather a martial voice accustomed to giving orders to his sailors, suddenly spoke in dulcet tones whenever he turned to

Eléonore. He was struck by her grace the very first time he had met her in Madame de Montigny's drawing-room. To see them together was like watching a vulture bending down to have a conversation with a wren. And what conversations! The Comte had distinguished himself in the Seven Years War. When his ship, the *Centaure*, had been cruising off the coast of Gibraltar, she had been attacked by four British ships. The masts had cracked and splintered like firewood, the sails were in shreds. He himself had eleven bullet wounds in his body. He held on until the last round of ammunition was used up. Then, nothing daunted, he ordered his own silver plate to be brought up on deck, to charge the cannon. Alas, the *Centaure* began to sink; he was taken prisoner by the English, and the Comte used to tell Eléonore: "Those good English took me to England, and there I was treated for two months with the utmost consideration—not as an enemy, but as a fellow sportsman who had unfortunately lost a round of an exhilarating game."

Eventually he had returned to the Court of Versailles, covered with glory. Louis XIV, welcoming the aged Condé as he slowly climbed the great staircase after his victories, had said: "Do not hurry, you are too weighted down with laurels." For the Comte de Sabran, Louis XV also found greeting exquisitely apposite. Turning to the Queen and the Dauphin, he said: "The Comte de Sabran is one of ourselves." This was a reference to his descent from the wife of Saint Louis, who had been a Delphine de Sabran. Every royal house in Europe could claim descent from a Sabran.

Eléonore mused on all this. "He would need me, and I have a great respect and admiration for him. Is it necessary to be passionately in love? Perhaps one is freer from worry without it. At least I would not be listening for him as he crept back at dawn, after bachelor parties! Yes, I've decided; I will speak to my uncle about it."

In a few moments, Eléonore, as fresh as a lily, had donned her *négligé* of white and mauve striped silk and was deep in conversation with her uncle.

"But, my little one, he is much, much too old for you."

"I shall be everything to him. He will love me, and protect me."

After a while she persuaded him.

"Very well. I will go and sound him immediately."

Arrived at the gallant Admiral's, the uncle delicately conveyed to him that, if he were searching for a bride, it would *not* be impossible for him to win the hand of his own charming niece.

The effect was electric. In the excitement of the moment the

Comte de Sabran became many years younger. His face, his very movements were charged with the fire and impetuosity of youth.

"My dear Monsieur de Montigny, surely you are mistaken? You cannot mean that your niece, so perfectly beautiful, so full of grace, so accomplished, would be willing to trust herself to an old fellow riddled with bullet wounds? Will wonders ever cease!"

Imperiously he pulled the bell for his hat, cape, and sword, he ordered his coach, and before the bewildered uncle could say one more word he was dashing off to the Rue des Vieilles-Audriettes, to lay his ancient name, his unblemished honour and his loyal heart at the feet of Eléonore de Manville. With quiet joy, she accepted.

Strangely enough, this plan met with no opposition. Both *grand'mère* and the Chevalier looked upon the Count as too old to be a formidable opponent to either of them; they thought he would soon be out of the way and Eléonore at their mercy again.

The marriage was hurried through, as every moment counted while the Chevalier could still wheedle sums of money out of her father. Quickly those delicious marriage invitations were brought to the houses of the guests by the footman. Perhaps Sieur Croisey, of the Rue Saint-André-des-Arts, had designed a pretty card; at the top a garland attached to a medallion in which two doves are making love. The invitation would be worded like this:

"M . . . .

"You are invited by Monsieur de Jean de Manville and Madame de Montigny to honour them with your presence at the Nuptial Blessing of Comte Elzéar Joseph de Sabran-Grammont de Beaudinar and Mademoiselle Eléonore de Jean de Manville, which will be given this day of 1769, at o'clock in the morning in the Parish Church."

The bridal gown was ordered, and the seamstress with her workroom of young girls feverishly set to work on the embroidery. The low-bodiced dress was not necessarily white; it might be cloth of silver decorated with diamonds, and the *Galerie des Modes* tells us of a wedding gown in Pekin blue ornamented with gauze and white flowers. The bride always wore rouge, patches, orange flowers and diamonds. Two gentlemen ushers led her to the altar. Nor was the wedding ceremony necessarily performed during the day, for there is a record of a society wedding at St. Eustache at midnight, with more than six hundred candles blazing.

In any case Eléonore must have looked lovely sailing up the

aisle in her great panniers. As she pronounced her vows her unawakened heart was full of peace. How could she guess that, one day, love in all its ruthlessness, passion that might not be denied, would wreck that peace for many years?

CHAPTER IV

PRESENTATION AT COURT

In those days a young society bride was presented to the King and Queen at Versailles almost immediately after a short honeymoon. Eléonore shared the doubtful honour of being presented in the same year as the Comtesse du Barry, who had made her formal curtsey before a scandalized Court on April 22nd, 1769.

The scene was the *Galerie des Glaces*, one June afternoon of 1769. The air was heavy with the many orange-trees in silver tubs which were always put out on ceremonial occasions. The pages, in crimson velvet and gold, darted about, arranging trains. A valet in blue livery was surreptitiously clearing away some litter left by the hawkers in the morning and the goats who brought milk to the princesses. Footmen took their mistresses' cloaks away for them. The Court was assembling to watch the young Comtesse de Sabran on her way to make her first curtsey before Louis XV and Marie Leczinska. Viewed from a height, all that could be seen was an expanse of swaying ostrich plumes, like a gigantic forest of trees fluttering in a breeze. The feather-crowned heads, which twenty years hence were to fall beneath the flashing blade of the guillotine and tumble headlong into the bloody baskets beneath, were now clustering for scandal. (Ah, the severed heads to be placed between the legs of their owners, furtively entombed by lantern-light, and sprinkled with quicklime, while the diggers fought about the clothes they had stolen from their victims. O witless heads crowned with plumes . . .!)

But to-day the lovely owners of these plumed and powdered heads were gossiping as was their wont. The Greek statues opposite those mirrors which had reflected the famous ball in '45 when the youthful Pompadour had bewitched the King, and later witnessed the presentation of her successor, now looked down as impassively as ever on these Court ladies whispering behind their fans.

"My dear, tell me that rhyme again; I must commit it to memory."

"Come nearer then: we don't want the Maréchale de Mirepoix to overhear us."

"But it was her nephew, de Boufflers, who wrote it, wasn't it?"

"Shush . . . ! Now listen:

Lisette, thy beauty's snares
Entangle all the Court;
In vain the Duchess glares,
In vain Princesses snort;
Venus was born, my Muse declares,
From the scum of the wild sea's sport."

"Miraculous! Divine! Really young Boufflers is cruelly witty. I'm not surprised that they are too frightened to have him here , quite apart from his blood-relationship with Her Majesty."

"It doesn't always do."

"Not *nowadays*. Things are so different. Now, my dear, in my time this state of affairs would not have been tolerated. The Mirepoix only presented la du Barry because she had lost so heavily at cards and needed a little financial backing. Why, a shameless strumpet . . . publicly presented at Court. Our poor Queen . . . how she must have suffered."

At this point the handsome Prince de Ligne, who had a great reputation for gallantry, interrupted them, also in a whisper.

"The King shows good taste. I think the Comtesse du Barry ravishingly beautiful. That auburn hair . . ."

"It's dyed."

"How do you know?"

"I'm afraid I can't go into details here, but I have it on good authority." (As a matter of fact she was right; when the du Barry went to prison, she came out with black hair, as, of course, she had been unable to get her usual hair dyes!)

"Well, let the hair pass: her complexion is flawless, like a very young girl's. It owes nothing to artifice. Her eyebrows are bows delicately drawn with Cupid's own arrow, and her eyes are like turquoises."

The ladies changed the subject of conversation.

"Talking of blue eyes, you will soon see a fine pair, irised with brown, when the young Comtesse de Sabran passes by on her way to their Majesties."

"I know! But have you looked at her feet? They are the tiniest I have ever seen. My maid tells me she never wears anything but satin slippers, even for the country, and she has two closets crammed with them. A real Cinderella foot."

"Cinderella, perhaps, but she hasn't picked on a fairy prince for a husband. He's old enough to be her grandfather; his devotion is pathetic—almost in bad taste."

"Oh, she will soon find consolation elsewhere, believe me. Perhaps she only got married to escape from that grandmother of hers, and enjoy a little freedom."

"No, no, I assure you," said the Prince de Ligne, "she is devoted to Sabran. I vow it is quite touching to see them together, for he is bursting with pride in her beauty and cherishes her with the tenderest care; in fact, with those old-fashioned courtly manners of his, you feel all the time that he is treating her like a jewel in a glass case. I wish she were more punctual, though. Why doesn't she come?"

"Sh . . . Sh . . . I think I hear the folding-doors being flung open: they are just going to announce her. Here she comes."

Upstairs, there had been quite another commotion behind the scenes. Poor Eléonore was in an attic of the Palace, surrounded by ancient chattering ladies from the provinces, relations of her husband's who were almost tearing her to pieces in a controversy as to how much rouge she must have on her cheeks and how tightly she must be laced. A full hour ago she had given up any attempt to protest: she just sat before her mirror being prodded here and there with pins, laced by harpy hands until she thought she would suffocate, having patches applied and as quickly taken off. She had not leaned back or reclined for many hours, but had been obliged to sit upright since early dawn, lest she disarrange the scaffolding of her powdered curls. She was weary after a week's rehearsal of curtseying under Monsieur Gardel, the fashionable dancing-master. How difficult it had been to smother her giggles at the plump little man, who, impersonating the Queen, had strutted about in panniers, false bosom and long Court train. Over and over again she had come into the room, walked the whole terrifying length of it, dropped her three curtseys, then holding her fan and taking off her gloves, she made as if to kiss the hem of the pseudo-Queen's robe, and then had burst out laughing. After regaining her composure she was made to practise backing out of the Royal presence, gently but firmly kicking her train out of the way as she went. Ouf! what a relief when she would reach the door at last, away from all those pitiless eyes, those tongues whose verdict could either make or mar a social reputation.

But now, how she longed to get away from this stuffy attic: *tante* Eulalie, from Provence, always chilly, had ordered a fire to be lit: after the manner of Versailles fires it smoked abominably, and soot fell in showers down the chimney. The windows, after the manner of Versailles windows, had been hermetically sealed all the winter and they had forgotten to open this one. Something suspiciously like a flea had sprung from *tante* Léonie's wig, and a moth had fluttered from *cousine* Aurore's antiquated fur pelisse. Every conceivable variety of rouge was littered on the dressing-table, from *Rouge Serkis*, to the famous carmine of Madame Martin.

All these attendant spirits talked or rather shrieked at once, and nobody listened to anyone else; and time was passing. . . . At length Eléonore felt she could stand it no longer. She rose to her feet, looking tiny but determined, raised her fan to command silence in the hubbub and said in a shaky voice:

"I feel that I am going to have the vapours; please all leave my room, or we shall be obliged to put off the presentation entirely. Believe me, *Mesdames*, I am my own physician in these cases. I must ask you to go *at once*, all except Minette, or I shall have hysterics and then all our plans will go awry."

They were too taken aback to speak. She started wafting and pushing them, until at last she was left alone with her maid. She locked the door, and, in a few minutes, revived by some Queen of Hungary water, she had repaired the damage done to her hair, washed off the surplus rouge and patches and loosened the excruciatingly tight laces of her bodice. At length she let in some air by breaking the window; the room stank, for these old ladies used a great deal of perfume to conceal what water would have remedied.

The eighteenth century was not all citronella and ambergris.

"How can I reach the *Galerie des Glaces* without falling into their hands again? They are all waiting for me outside the door, ready to pounce. They are rattling the handle. I know! We must open this window completely. I will climb out on to the parapet and try to find my way through some other window. I must take care not to be late. What a good thing that I can see the clock on the turret. Come along, Minette. Help me."

It was lucky that the little maid had been in service at the Palace before, in attendance on a frisky lady-in-waiting who had often roamed on those intriguing roofs of Versailles; she knew her way about, and rather enjoyed this. The golden urns—now gone—glowed on the façade of the roof-top. Eléonore was as agile as a little chamois, and had by now quite recovered her spirits. Sometimes she paused to tap at some dormer window, just to frighten the people inside. From a space among the chimneys she peered down at the great expanse of the lawns below, and gazed at the geometrically planned flower-beds hemmed in by the embroidery of dark green box. Far away she saw a lady in satin the colour of apple-blossom, mincing her way towards Trianon, a long jade green parasol held over her head by a little nigger boy in orange brocade. Could it be the favourite with Zamor? Beyond . . . beyond . . . she gazed at the encircling woods of the Royal hunts topped by frolicsome June clouds, billowing in the breeze like her own swaying skirts. What fun if Boreas puffed strenuously enough and blew her detachable train away. What would her husband say when he heard of the escapade, and her grandmother and her stepmother, and the Chevalier; and oh! Sister Agatha at the convent? How carefree life was, now that she was away from all those women, just being spoilt by her husband, and making him happy in return.

At length they scrambled into an empty room in the late Queen's suite overlooking a dark inner courtyard. Eléonore glided through a closet where Louis XIV had kept his countless wigs in wall cupboards, and at last she found her way to her husband, only just in time. She had gone by a twisted, secret staircase and through a concealed door, into the bathroom of the late Marquise de Montespan overlooking the Ambassadors' staircase. In the meantime, the relations, wondering what had happened to Eléonore, broke into the room, and, finding her gone, concluded that a ghost had spirited her away—one of those rather sinister *dix-huitième* ghouls who haunt palaces where many souls have sinned.

The young Comtesse de Sabran's progress through the *Galerie des Glaces* was a triumph. "*Fleur-des-Champs!*" exclaimed the Prince de Ligne; the name remained hers for the rest of her life. Indeed, she was a field flower, a lily-of-the-valley, in all its simple loveliness, glowing in contrast with those artificial peonies, parrot-tulips and spotted orchids.

Many, many years afterwards, when Eléonore was an old lady who had seen revolution, exile and the downfall of Napoleon, did she remember that day when she made her first curtsey to that King who is reputed to have said: "After me, the deluge"? Was she too shy to look up at the face of this man who, falling a prey to the sick boredom of the over-civilized, was now leading a life of vice?

The old ladies smiled at her little *gauche* ways and all the timidity of innocence. Most older women praised her. They had that boldness of the great old ladies of the day, who would say in a loud voice, perhaps on purpose to make her blush: "Ah, but she is really adorable, that little Sabran." One could overhear: "What tiny feet! Charpentier must delight in making her shoes. What freshness. She should be a very graceful dancer; her movements are *perfect.*"

A woman may be as lovely as a rose, but if her beauty is not in the fashion of her day she might just as well retire to a convent for all the notice the social world will take of her. Eléonore typified a beauty that was fast becoming contemporary; Greuze and Rousseau were beginning to cast their spell. Like an old man who has tasted every pleasure, the century now relished innocence, casual white dresses and an air of simplicity, after a surfeit of artifice and sensuous perfection.

The powdered exquisites in their brocaded coats lifted their lorgnettes, shrieked out some compliment to her very face, in the embarrassing manner of princes at Court. But they sensed that in spite of the white hairs of her husband, the young Comtesse would not be one to indulge in flirtations. As for the young women, they recognized one who was far above their little machinations, for she would neither steal their lovers nor intrigue for money and position. It was rumoured that her conversation was fascinating and that whoever frequented her drawing-room in the future would never know *ennui*. Was she not studying Latin in order to read Virgil and Horace? The Abbé Delille and other famous men of her day, struck by her intelligence and the interest she took in serious conversation, guided her private reading. She read a lot, and with profit, though she complained, all the time, of her bad memory. During her sad girlhood she had acquired a solid foundation of good literature: this gave an original charm to her conversation, without, however, depriving it of sprightliness. In one so shy, it was piquant to hear her coming out quite simply with an historical quotation or a sound piece of literary judgement on one of the old French authors.

From the very first day, Eléonore captured the imagination of that declining Court, and particularly of the women. Her timidity was one of her most endearing qualities. Monsieur de Puységur, who witnessed her début in society, said: "At Versailles one always had to fetch her from behind the most voluminous panniers belonging to one of these ladies, for she made them a rampart and a hiding-place." At the beginning, she belonged to a group of young women called "La Brochette", because their shyness made them cling together. But after a while everybody was saying: "Have you seen her?" Her great beauty never created envy. This was particularly evident on one famous occasion. In those days it was the fashion for ladies of exalted rank to take round the alms-bag at Mass. Marie-Antoinette herself used to go round the chapel at Versailles with her silk bag and collect golden *louis*. ("So expensive" grumbled the courtiers!) The *curé* of Saint Roch, in the Rue Saint-Honoré, was in the habit of inviting the most beautiful Court ladies to collect for the poor of his parish. The renowned beauty of the year before, the Comtesse d'Egremont, had collected a very large sum. When the *curé* heard of Eléonore's great loveliness, he said to himself: "Ah! Providence has sent me an angel for my poor." Indeed, on that day at High Mass the church was packed. There were no grumbles from the dandies this time: each accounted it a privilege to give his golden *louis*, for he was rewarded with a smile such as goddesses sometimes bestow on more favoured mortals. Even the organist scrambled down hurriedly from the organ loft to give his contribution. What a pity that the scene has not been immortalized by Cochin—that exquisite engraver of church ceremonies, of funerals where even Death is decorative, and becomes a *Pompe-Funèbre à la Pompadour*. He alone could give the detail, the serried ranks of tiny powdered heads, the be-ruffled hands holding heavy missals embossed with family arms, those lackeys in livery carrying the great velvet sacks for the missals and settling their masters and mistresses comfortably in their chairs. . . . One can picture the whole scene, aided by the knowledge of other delicious engravings. At last it was all over. Eléonore took her heavy bag to the sacristy. The Comtesse d'Egremont hurried after her to find out how much Eléonore had collected, and when she was told that the bride had outdone her she was the first to congratulate her. Hour of triumph, not only for the good *curé* of Saint-Roch, but also for Eléonore's husband, who was so proud of her.

Looking at the portraits of famous contemporary beauties, it is hard to discover the secret of what charms a particular century; that is because we look for perfection of feature and colouring. Like a lover, the fashionable world falls in love with a woman, not so much for obvious qualities, but because it revels in her "atmosphere", loves to bathe in her climate, so to speak. Alas, the charm has almost entirely vanished, like a delicate perfume. Any attempt to recapture it by description becomes mere enumeration of good points. A woman's "atmosphere" is made up of a synthesis of various things—her dress, her small talk, her house, her garden, her personal maid, her intimate possessions! (Historic secrets are revealed if we touch the dead woman's fan, her slippers, her ear-rings.) Eléonore dressed with subtle simplicity. She had made an art of this. In the *Galerie des Dames Françaises*, an onlooker records that "she never wore anything that glittered, but with infinite skill made use of the simplest ornaments. She appeared to have arranged nothing, and left everything to chance, but when one looked at her closely one saw that nothing had been forgotten". (Oh, forerunner of that expensive simplicity which made Marie-Antoinette run up such lengthy bills *chez* Madame Bertin, merely for white muslin dresses tied tightly round the waist with blue silken sashes.)

Here, indeed, was the naturalness towards which the jaded century tended with longing, that charming casualness which Madame Vigée Lebrun has recorded in her memoirs. She describes her as "very pretty", and in painting her she immortalized what Mrs. Webster called "that look of teasing tenderness, that enigmatic smile, the rebellious hair, the wit, the whimsicality, the careless attitude so natural to her".

Thus Eléonore's first season at Court was an unqualified success. As the Comte de Sabran reviewed the panorama of the presentation, the first ball, the collection of Saint-Roch, he glowed with pride. This young woman had come suddenly into his life with her hands full. She brought beauty, virtue, devotion, and, most unexpectedly, charm of conversation; and it was this last attraction, in an age which set great store by intellectual pleasures, that filled the Sabran drawing-room and brought Eléonore into contact with some of the most interesting men and women of France. The days passed in quiet happiness. The Comte adored his wife, and did all he could to make her forget her unhappy childhood by creating a background of quiet protection for her.

Soon a little girl, Delphine, was born to them. As Eléonore held her in her arms for the first time, she remembered her own mother who had died at her birth. She clasped the frail creature to her and cried: "You, at least, shall know a mother's love."

CHAPTER V

THE CORONATION

Louis XV was dead, and now a new reign had begun. At Court, the Queen's ladies were preparing for the Coronation of Louis XVI at Rheims Cathedral. The wardrobe women and numberless tire-women of Queen Marie-Antoinette were at sixes and sevens: there was such a deal to think of. It all seemed perfectly simple from Her Majesty's point of view, for she had only to place a pin every morning in her clothes catalogue, opposite the samples of the dresses she had decided to wear. But up in the attics, among the rows of hanging wardrobes, there was scurrying and quarrelling, ironing and goffering, the folding of gowns on long tables, cleaning of jewels and crisping of plumes, packing and making of inventories; and, above all, there was the snitching of perquisites by the ladies of the wardrobe, which made Her Majesty's dress allowance vanish so quickly. Indeed a Coronation was a tremendous upheaval where the women were concerned.

But calm reigned in the apartments of the Queen's sisters-in-law. Madame Clothilde, who was affectionately called *Gros-Madame* because of her plumpness, had an agreeable wit, and was loved by her friends because of her endearing graciousness and thoughtful attentions. The devout Madame Elizabeth was spirited and imperious, with the real Bourbon nose. *Madame* had been given leave to summon a very favoured few. The two sisters were choosing their guests one May evening in the large south drawing-room overlooking the Orangery, where all the orange trees were in full flower. They had dismissed their enormous private households of pages, equerries, lords and ladies-in-waiting, footmen and reading-women. The sisters were sorting out *layettes* for the poor of the parish, for they were always helping them from their privy purse. They were wondering whether the Queen would allow them to invite Eléonore de Sabran to the Coronation. They had talked a great deal about their childless sister-in-law that morning, because of an unfortunate incident a few days before; Marie-Antoinette was out driving near Louveciennes and a little village boy of four had been nearly killed under the horses of her carriage. Hearing that he was motherless, the Queen, with her usual impulsiveness, decided to adopt him on the spot; so, after making enquiries she carried him off with her to the Palace. Jacques had kicked and screamed, crying with intolerable shrillness that he wanted his grandmother, his brother Louis, and his sister Marianne. Two days later, divested of his little red frock and wooden shoes, he had appeared, resplendent in a long white frock trimmed with lace, a rose-coloured sash edged with a silver fringe and a preposterous hat decorated with ostrich feathers! The whole affair had aroused a lot of whispered comment; the King had been secretly ridiculed.

Any action of Marie-Antoinette's was criticized, for her grace and beauty aroused great jealousy among the women. Had they only known the secret cause of all her little follies! "*I am afraid of being bored*," she is reputed to have said. Terrible words, in which are epitomized the tragedy of a whole century, and the particular tragedy of one woman.

With a sigh, the two sisters turned the conversation to Madame de Sabran. "I wonder whether Eléonore has been very busy with her *Société de la Bienfaisance,*" said Madame Clothilde. "I hear that the members go in pairs, every week, to distribute small sums to the poor."

"I think she has been absorbed in her home. Her husband is ailing, and she has nursed him devotedly, and of course there are the two children."

Three years after the birth of Delphine, Eléonore had a son, and called him Elzéar. He had been born a week before Louis XV's death from smallpox. He was extremely delicate, and his life had been despaired of. Eléonore always wore a bracelet representing a nest, over which were engraved the words "O may they live". At the time of the Coronation, Elzéar was a year old. His father had lived through three reigns, and was now too old to make the journey to Rheims to see Louis XVI crowned. But Madame Clothilde, always rather touched at the way that Eléonore, as a débutante, had sought her advice in the shifting quicksands of Court life, finally decided that she must be invited to come with them, even without her husband.

What a magnificent pageant was this last important Coronation of a King of France. Indeed, it was a spectacle for the memory to treasure in the fullest detail. Eléonore laughingly planned to describe it from her arm-chair fifty years hence to a crowd of listening grandchildren around the fireside. Lovers of the *dix-huitième* who have not had the privilege of speaking to any of these grandchildren, must be content with the gleanings of memorialists, and, above all, study with a magnifying glass the superb engraving, by Moreau le Jeune,[1] of the scene inside Rheims Cathedral. This is the most comprehensive and detailed French engraving of the eighteenth century. It gives a bird's-eye view of the middle of the chancel, embracing the gorgeous high altar on the left, the King on his throne on the right, surrounded by priests and dignitaries of the Church, and in the vast space in the middle great nobles in fine attitudes, wearing their traditional costume of white silken hose, cloaks and swords, and hats with swirling plumes. Here, on a small piece of paper, is depicted all that this proud land of France boasted of aristocratic holders of ancient privilege, almost arrogant in their proud obeisance to the King whose throne their disloyal mockeries would help to overthrow, in spite of all their vows of allegiance on this most solemn day. And then, higher up in the background of the picture, there rises the enormous many-tiered balcony, like a huge flower-bed with a myriad flowers clustering around the

[1] Not to be confused with his unfashionable brother, Louis Gabriel Moreau, who painted enchanting landscapes. Reproductions in Art Room of Victoria and Albert Museum.

central rose—the bejewelled young Queen in her enormous panniers and the plumes of her high, powdered head-dress. She is surrounded by her ladies-in-waiting, her household, the King's aunts and sisters, with their ladies-in-waiting and households. Each lady is jewelled, crisped, curled—the finished product of many hours of artistic effort by tire-women, seamstresses, hair-dressers, and maids, jewellers, and fan-makers from the Rue Saint-Honoré, silk weavers of Lyons, the despoiled ostriches of Africa, not to mention the creators of perfume, patches and rouge from all over the capital.

The Comtesse de Sabran was up in that balcony. Eléonore had blossomed out after six years of quiet married happiness. She was in the full bloom of young motherhood, and its sweetness glowed in her expression. As for her *toilette*, it was the acme of all that great wealth and perfect taste could lavish on a Court robe. She had said good-bye to her husband with great tenderness, and now, as she sat watching the ceremony, she kept reminding herself that she must treasure this, that and the other little significant details to tell him when she came home, for he, with his long memory of three reigns, would find everything of great interest. "What a pity I have such a bad memory," she sighed to herself. It so often happened that during the important days in life it was the foolish little whisperings which remained in her mind, mingling incongruously with the shouts of "*Vive le Roi!*" which rolled along in waves of thunderous enthusiasm up the vast chancel and were echoed and re-echoed by the crowds massed outside the great West door. For instance, at the very moment that the ancient crown of Charlemagne was placed on Louis the Sixteenth's head, Eléonore distinctly heard the King mutter to a prelate standing near: "It's uncomfortable." Omen? Then he had glanced up at his wife in the royal balcony with a look of love. Later, the Queen fainted from emotion, and had to be led out and revived. She retired for a moment to that much-talked-of innovation, the *lieu-à-l'anglaise* which had been installed behind the Queen's tribune. At this point there was a malevolent cackling from the King's old spinster aunts, who had emerged for the occasion from their retirement at the Pompadour's palace of Bellevue, where they had put fig leaves on all the male classical statues. To-day they had sailed forth in formidable battle regalia to watch their nephew's Coronation, and to ooze with malevolence towards their detested relative, the Queen. (Oh, shades of the Court-painter Nattier, rise and behold the three sisters, Adelaïde, Victoire and Sophie, whom you had painted all-begarlanded with such delicious deception in the bloom of their early girlhood. Now a later artist, Madame Labille-Guiard, was waiting to pounce with her relentless brush, showing up all the hideousness of envious, thwarted spinsterhood, the macaw-like cheeks, too furiously rouged, the antiquated turbans, the three-fold vulture chins, the eyes of hatred.)

The Queen returned, and the three aunts donned their masks of smiling hypocrisy again. The ceremonies continued. . . .

At last the Coronation was over.

The Prince de Ligne took Eléonore back to her lodgings in his coach. It was a huge, gilded affair with the princely crown on top, wheels spoked with wavy sunrays, the interior upholstered in yellow satin, and the doors painted with an allegory depicting—most irrelevantly—the Triumph of Virtue. In spite of every effort made by the footmen at the back to hold it down with straps, this ancestral coach was so badly sprung that it jolted horribly from side to side, and made Eléonore feel bilious. However, women were never sick in the eighteenth century, they took out their vinaigrette bottles, and smiled and gossiped—while inwardly they felt like death. Eléonore was deafened by the booming and clanging of all the cathedral and church bells and by the roars from the crowds who were surging to the very windows. As the coach moved at a snail's pace, she could see some of the happy faces quite plainly. She turned to de Ligne impulsively: "I'm glad to see the people enjoying themselves. They've given the King and Queen such a welcome. Perhaps they realize how kind they both are, so full of good intentions. Don't you feel, Charlot, that to-day you and I have seen the birth of a new era?"

"How, my dear *Fleur-des-Champs?*"

"I don't know. There's a feeling of kindness and benevolence in the air; they say the Queen is very good to the poor."

"Bah, *ma chère*, it will never prevent sedition-mongers from doing what they want with the mob when the time comes. Charity and patronage exasperate them."

Eléonore, a little baulked by his cynicism, persisted in her praise: "And then, the King and Queen have strict views, they will set a new standard of morality. The first act of their reign was to put the du Barry into a convent."

Ligne smiled knowingly, and said nothing. An ardent admirer of the du Barry's, he had gone to cheer her solitude in the nunnery, and had come away assured that this beautiful creature was making the best of her enforced retirement. The nuns were vastly intrigued by her, the whole convent in a flutter; and she herself was pulling strings right and left to secure her release so that she might live at Louveciennes again, where she had amassed many treasures. Though now a little plumper, she was still very lovely, and good for many more years of amorous dalliance.

Eléonore changed the subject. "I've heard rumours that the King intends to summon the States General. I think that's hazardous, after such a long interval."

"I agree, there may be trouble, unless he can make the people realize that he is master of any situation. I feel he lacks decision. And then—I can say this, for I am a foreigner—he is surrounded by disloyal courtiers. Oh, if I were in his place, I know what *I'd* do to keep order."

"Tell me."

"You won't agree, for you love your life at Court: I wouldn't allow so many members of the nobility to leave the provinces and live at Versailles. I'd encourage them to stay on their own estates. They belong there. As a great many nobles are poor, I'd make a tour in various provinces and give emoluments to those who were the best landlords, and who took the most intelligent interest in agriculture. We should imitate the English squires. In Brittany, for instance, there is such neglect—the land is just wild, uncultivated heath, or undrained marshes. All those acres untilled, and the owners are living all huddled up in some out-of-the-way garret at Versailles."

"Yes, I agree, Versailles is like a great octopus, sucking the life blood of our aristocracy. But, you know, we all feel at home there; I don't think many of us at Court take naturally to country life."

"I know! Whenever I invite my friends to stay at Bel-Oeil, they rise at noon, live for the post and the arrival of the news-sheet, play cards and act plays all day, and at night, pay visits to each other's rooms and gossip till dawn."

"A woman, alas, unless she is a widow, only goes to the country to restore her complexion, or economize to pay her card debts. What a lot she misses!"

Just then the coach stopped dead, and a footman appeared at the window with a sealed note which he handed to Eléonore. Glancing at her apprehensively, he explained that a courier from Paris had brought it an hour ago, but the crowd was too dense for him to reach her before.

Eléonore looked very worried. "I wonder if the children are ill? Elzéar had a little cough before I left." She broke the seal. The letter told her briefly that her husband had died suddenly after a paralytic stroke.

CHAPTER VI

"THESE SPRING EVENINGS ARE DANGEROUS"

"A WOMAN, alas, unless she is a widow . . ." A year later. A year of strictest seclusion for a young widow. Eléonore had gone with her two children to stay with her husband's thirty-five-year-old brother, the Bishop of Laon, Monseigneur de Sabran at his château of Anizy, near Laon. This little Renaissance château, to which his predecessor had made considerable additions, was a miniature jewel of architecture. Its delicate turrets rose out of a setting of lush meadows and pretty woodlands. The clergy, the shepherds and other country folk were all devoted to their bishop, who, though lacking, perhaps, the fire of an apostle, was well-endowed with urbanity, humanism and the spirit of hospitality. His eighteenth-century Benedictine biographer said of him that the *douceur de ses mœurs* and the qualities of his mind and heart promised an era of happiness to his diocese under a peaceable and wise rule. Like his dead brother, he was a traditionalist, thoroughly loyal to the monarchy, and a firm believer that the present state of things was the best for all concerned. The morals of Louis-Hector-Honoré-Maxime de Sabran were beyond reproach—else later in his career he would not have been made Grand Almoner to the Queen. But that did not prevent him from being a shrewd judge of a horse or the bouquet of a wine; and he enjoyed intelligent conversation. He liked Eléonore because she was very delightful to talk to, and she helped him to entertain his canons and other diocesan dignitaries with consummate grace.

It was a May evening; brother and sister-in-law were having a collation together at a small round table in the centre of a large dining-room. Sunlight glowed softly on a bowl of early strawberries, the tall-stemmed wine glasses which the wine had first goldened, then reddened, the greyhounds nuzzling into their master's fine hand, and on the little white cap which completely hid Eléonore's curls. In his choice of dishes, the bishop showed himself to be an epicure rather than a *gourmand*. First a pigeon reclining on fried croutons surrounded by a subtly-blended sauce; then a large silver dish of the tenderest little peas cooked with cream, onions, sugar and lettuce, An omelette of Gruyère cheese, grilled golden brown and surrounded by minute button potatoes sizzling in country butter. A few crisp lettuce leaves dressed with care by the bishop's long fingers. Finally, pine-apple hollowed and filled with vanilla ice and fragments of *marrons glacés.* A small meal for the eighteenth century: only one main course, no soup, no fish!

"*Ma Sœur*, what did you do to-day?"

"*Mon Frère*, I spent a very quiet day. This morning I taught Delphine her letters and then showed her Sacy's Bible. Elzéar was rather naughty and kept climbing up and interrupting. Then I brought out my pastels and tried to do their portraits, but it was no good, as they would not remain still. Then this evening I took my Virgil with me, and went for a walk."

"I'm sure you did no reading!"

"I didn't. Oh, what a lovely evening. Do you know, this is the first time in my life that I have really tasted the pleasures of country life."

"You must ride again," said the bishop, "and then you would be able to roam farther afield. So you enjoyed this evening?"

"Very much. 'Nothing to be seen but meadows bejewelled with flowers, little cottages at intervals to rest the eyes, and nothing to be met but pretty little sheep and young shepherds. I think they are much prettier than our modern shepherds; they were crowned with lilac, and were eating large slices of black bread and butter with very white cheese. I love to hear them singing in unison about the simple charms of their shepherdesses. The peace that reigns in this solitude goes to my heart'."[1]

Aloud the bishop said: "Indeed, my dear sister, you almost reconcile me to my exile here." But he thought within himself: "She sees love all around her, even in the shepherds singing to the shepherdesses, and love makes her sad." To distract her, Monseigneur de Sabran told her how this morning he had received the visit from a canoness of the noble chapter of Lyons, and that she wore a fashionable dress of black silk on panniers, and great ermine sleeves. "She was extremely diverting to talk to. She knew all the latest Court gossip."

"Yes," continued the bishop, sugaring a strawberry with exquisite fastidiousness, "women very rarely shed their vanity when they go into religious orders. She was telling me about the convent of the Abbaye-aux-Bois, where Charlot de Ligne's daughter-in-law, Hélène, went as a boarder. They say that the apartments of the former *abbesse*—a daughter of Louis XIV and Madame de Montespan—were haunted. At night, the nuns said, they heard shrieks and smelt sulphur. No one would go near that suite, and it took six nuns in a bunch to sweep it twice a year. Some of these *abbesses* never shed their exorbitant pride of race.

[1]This paragraph is an extract from a letter of Eléonore's (to the Chevalier May 15, 1787).

I've heard it said of Madame de Torcy that she became a nun because Jesus Christ was the only fit spouse for her."

Eléonore smiled. "That reminds me of the mad old Maréchale de Noailles, who was always writing notes to the Blessed Virgin and leaving them in a nook in the garden. Her husband used to write the answers, and leave them there too. But the Maréchale was quite scandalized when Our Lady addressed her as 'my dear daughter'. 'What, a little *bourgeoise* from Nazareth daring to address me like that'!"

The bishop dipped his fingers into a finely-wrought silver bowl, full of scented water, and dried them carefully on a diaphanous linen towel. He pushed a tray of preserved fruits towards Eléonore, leant back in his chair and gazed out at the green mosaic of trees in the park, unearthly in the liquid ambers of a May evening.

Suddenly he said: "I can always tell you my blasphemous stories and you are never scandalised. It has often occurred to me that in order to be really blasphemous one must be a believer at heart. You've heard of that charming, witty fellow Stanislas de Boufflers, who left the seminary and has since been fighting and roving the world? His little blasphemous rhymes are masterpieces."

"I've never met him. I've only heard of him."

"I love his verses, I suppose they ought to shock me, for I can't quote them to my canons here."

"Why did the Chevalier leave the seminary?" asked Eléonore.

"Well, you can't imagine that such a versifier would be popular at Saint Sulpice? Besides, he was too much of a social butterfly. The superiors tried in vain to curtail his visits, but he was loud in his lamentations. He never really wanted to try his vocation at all, but was forced to do so by his mother. However, in the end he had the honesty to see that he simply couldn't just stay in the Church solely for a livelihood, and he left just in time. Yes, he was thoroughly honest. I hear, now, he's become a great favourite of Voltaire's. Yes, I think he won the old man's heart by reciting his verses, and then by quoting the famous story of the Abbé Prévost to him."

"What was that?"

"The abbé wanted to be almoner to a certain nobleman, and when he presented himself the nobleman said to him: 'I don't need an almoner, as I never hear Mass.' And the abbé replied: 'It is precisely for that reason that I have the honour to apply for the appointment, and that I think it was made for me, because if you never hear a Mass I, on my part, never say one.' Yes, a story like that was exactly in the style of Boufflers. He comes from a family whose tradition forbids bigotry and pretentiousness in any form, a family which judged that *le ton* was everything in a man, and that there is a subtle connection between elegant manners and elevation of mind."

"Yes, I know. His great-aunt, the Maréchale, even believes that it is pleasing to God to address him in prayer in a courtly manner. I shall never forget, when we were visiting the Prince de Conti at l'Isle-Adam, we were all waiting to go into Mass, and had just put down our missals on a table in the drawing-room. The Maréchale picked up one of these missals, and began to criticise some of the prayers furiously, and say that they were in bad taste. Another woman said to her: 'Surely, sincere piety is more important to God than *bon ton*,' and she turned round sharply and said with the utmost seriousness, '*Eh, bien, Madame*, don't you believe it'!"

A little later, Eléonore, a slight figure in her black ninon panniers and widow's cap, was leaning over the balustrade of the terrace absorbed in the beauty of the view. She had a faraway look in her eyes. The bishop, knowing how easily his sister-in-law caught chills, interrupted the recitation of his Breviary to ring for her furs. "These Spring evenings are dangerous," he said, not without meaning; and, taking off his episcopal tricorne, with its gold tassels, he murmured the words from the Office of Compline: "Our adversary the Devil, as a roaring lion, goeth about seeking whom he may devour." [To a man as enlightened as Monseigneur de Sabran, the Devil was merely an interesting relic of the Middle Ages, but still very useful to frighten the ignorant masses of the faithful.] His mind was absorbed in anxiety for Eléonore, who had been his guest for nearly a year now. Lately he had been struck by her thinness, her languor and depression, and he thought: "Alas, happiness is a mighty physician, and if he does not cure, at any rate he makes you forget your ills. She is much too young and beautiful to spend the rest of her days in country retirement. How bored she must be by my canons, with their addiction to the pleasures of the table. And yet, that is the only society I can offer her. The conversation of a Boufflers, for example, would be more bracing—(that most charming of madmen!) If she left Ainzy, I should be the loser, but it might be best for her to return to Paris. She must not take root in the dangerous pleasures of solitude, and become quite unfit to converse with friends of her own age."

During that time, Madame de Sabran was day-dreaming, thereby fulfilling the bishop's worst fears. She had been reading Virgil again, and the little volume had slipped from her hands as she read: "*Sunt lacrymae rerum, et mentem mortalia tangunt.*" She was regretting that the hour of conversation had passed so swiftly. Almost unconsciously, she clung to the society of her brother-in-law, and found mental solace in his cynicisms, in his open mind entirely free from bigotry, and the distinction of his very presence.

"These Spring evenings are dangerous." She had not told her brother that she had also been reading Rousseau that morning; Rousseau, so long shunned during her girlhood, was now distilling his slow poison in her veins. In the Elysium of Clarens, Eléonore wandered in that Paradise Lost of lilac groves and winding alleys, drinking in the solitude and shade, listening to the sounds of running water and the song of the nightingale. And now she longed for someone to share the Paradise. Oh, barren century, where woman in love never invoked Nature to echo her transports until Rousseau taught her the art. Hitherto, the God Cupid had reigned in candlelit alcove or airless *boudoir*, never in field and woodland.

With a start, Eléonore realized that she was thinking not of her dead husband but of some nebulous creature of her imagination, who was young, like herself. How wonderful if only she could be in the company of someone of her own age, a friend to whom she need be neither daughterly nor protective, but quite simply herself.

And she had not told the bishop that, on her walk this morning among the shepherdesses, she had called at a thatched cottage where buttercups were splashing the very doorstep in gold; the young mother of a copious family had offered her a bowl of the creamiest milk; then the woman's husband came in from the fields, and looked at his wife for a moment as she was feeding the youngest baby. The quiet happiness of the woman basking in the love of her young husband had haunted Eléonore for the rest of the day.

"I must distract myself and not succumb to melancholy," she whispered. Just then the bishop murmured his final "*Gloria Patri*" and made the sign of the cross.

"I had quite a quantity of letters from Paris this morning," said Eléonore, turning to him.

The bishop was glad of the distraction, so he settled in a chair near her, and deftly led his sister-in-law to talk about her many friends. He always relished any gossip from her letters. Was the world going mad? Oh, the names of the fashionable colours! —thigh of emotional nymph, Paris mud, goose-dung, and above all, *puce*, or flea-coloured, with all its variations of old flea, young flea, tummy of flea suffering from milk fever! "How did this enchanting colour ever come into vogue?" he asked, taking a pinch of snuff.

"Don't you know? A woman at a card party was examining

a dead flea on her nail. 'Look, *Mesdames*, at the colour of this flea! It's a black which isn't black, it's a brown which is too brown, but really, this is a *delicious* colour . . .' In Coronation year you only had to wear that shade to be a raging success at Court, for it was the King himself who had named it."

"Indeed," said the bishop, twirling his amethyst, "to describe a subtle colour accurately is a mark of a highly-developed mind. The violent colours belong to a cruder age. But, tell me, *Ma Sœur*, what is that new head-dress which is called *pouf à la grand'mère?*"

"Oh, that's a coiffure which you can lower two feet by pulling a string, when you visit your grandmother, in case she disapproves."

Eléonore patted her hair under its cap, and looked rather frivolous for a fleeting moment.

"What a good thing I don't have to worry about that," she said, not altogether convincingly.

The bishop threw up his hands in mock dismay. "What, have you renounced the pleasures of the *toilette* for ever? I don't believe you! When you were reading the letter of your school friend the other day, in which she told you of her four changes of dress in one day, you got quite excited. Come, think now, my dear. You remember your friend was giving you the time-table of her days."

With great wiliness, he led her to recall the chiffon of a letter which began with an entrancing afternoon spent in the Rue Saint-Honoré, shopping with a maid, visiting the famous doll in a shop window which served as mannequin to the rest of Europe, then a musical tea-party *chez le Prince de Conti*, at the Temple, a visit to the Opéra where it was fast becoming the fashion to appear in one's box in superb furs, and to shed them with all the languorous art of a coquette, and finally a night party near the Orangery of Versailles which lasted until dawn.

The whole account was perfumed with feminine vanities; one could almost picture Eléonore's little friend at her *toilette*, surrounded by a chattering crowd of monkeys, angora cats, spaniels, parrots of bright plumage, tame abbés reading verse, a flower-merchant bringing sweets and scent, dressmakers displaying their wares in chintz-covered boxes; and in the background the bevy of light, fluttering maids who lend such charm to the engravings of Baudouin. The letter seemed almost calculated to entice the most retired young woman back to Paris. Scribbled in haste on the corner of her dressing-table, it conjured up all the graces which these women had learnt before their mirrors—one could see slender fingers on the handle of fans, the indiscretions of high heels glimpsed under foaming skirts, tricks of deportment, the coquetry of little gestures and the play of shoulders; in brief, all the touches which made woman a finished work of art, the paragon of her century, and desirable to man. . . .

And the missive concluded with an appeal from the writer to her dear friend Eléonore to return to this social *milieu* which was hers by right of birth and fortune, a life whose sweets she had never really tasted. "You are twenty-eight, *ma chère*, time is slipping by. Do not heap up for your old age a store of regret for the pleasures you have left untasted; far better to experience life fully and to suffer thereby, than not to dare and later to pine away in futile regrets."

"My sister"—and here the bishop was clever—"you must not only think of yourself, but of Delphine and Elzéar. How can their education be pursued here, far from dancing instructors and drawing masters, away from professional actors who could coach them in their little theatricals? And then they are separated from other children of their own world."

And it was this last argument which finally made Eléonore de Sabran decide to flee the dangerous pleasures of solitude and drown her sadness in the feverish life of Paris.

END OF PART I

PART II

STANISLAS

CHAPTER VII

A CONFINEMENT ON THE HIGHWAY, AND SUBSEQUENT EVENTS

"When I remember that court of Lunéville, I seem to be recalling the pages of a novel, rather than the years of my own life."

STANISLAS DE BOUFFLERS.

ON May 31st, 1738, the Comtesse de Boufflers decided to transact some business in the town of Bar-le-duc. She was living at Commercy, in the Palace of her royal protector, the enormously fat Stanislas Leczinski, ex-king of Poland, and father of the Queen of France. She jumped up into a high gig, taking with her a great admirer, a sedate magistrate. They trotted off at a good pace. Members of the little Court stood on the terrace and waved to her in the sunshine. Numerous fountains flung up glittering cascades while swans and elegant galleys glided by on the silvery expanse of the canal. Commercy was the King's favourite residence.

"Now let us enjoy ourselves," cried the Comtesse. What *joie-de-vivre!* She had already chosen her epitaph:

A lady of pleasure, and frolic and passion
In deepest peace and rest here lies.
To be on the safe side, in wisest of fashion
In this world made her Paradise.

She always wore tiny rose-coloured slippers and enchanting dresses of bright silk over her voluminous panniers. All day she sang to the harp and harpsichord songs of her own composition, gambled recklessly, indulged in witty conversations and ephemeral flirtations. The rooms of the Palace echoed with her peals of delicious laughter, for life was so gay and she lived only for the moment. She was always surrounded by a retinue of adorers and friends, and they remained devoted to her for the rest of her life. Her son said of her long after: "Her gaiety was like a perpetual springtime in her heart that brought forth flowers to the last day of her life." She did not love the plump old King, but she had grown fond of him, and could not endure the idea of causing him pain. So she kept her infidelities dark. Though she was far too inconsequent to feather her own nest, and, according to Voltaire, sometimes even lacked money to buy petticoats, she found that the care-free life at Commercy and Lunéville suited her temperament admirably. King Stanislas knew how to make his guests feel at home, she was surrounded by kindred spirits, and she was indispensable to all.

Later in the afternoon, after finishing her business at Bar-le-duc, the Comtesse took the road back to Commercy. It was a fine May evening and she had given over the reins to the devoted admirer who, wishing to prolong so pleasant a *tête-à-tête*, slowed down to a moderate trot. His wiliness was rewarded, for, no doubt inspired by the example of numerous yellow-hammers twittering in field and copse, the Comtesse showed signs of an inclination to gentle dalliance. Occasionally her little hand slipped into his and pressed it, quite ardently! She did this at almost regular intervals. Fearful of believing in his good fortune, the magistrate stole sideways glances at her, and could not help admiring the glow of her flushed cheeks. Again the pretty hand stole out, this time the pressure had become more affectionate. She gave a little sigh.

"Shall I harness the horse while we rest by the roadside awhile?" he asked, almost timidly.

"Oh yes, *please* do."

He jumped out, and, hardly able to contain his impatience, lifted her down in his arms. Her breath was hot against his cheek. He carried her to a grassy spot by the roadside, put her down gently, and went to harness the horse to a tree. This took longer than he had expected, for the tiresome animal was nibbling a particularly enticing patch of clover, and could not be induced to leave it for some time. Another deep sigh from the Comtesse made him hurry to her side. She was lying back amongst the daisies, looking quite adorable in her rose-coloured panniers. He was about to declare his devotion, when she clutched both his wrists and said most unexpectedly: "Fetch the provision basket, quick, but quick." A little piqued that she showed such a tantalizing and unflattering preference for Epicurus, at a moment when the little winged god should have reigned supreme, he resentfully fetched the hamper and put it down by her side. Then she said: "It will have to be washed in champagne and wrapped in my table-napkin. Bring out the knife and some string. Do you know how to cut the cord?"

"What *are* you talking about?" he said, mystified.

"The baby, of course, *imbécile*!"

"What baby, dear Comtesse?"

"Oh, you clod, the baby I'm going to have any minute now. Didn't you know? Ah, well, even *I* thought it might be colic after that excellent *foie-gras*, but . . . Ai! hold my hand, you great fool. I always felt you might be a little stupid, but this time I'm *convinced* that you're an idiot."

And that is how Stanislas, Chevalier de Boufflers, one of the most renowned wits of eighteenth-century France, made his first bow to this world.

At the palace of Commercy, King Stanislas and his guests were getting anxious. The sun had set, and there was no sign of the Comtesse.

Much later that evening they espied the empty gig coming at a snail's pace, led by the admirer, who looked very pleased with himself. "Where is the dear Comtesse?" they cried.

Without a word, he pointed rather bashfully to the inside of the gig. They all crowded around. There, propped up on cushions on the floor, lay the smiling Comtesse, holding in her arms a little bright-eyed baby wrapped in a table-napkin, who suddenly threw out its tiny arms, made a square mouth, and began rending the air with its yells!

Everybody wrote his own epitaph in those days. The Chevalier in due course followed the prevailing fashion:

Here lies a Knight whose life was one mad rush,
Who on the great high roads was born, and lived and died.
To prove the truth once uttered by a sage,
That life below is nothing but a journey.

The Comtesse had no time for babies. She sent little Stanislas out to nurse with a peasant woman of Haroué. If ever he was lost, they said: "Better go and look for him in Pataud's kennel." Dog and child were so inseparable that both got called Pataud or Lout, indiscriminately. Although he was given the name of Boufflers, there is little doubt that Stanislas was the Polish King's son: there was, moreover, in his character a strain of ruggedness and passionate wildness which was essentially Slav, though he was to inherit all his mother's French wit and gaiety. After a while, he was sent to his aunt, the Princesse de Beauvau. He stayed away nine years altogether.

1747. Nine years later. The Pompadour had been Louis XV's mistress for the last two years. At Lunéville, King Stanislas said one morning to the Comtesse, who was as frivolous as ever: "Well, my little namesake comes back to-day."

"Let's hope he's not as dull-witted as they say. I'll have to play little games with him to develop his intelligence."

"*I* don't want to play with him," said his six-year-old sister, Catharine, an ugly, spiteful litt e girl whom her mother spoilt and adored, and most ineptly called "*La divine Mignonne*".

"Nor I," said his elder brother Charles.

Unluckily, young Stanislas arrived before he was expected, when everybody was taking an evening walk to look at the new waterworks which were the King's passion. In that vast household, swarming with servants—(fifty-six in the kitchen alone)—there was no one to show him to his rooms and make him feel at home. Rather upset by this, for he was longing to see his mother, the child wandered disconsolately through the gardens till he reached a stone seat in the niche of a yew-hedge. He sat down heavily and began thinking sadly of Pataud, his old Nanny sheep-dog.

They say it takes a wise man to play the fool. The circumstances of this lonely boy's life had forced him to put up a façade of dullness so that people would leave him alone and he could creep away unnoticed. He had all the marks of a neglected child—clothes put on anyhow, indifferent teeth, rather unkempt hair, and an ungainly way of walking and of twiddling his thumbs for which he later became famous. However, he had the white, smooth skin of the aristocrat ("*ta peau blanche et fine*"),[1] and a serious face. The Prince de Ligne, who adored him, says of him: "There is childishness in his laugh and awkwardness in his bearing; he holds his head down and twiddles his thumbs in front of him like a Harlequin, or else keeps his hands behind his back as if he were warming himself; his eyes, small and agreeable, seem to smile; there is something kindly in his face, something simple, gay, and naïf in his manner; there is heaviness in his figure and carelessness in his person. He sometimes has the stupid look of La Fontaine, and one would say he was thinking of nothing, when he is thinking the most."

At that moment, Stanislas was looking more vacant than usual, kicking his heels and biting his nails. He was very hungry.

"Feeling bored?" said a piping voice from the region of his elbow.

The boy started, for the voice seemed to come from nowhere.

"Look down, but don't tread on me," the voice continued.

Rubbing his eyes and wondering whether he was dreaming, Stanislas looked down and saw a fairy. This is the sober truth, and not an invention. He saw a little man, very pretty and beautifully proportioned, two feet high, dressed in breeches, coat, gorgeous waistcoat and lace ruffles. Stanislas stared hard, and then crossed himself.

[1] Madame de Sabran said it of him.

"Don't do that," said the little man, stamping his foot angrily. "I'm not the Devil, though everyone here seems to think I am."

"I beg your pardon."

"I should think so. And who may you be, pray?"

"I'm Stanislas de Boufflers. I've come to live with my mother."

"She'll have no time to spare for *you*, my boy. She's flirting with her latest adorer. No one wants you."

At that Stanislas lost his temper, and, fairy or no fairy, bent down and, seizing the little man round the waist, shook him violently. The dwarf—for so he was—started biting and screaming and kicking. He made as much noise as a very angry, squealing baby. Suddenly, as if in answer to his cries, a *chef* rushed out from the servants' wing of the palace, and, running as fast as he could to the yew-walk, stopped dead when he saw Stanislas. The dwarf ceased screaming. Gilliers, the *chef*, doffed his cap, and twirling it awkwardly in his hands, stammered to Stanislas:

"Beg pardon, sir, but I shouldn't do that, sir. His Majesty will be displeased. Nicolas is due to be popped into a surprise pie I'm making to-night: I don't want him all upset. *Please* let him go."

"But he was insolent and I won't have it," said Stanislas. "Who is he, anyway? I thought he was supernatural."

"I'm Bébé, and I won't be put into a pie. And I'm not supernatural. Let me go, you son of a harlot, or I'll poison the rest of your days here."

The *chef* threw up his hands in horror, and Stanislas, by now quite beside himself with rage, picked up a twig from the ground and started lashing the dwarf across the face with it. With piercing screams and yells, Bébé tried to wriggle away from his executioner, but Stanislas' wrists were as strong as steel, and he was very angry.

Gilliers, the artist-*chef* who was responsible for King Stanislas' sweetmeats, suddenly had a bright idea. He came nearer and dangled a candied orange in front of the infuriated boy's nose; the trick worked. Stanislas let go. But before he could take the sweetmeat, Bébé, quick as forked lightning, seized it and ran away in the direction of the house, chattering like an angry monkey.

Gilliers sighed with relief, mopped his brow with the back of his hand, and fishing into his pocket, brought out a comfit box and respectfully offered it to Stanislas.

"Tell me about the little beast," said Stanislas, a trifle restored. (He loved sweet things.)

"Nicolas Ferry, sir. That's His Majesty's great pet. He only weighed one and a quarter pounds at birth, and was carried to church on a plate. A clog was his cradle. Between you and me, sir, I can't say that his christening did him much good."

"I can see he's got a horrid nature."

Gilliers said in a whisper: "He's obstinate, very bad-tempered, lazy, greedy, sensual, and above all, very jealous. The *Princesse* Talmont was the only person who ever had any hold on him, for she tried to educate him. Bébé, for once, showed a little gratitude by loving her with such passion that when she caressed her dog one day he threw it out of the window. The poor *Princesse*, however, soon renounced any hopes she ever had of educating him. He has no reason and no judgement, and he cannot be made to understand the idea of God and religion. Of course he's very jealous of you."

"Why is he kept, then?"

"Oh, sir, he amuses His Majesty, though I often feel he's more trouble than he's worth. If he's thwarted in any way he breaks the china and glasses on His Majesty's table. We can only persuade him to obey by bribing him with sweets or a new costume. Once, when he was leaping out of a pie, he shot a pistol at the ladies. He hates the noise of *tric-trac*, and when the King is playing, he jumps on the pile of counters with a bang, and everybody is obliged to stop playing."

Stanislas laughed. "Why, that's like my Aunt de Mirepoix's cat, who pushes the counters on the loto-table with her paw." He added hopefully: "Perhaps Bébé will get lost one day. He's so small."

"We all profoundly hope he will," said Gilliers in a whisper. "The servants are terrified of him. As a matter of fact, he nearly did get lost in a field of high grass the other morning; we spent the day looking for him. The ladies are always afraid of squashing him with their panniers. His insolence is disgusting: when he's sulking, he locks himself into his little castle and calls out through the window: 'You will tell the King I am not at home'."

By now, Stanislas had finished the comfits and was sticky all over. The clock in the stable yard struck the hour. He suddenly crumpled up, weary with hunger and disappointment and rage.

"I wonder when they are coming home?" he said, almost in tears.

Gilliers felt sorry for him, and thought what a shame it was, to return after nine years and not find his mother at home. He took the boy by the hand and led him towards his own special quarters, where he was preparing the dessert for supper that night. He ordered a tray of hot chocolate, *brioches*, and some special candied fruits to be brought. Then he installed him by his side as he worked. After a while another white-robed *chef* came in and bowed to Stanislas.

"Cyfflé, at your service, sir," said he.

Gilliers pointed to him and said: "His Majesty's superintendent of table-decorations, sir. He is a great artist. What are you doing to-night, Cyfflé?"

"I'd planned to devise a stag-hunt on the table, but Bébé has broken the stag, so I will have to fall back on a mythological scene—Leda and the Swan, for example. I came to ask you whether you would lend me a few bits of angelica for reeds."

"With pleasure, Monsieur Cyfflé, with pleasure," said the amiable Gilliers, taking out his bunch of keys.

Cyfflé smiled with smug mock humility and turned to Stanislas: "Monsieur Gilliers, my esteemed friend, is as gifted as he is charming. Do you know, sir, it is no ordinary man that you see before you. He is an artist who has left a large monument of his art for posterity." He went to a bookcase and pulled out a magnificent quarto volume with numerous mouth-watering illustrations, and read the title-page aloud: "*Le Cannaméliste français:* being the customs, choice and principles of all that is used in the preparation of candied fruit, dry or liquid, or preserved in *eau-de-vie*, sugar confections, long drinks, sweets, *bon-bons*, snows, *mousses* and *glacé* fruits."

"I should like to read that book," said Stanislas. "I love the pictures." Then, looking up, "Are you really doing Leda and the Swan to-night?"

"On second thoughts, sir, in honour of your home-coming, I think I'll do a little park in the manner of Monsieur Lenôtre. His Majesty loves waters splashing everywhere, so I might contrive that tiny fountains play into miniature ponds on the table. I have been fortunate in getting some little Sèvres statuettes of Courtiers and Court ladies, so I can scatter these charming figures, strolling at leisure amongst fruits and flowers. My confederate, Monsieur Gilliers, will make cypresses and rose-bushes for me out of coloured icing sugar."

"What fun," said Stanislas, by now completely fascinated. "You will end your days at Versailles, in the service of the King."

The two *chefs* exchanged meaning glances. "Never," said Gilliers. "I know too much about the riff-raff serving in those kitchens and still-rooms there."

"Yes," said Cyfflé, "a rabble of thieves, nothing less. Just to feed His Majesty there is a staff three or four times as large as this one. At Versailles the *chefs* allow their friends and relations to swarm into the royal kitchens and filch any amount of morsels away. All food coming out untouched from the royal table is sold in the town at a great profit. It will cause trouble one day. It isn't His Majesty who should be blamed."

"And then," said Gilliers, "there's this system of perquisites. My cousin, who is *chef* to *Mesdames*—and their Lenten fare is renowned—my cousin tells me that every single candle in the royal apartments, whether used or not, becomes the property of the ladies-in-waiting at the end of the day."

He drew back from his table, and surveyed his park critically. Then he turned to Stanislas and bowed respectfully, and said: "Now, sir, I'm sure His Majesty will return at any moment. Shall I lead you into the alley through which he usually comes?"

And that is how Stanislas made two friends on his first day at Lunéville. And throughout his boyhood, they both spoilt him so much with little gifts of sweetmeats that they contributed not a little to those torturing attacks of toothache which racked him at intervals for the rest of his life, and which, in one instance, ruined his diplomatic career by making his cheek swell at the wrong moment!

CHAPTER VIII

THE EDUCATION OF A WIT

In a few days the boy had settled down quite happily. Out-of-doors, he kept the jealous Bébé away by hissing at him whenever he came in sight of his little cart drawn by four goats. The Comtesse treated her son like a grown-up person, and soon won his adoration with her gaiety and her accomplishments. As for King Stanislas Leczinski, he took an instant liking to the clumsy-looking boy who had so many foibles in common with him! He soon found that he had a prodigious appetite, as if he had been half-starved until now. In spite of a hot temper he was a warm-hearted, impulsive lad, craving for affection; he seemed to have an inexhaustible fund of health and gaiety, and an enormous capacity for enjoyment. Above all, even at that early age, he shared some of the King's rather advanced democratic views. One day the King and Stanislas were showing some officers from Nancy the new pavilions which were being made in the park for the privileged courtiers. Within hearing of the workmen one of the officers had said: "Here are some logs who are fashioning stones."

The King interposed, with ill-concealed annoyance: "You are mistaken. All men have a relative value, whatever their condition." Then, turning to the workmen, he said to them: "Now, what do *you* think of soldiers—no doubt you think they're very inferior to masons."

"Indeed we do," replied the chief builder, "for masons build, and soldiers can only destroy."

"Ah! ha!" said the King, "listen to your logs talking."

The officers looked so thoroughly discomfited that one of the workmen said: "Oh, well, if perhaps these gentlemen cause a death here and there, on the other hand they are responsible for plenty of christenings at Nancy."

Stanislas burst out laughing. The King followed suit, and exclaimed: "Well, really, the devil take the hindmost. We've made the logs talk. I notice that their bite is cruel."

Thus did the King find that young Stanislas completely shared his view, that each human being, however low in the social scale, had a unique value of his own, and should be justly treated.

The boy had a grand sense of fun. On the day that the Emperor of Austria sent his yearly barrel of Tokay to the King, in a coach decorated with the arms of Austria and Hungary, escorted by four grenadiers, King Stanislas took him to the courtyard of the château to receive the gift in person, and then led him to the royal cellars. Here, dressed in an apron and in the company of a discreet acolyte who was sworn to secrecy, the King, puffing and panting with obesity and excitement, mixed his own potion of Tokay with Burgundy and other wines, put the hideous concoction in bottles specially manufactured and labelled for the purpose, and then had them sent to his friends! And no one was so unwise as to ask how he could possibly spare so many bottles of this precious Tokay! And the ignoramuses, whose palates were vitiated by snobbery, would roll it round their tongues, close their eyes and say: "Perfect!"

Unfortunately, the old King was a *gourmand* rather than a *gourmet*. His appetite was so violent that he would often have dinner an hour earlier—to the dismay of his *chefs*. Someone said to him: "If your Majesty continues like this, you will finish by dining the day before." He would eat his meat cooked with fruit, and showed a decided taste for raw sauerkraut and shredded cabbage powdered with sugar.

This childlike old man, who loved making everybody around him happy, and who revelled in practical jokes, never found anyone like Stanislas to appreciate the wonderful clockwork village he had invented. Day after day the boy would make him waddle along to it and set the machinery in motion. The village was built on an artificial rock, and was complete, with life-size peasants in painted wood. There were houses, a hermitage, and even a tavern. The three hundred people, with their animals, were set in motion by the action of water. Cocks crew, lambs grazed, goats fought, the cat pursued a mouse, the drunkard returning home at night had a pail of water thrown over his head from a window. A woman worked at her spinning-wheel, and a carter whipped up his horses. What a ravishing plaything for a boy, and what fun to see it coming to life all of a sudden!

The boy's admiration for his mother was so blind that he lost all power of making independent judgements with regard to her morals. In fact, he was brought up in a completely amoral atmosphere. At the time, a certain Comte de Tressan had won her favours. When he, in his turn, was dropped, he wrote long letters to a former lover of hers nicknamed Panpan, saying he longed to hide his heart in "one of her little pink slippers". He was in ecstasies when the "*divine fauvette*" had sung to him alone on her harpsichord. Stanislas was a witness to all this, and sympathized with the victims a little.

After a while, Stanislas began to understand why his mother was universally loved. "To listen", that was the secret which endeared Madame de Boufflers to her admirers. She believed, with Solomon, that silence was woman's best ornament. Also, the brevity of her wit was delightful: she had her own views on this, and she aired them in verse. Her brother said she brought her lovers to despair, more by her wit than by her infidelities. After a while Stanislas caught the fashionable fever of versifying from her, and developed a talent which later was to make him beloved in all the wittiest drawing-rooms of the century.

To our so-called civilized ideas, it might appear shocking that the child grew up in surroundings where pure married happiness was deemed ridiculous. It is necessary to get "inside the skin" of the people of the eighteenth century in order to realize that they had a justifiable point of view about this, and, in fact, *almost* an excuse. In France, where the security and perpetuation of the family counts for more than the happiness and freedom of the individual, marriages in the upper classes were arranged as if they were financial contracts. Mutual passion did not come into this. (Sometimes it worked, and there is quite a long record of happy marriages, which remains almost forgotten because it has escaped the notoriety of sin. For instance, there is the moving picture of a young bridegroom who, knowing that his adored wife would die very soon, sold all he had, in order to buy her a magnificent diamond necklace and tried to make her believe that she was going to wear it at Court in the near future.) More often the system did not work. The husband sought distractions with a mistress quite soon after marriage, leaving his wife to her own devices, often without children, always without the busy household duties of the medieval housewife, religious only in so far as it was the *chic* custom to go to

Mass on Sundays, surrounded by friends who were, at best, completely uncritical about moral matters. She might resist for a time, but after a while everything would conspire towards her downfall. All the world about her breathed one word alone —Pleasure; for love was no longer the heroic fire of Racine's time, but appealed chiefly to the senses. All material things themselves spoke that word—Pleasure, *Volupté*—the downy, comfortable arm-chairs of the times, made for confidences and *tête-à-têtes*, the voluptuous beds in their alcoves, the semi-obscurity of the *boudoirs* with their heavy curtains and rich draperies, the engravings on the walls—Baudouin, Regnault, Lavreince, Eisen—which never respected the privacy of woman in bed or at her *toilette*, and which even intruded upon the intimacies of the wedding night; all those many engravings with titles like: "*La rose mal défendue*," "*Le secret*," "*La comparaison*," "*La toilette intime*," "*L'amant indiscret*," and so on. And those dresses of the woman of the time, designed, as it were, to equip her for the battle of love and to attract desire, the neck greatly *decolleté*, the bodice tightly laced to accentuate a slender waist, those inspired little shoes called *Venez-y-Voir* (Just look at it), those voluminous skirts which billowed on either side as a woman glided across a room, making her look like a rose emerging from a large calyx, the make-up and head-dresses, subtle enough to hide any natural defects and bring out every hidden beauty. Everything conspired to make these men and women of the *dix-huitième* think that the sole aim of life was the perfecting of your material tastes, so that you drew the acme of enjoyment from your surroundings, and enjoyed the pleasures of love in a perfect setting. And the mother of Stanislas, who had called herself "*la dame de volupté*", was, above all, in her search for pleasure, only a woman of her century.

The account of this miniature court which had all the brilliance of Versailles without its etiquette, makes the most fascinating reading. One gets the impression of a prolonged house-party composed of nobles, pretty women, poets, philosophers, artists and literary men. There was music at all meals, played by an orchestra whose violinist had been a friend of Lulli's, nocturnal wanderings in the bosquets of the park after the King had gone to bed, exchange of gifts like porcelain Cupids, accompanied by suitable little poems. And on Sundays, after Vespers, they would accompany Madame Durival, of whom Stanislas was very fond, and dance wild "*rondes*" in the fields with all the young people, while Madame Durival sat on a tree-trunk and played the guitar. (This great friend of the Marquise de Boufflers was beloved in the country round, for she would tour the villages in her big straw hat, carrying an apothecary's bag under her arm, to cure all the sick and poor.)

To add spice and diversity to this life which seemed like an "*embarquement pour Cythère*", there was an open feud between the Marquise de Boufflers and the Jesuit confessor: both played in turns on the imagination of the King. When the priest prevailed and frightened his royal penitent into making a retreat for the good of his soul, the Marquise lost nothing, for she seized the opportunity to deceive the King in his absence with a succession of other lovers.

Stanislas may not have received a conventional education, but very soon he had become a good deal more accomplished than many of his contemporaries. By eighteen he rode magnificently, danced, sang, was a keen and selective Latinist, painted in pastels and in oils, acted brilliantly, played the violin, composed light verses which were the admiration of his mother's circle, and was altogether a charming companion whose witty silliness concealed a strange streak of seriousness.

Alas, this streak of seriousness shown in his rapt attention to the sermons of the Père de Neuville, a Court chaplain, proved to be his undoing. It so impressed the King that he said to his mother: "The boy is a flower destined to adorn the altar," and from that day he planned that he should have an ecclesiastical career. Accordingly, in spite of Stanislas' anguished protests that he had no vocation to the priesthood, the King entrusted his education to a tutor, the Abbé Porquet, and told him to begin his theological studies.

Stanislas loved him at sight. He was only ten years his senior. He was extremely clean and tidy: his wig and his clothes were in such perfect order that his best friends used to tease him, for he resembled a fashion-plate. "H'm," thought Stanislas as he looked down at him appreciatively, "there will be a feud between you and the Jesuit confessor before long." This tiny little person was not at all strong; he was gay, irresponsible and silly, and had all the same tastes as his pupil. And a wonderful versifier into the bargain. What luck! They found that they shared an admiration for the great Voltaire, who, accompanied by his "divine Emilie" came to visit Lunéville when Stanislas was ten. "Do you know what I like in Monsieur de Voltaire?" said the boy to his tutor. "It's his unbounded personal kindness. What a pity that he's always in trouble with the clergy. Oh, well, I'd rather be 'a good devil' like him than 'a bad saint' like so many pious people, wouldn't you, Monsieur l'Abbé?"

"Come, come now, my little friend; you think too much for your age. It's not healthy. The principal thing in life is to enjoy oneself. I could prove to you from dogmatic theology that an appetite for enjoyment is the chief propelling power of mankind, the *raison-d'être* for our very existence." And he sang, in a high but particularly tuneful treble, verses of his own composing:

Pleasure and fun, no matter how—
That's all my life's philosophy.
The only moment lost I vow
Is when with boredom's yawns I sigh.
And if I find before I die,
I've lived as well as I do now,
On youth misspent I will not cry.

On the first day that this charmer adorned the royal table, he was asked to say grace. He said he did not know the Benedicite. "I prefer reading Voltaire to learning prayers." That didn't matter, for the Comtesse and the King loved Voltaire, and the little abbé's wit sparkled so brilliantly, his cynicisms about religion were so deft and pointed, that they almost forgot the purpose for which he had been engaged. The King pulled himself together for a moment and said: "Monsieur l'Abbé, you must really moderate your views. Try to believe in the religion of which you are the apostle—I give you a year in which to do it."

After dinner, the Abbé Porquet was given another chance to reinstate himself. He was asked to read the book of Genesis aloud to the King before he retired for the night. Well, the abbé was *very* sleepy, having dined well after a day spent riding with his pupil, and the print of the sacred text kept dancing and getting blurred before his eyes in a most provoking manner. He read "God appeared to Jacob *disguised as a monkey*," instead of "God appeared to Jacob in a dream". (*Dieu apparut en singe à Jacob*—instead of *en songe!*) The King sat up and questioned the accuracy of that statement. But Porquet was equal to the occasion. He drew himself up proudly, fully conscious of his ecclesiastical dignity, and said crushingly: "Ah, Sire, with God all things are possible."

Some years later, Stanislas, wondering how Voltaire could have forgotten Porquet during his visit to Lunéville, said exquisitely: "It is the tiniest gems that are the soonest lost." Even his mother started flirting with the abbé.

When Stanislas was eighteen the King, who had never made any provision for the scatter-brained Comtesse, bestowed two livings on her son, and he was henceforth known as the Abbé de Boufflers. But he was abbé only in name. In company with Porquet, who had tactfully reduced his theological studies to a minimum, he composed naughty poems, rode to hounds, acted, sang, danced. Together, they rhymed on "woman, love and folly". Here is a priceless quatrain on Lot (it *would* be a scriptural one)—which Boufflers composed:

He amorous grew
As he drank some more.
And then he became
His own son-in-law.[1]

He wrote several very shocking poems, too indecent to quote, plenty of love-poems, and one or two couplets celebrating the joys of freedom, and poking fun at the shackles of matrimony.

Then the strangest thing happened. Boufflers' talent for verse-making provoked so much admiration at Lunéville that when he was twenty the Académie at Nancy decided to make him a member! One can imagine Porquet and his pupil sitting side by side and trying to keep their faces composed during the speech with which the president regaled Boufflers:

"Until now, you have devoted yourself to the study of sacred books and theology, because you were born to enlighten vast dioceses and to be placed hereafter amongst the foremost pillars of the Church."

Alas, when he returned to the palace, his mother announced to him that he must now pack and prepare to go to Paris, to the Seminary of Saint-Sulpice and train for the priesthood. The dreaded hour had come, that hour so often forgotten in his mad scampers with Porquet. What, good-bye to his beloved tutor, to Panpan, to the Comte de Tressan and the intimate gay little circle of Lunéville, good-bye to Gilliers and his comfits, to Cyfflé and his table decorations, to the antics of Bébé, good-bye to versifying and card-playing and dancing and flirting, and wild gallops across country on his English hunters! (Good-bye for ever to the fair lady—one of many—whom he had visited at night in the palace of Commercy, and when he had returned to his own quarters, at two in the morning, he found his bedroom was on fire, as a candle had set the tapestries alight!) In imagination he heard the door of the seminary closing on him for ever, and he could visualize the long days of silence and study, asking permission for everything—he who adored freedom; fasting and abstinence, for one whose appetite was so voracious. And he would have to wear a long black cassock and a biretta. No, it was impossible. His mother tried to cheer him up:

[1] Il but
Il devint tendre;
Et puis il fut
Son gendre.

"But think, my dear, what a good time you'll have on your free days. Everybody is in Paris—your great-aunt de Luxembourg, your three aunts de Beauvau, de Mirepoix and the Abbess of Saint-Antoine. I'm sure your aunt de Mirepoix[1] will see to it that you meet everybody. Rather a blot on the escutcheon—her many card debts I mean, poor dear, but she is *so* agreeable. Then there are the de Contis and the de Choiseuls and the de Lignes, who are sure to ask you to come and stay. You must also go and call on Madame du Deffand, and bring her all the gossip. Oh, and I'm forgetting; of course His Majesty's daughters will be kind to you in remembrance of the post I held with them. Don't take your duties so seriously. Take things lightly, easily, like a man of the world. You're not thinking of going in for sanctity, are you? Haloes are not traditional in our family."

He told his mother quite simply: "Mama, I've got no vocation." She replied: "But, you silly, what do you want with a vocation when so many priests get along beautifully without?"

In despair Boufflers went to the King, who was usually so sympathetic, and implored him not to force him to take this terrible step. The King tried to tempt him by dangling prospects of future greatness before him, of a dazzling ecclesiastical career.

Boufflers replied:

"I would rather be happy than great."

However, both his mother and the King remained adamant, and one morning, with tears in his eyes, Boufflers bade them all farewell and rode off to Paris with a very heavy heart.

A chapter in his life was closed.

Recalling his boyhood, he wrote later:

"When I think of that court of Lunéville, I seem to be remembering the pages of a novel, rather than years of my own life."

CHAPTER IX

THE SEMINARY

1762. Boufflers was twenty-four. The Pompadour forty-one, George III of England had been reigning two years. Eléonore was thirteen years old, and had already gone to the convent school of the Conception—not so very far, after all, from the Seminary of Saint-Sulpice.

[1] Horace Walpole said of her: "she is *the* agreeable woman of the world, when she pleases—but there must not be a card in the room".

Boufflers had been at the Seminary for about two years. One morning in April the Superior of Saint-Sulpice, Monsieur Couthurier, summoned his staff to his room to discuss a matter of importance.

Boufflers wrote later to Porquet: "Think of the bitter hatreds, the black jealousies, the miserable perfidies, that reign even more in the hearts of priests than other men . . ." He must have been thinking of the priests of Saint-Sulpice.

Monsieur Couthurier's room was what a French priest's room might look like unless he is effete, a cardinal or a saint: untidy, dingy, dismal.

The black crowd drifted in. The apostles of a religion of universal charity eyed one another—a long time after Monsieur Olier and a long time before the Curé d'Ars. "Is there anything more depressing than an ill-assorted mass of bachelors?", Stanislas would have thought, if he'd seen them that day.

Some of the priests were old, very old, and afraid of anything young and dangerously alive within their orbit. Only one of them was adorned with the beauty of holiness, and he unfortunately looked apprehensive. Totally unambitious, he was at a discount among his brethren, who thought him rather insignificant. His name might be Père Tourniquet. He was the only one who devoured the works of Blessed John of the Cross, whose nuns had appeared in France in the last century: and he was the only one there who had a secret liking for Stanislas de Boufflers.

They all stared at one another, trying not to say what was completely obvious:

"*Mon père*, you've got ink smudges on your fingers and your forehead."

The Superior broke the tension. "*Messieurs*, I see that the Abbé de Boufflers has again been pouring ink into the holy-water stoups. Pray be seated. I suggest that we all adjourn after this meeting and call for hot water and pumice stone."

In a distant corridor, a cock crew: this surprising sound was followed by a frightful cackle of hens, geese and turkeys. The Superior questioned the community with a look. L'Abbé Rochet explained: "*Mon père*, young Boufflers, amongst other things, has been gifted with a remarkable talent for imitating the sounds of a farmyard. The other day he enlivened my discourse on Saint Peter's denial by crowing at the appropriate moment."

Père Tourniquet burst out laughing. The others turned on him with a sussurating sound, like affronted adders. The poor man lost his nerve and found he could not stop laughing. Oh, it was agony, this uncontrollable wobbling of the shoulders in front of all the brethren! However, when at last he had restored his equilibrium by taking a few pinches of very good snuff, provided for him by the Carmelites of the Rue Saint-Jacques, the Superior, looking patient but pained, continued.

"*Messieurs*, I have summoned you in order to discuss, point by point, all the reasons why, in my humble opinion, Monsieur de Boufflers has no priestly vocation."

Père Tourniquet said in a timid, piping voice: "He already knows that. He's told us so a thousand times. His motto is 'I would rather die than cease to be honest'."

The Père Couthurier waved his hand without looking up, as if he were brushing away a fly, and went on: "The restraints of the Seminary only whet his appetite for pleasure. He seems . . . er . . . to *burst* whenever he gets out. I have a letter here from the domestic chaplain of the Prince de Conti. It appears that when young Boufflers went to L'Isle-Adam at Christmas, he let himself be carried away at a champagne supper-party into singing an impromptu song, which is so indecent that I cannot repeat it here; it reached the ears of Monsieur le Dauphin at Versailles and he sent him a severe rebuke. Fortunately even the culprit recognizes the enormity of his fault; I have availed myself of our privilege of opening letters,[1] and I see that he writes to that ill-starred tutor of his, the Abbé Porquet: 'I was unanimously condemned, and unfortunately with justice.' After the same visit he writes to his mother: 'We are here in battalions . . . and there are pretty women by the dozen. I could imagine myself at the *salon* where everything enchants the eye but nothing holds it, so I have made up my mind to love everyone at once.'"

There was a murmur of disapprobation from all in the room, all except Père Tourniquet, who took another pinch of snuff.

The Superior continued: "Here is the latest extract from his letter home: 'My health will soon be like that of nearly all the others here, who are ruined, for no apparent reason, by frequent prayers on their knees.' And then again: 'I have just heard a frightful thing! I am only to be allowed out twice a month instead of twice a week, and then I must be in by five o'clock.'"

The dean broke in at this point. "*Monsieur le Supérieur* did right to take such steps: we are all very concerned that Boufflers is always riding off to Versailles on that great devil of a horse to visit the Marquise de Pompadour at her house in the Rue des Réservoirs. Later, he joins in the circle of the Docteur Quesnay, in the palace itself. It is all very suspect. The members call themselves social reformers, but, believe me, this society is

[1] Stanislas was so frightened of this that he asked his mother to send his letters to his aunts.

nothing less than a hotbed of ardent materialists, the laboratory for an enormous social revolution which will overthrow Church and King and sweep us all away in a deluge. Besides, I do not like the fact that he excites so much admiration in Monsieur de Voltaire, who said of our young Boufflers: 'It seems to me that his special calling is to give much pleasure to men.' Can such a young man be destined to the priesthood?"

Loud cries and murmurs of: "Shame, certainly not."

"I spoke to him about it—tactfully—for he is very hot-tempered, and I don't want to get involved in disputes with King Stanislas. I suggested that he should employ his talents in writing something really useful, which would benefit society instead of destroying it. Soon after, I found, to my satisfaction, that he seemed to be deeply engaged in literary work in his cell. For a time, he was quiet. Then, it was brought to my notice that all the Paris *salons* were raving about a new licentious tale called *Aline, Queen of Golconda*, by an unknown writer. It relates how a certain obscure milkmaid, by the exercise of her charms, rose to be Queen of Golconda. It seems that the Marquise de Pompadour is so impressed by it that, under its influence, she has conceived the idea of a rustic farm at Petit Trianon where she will milk cows and keep them herself, dressed up in the corselet . . . and er . . . white petticoat of this fashionable heroine Aline."

At this point, l'Abbé Tourniquet sat up, put on his spectacles and brought his own copy of *Aline* out of his pocket. All the others were too greatly devoured by curiosity to protest: "If *Monsieur le Supérieur* does not object, I will prove to him and to the community that this is not a licentious tale. It is merely a charming absurdity, and only shows nostalgia for the pleasures of country life. Young Boufflers feels stifled and cooped up here after Lunéville. You see, I know that up till now he's spent all his time out-of-doors, hunting and shooting. Considering how very hot-blooded he is, I'm surprised he's not broken out more violently."

"Yes, I know," said Père Couthurier, "but in these times, when everything seems to point to change, don't you see the danger of this 'getting back to Nature', throwing off all the restraints which keep men civilized? Why, it's sheer Rousseau. And Heaven knows how many women's pates *he's* disturbed. However, read on, *mon père*. I myself was unable to procure a volume."

The Père Tourniquet glanced round a little indulgently at the flutter he had aroused, and began quoting extracts:

"I lunched on bread and cold partridge, in a smiling little valley formed by two hillocks crowned with green trees: in the distance I saw a hamlet rambling up the slopes of a hill: I was separated from it by a vast plain, covered with rich harvests and pleasant orchards.

"The air was pure and the sky serene, the earth still glittering with the pearls of the dew; and the sun which had only run a third of its course, shone with temperate fires, which a gentle zephyr moderated with its breath. . . ."

One or two less prejudiced listeners in the room wished to say that this was not only quite harmless, but indeed refreshing; in a century whose novels breathed a hot-house atmosphere, it was better than Crébillon fils; but they were afraid of the Superior. Père Tourniquet went on:

"And the setting sun in the distance, summoned the shepherds to return to their huts, and the flocks to their stables: the air echoed with the sound of bagpipes, and the songs of workers returning to rest."

He stopped, and without looking up, he said eloquently: "Boufflers dares to be perfectly natural. That is what makes the charm of his personality. That is why I have always liked his little verses: they have a whimsicality, an unusual turn to be found nowhere else. The Prince de Ligne wrote to me the other day and praised the charming carelessness, the gaiety in every verse, the good taste amidst the bad taste."

The Superior interrupted him impatiently. "But, my good Father, we are not here to give literary criticisms. That is neither here nor there. The point is: he should be devoting himself to the study of the Sacred Scriptures, and not causing this hubbub in Paris and at Court by writing silly tales about milkmaids in white petticoats."

In the meantime the object of all this commotion was in his cell, after putting bunches of nettles in various beds. He was in wild good spirits, writing a letter to his aunt, the Maréchale de Mirepoix. He had just dipped his quill in his musty-looking inkpot, when a bell went. Boufflers looked up at the Crucifix and exclaimed with a bitter-sweet irony, which showed that his relations with God, if somewhat original, were nevertheless based on mutual understanding: "What! *More* services! Oh, my God, only *You* have a fund of gaiety great enough to prevent You from getting bored with all the homages You are always receiving![1] As time does not exist with You, I implore You to wait a moment." So he took the liberty of ignoring the bell, for the time being, and bent his head over the sheet of paper:

"I must beg you, Madame la Maréchale, to pay yourself my compliments, to assure yourself of my respects, to ask yourself

[1] Boufflers did say this!

whether you are well, whether you had a good journey and whether you are not very tired. . . . I have just been obliged to leave you for a moment in order to lunch on half a pie that the Princesse de Chimay sent me; from it I have derived invincible courage wherewith to brave the diet of the seminary, and lay up a store of sobriety for the whole day. Madame du Deffand sent me lately two excellent cold partridges. . . . Monsieur le Président sent me a tongue much better suited to the seminary than my own, for it is stuffed, and I am glad of it, as thus it is not in a condition to tell Monsieur Couthurier of my behaviour. . . . You see, by the account I have given you of my provisions and my verses, that my room is half Parnassus and half larder, and he who inhabits it is half poet and half ogre—but more ogre than poet! There, my dear aunt—give my respects to my grandmother and kiss yourself from me on the forehead in the looking-glass—I hear a bell ring, so I take my surplice and hood and fly to service. . . . If I am scolded I shall say it was you who kept me! Good-bye—Good-bye!"

That evening Boufflers was told of the conference, and informed that his superiors had grave doubts concerning his vocation. He agreed heartily, and said he wanted to be a soldier: there was a war in full swing, and he simply couldn't keep out of it any longer. The Père Couthurier said he would write and tell his family.

Boufflers saved them the trouble! He wrote a long and serious letter to Porquet, saying, among other things: "I would rather die than cease to be honest. . . . The first rule of conduct is not to become rich and powerful, but to know one's real desires and follow them." Then, very early the next morning, before anyone was up, he donned his secular clothes again, packed his few possessions, left an affectionate little note to the Père Tourniquet, together with all the contents of his larder, and slipping quietly out of a ground-floor window and darting across the garden to the great enclosure wall, he clambered over it with some difficulty. He landed almost in the arms of a girl selling early morning *café-au-lait*.

"*Dieu*, be careful, you might have spilt the lot."

Boufflers took no notice. He was in the wildest of spirits, the sun was about to rise, it was early April, the chestnut buds were opening, the birds were twittering madly, it was good to be alive. And inside there, his unshaven fellow students, poor devils, would soon be rising for Matins. He seized the astonished girl round the waist and said:

"What's your name?"

"Annette, sir."

"I thought so. Annette, beautiful creature, give me a bowl of that steaming coffee, with six lumps of sugar, and I'll tell you what I am doing here. Thank you. You are as good as you are beautiful. Well, I'll tell you, Annette: this morning I made a great sacrifice, I renounced a brilliant ecclesiastical career, possibly the Cardinal's hat or even the Papal tiara, so that I might be free to make love to grand girls like you."

And going off into peals of laughter, he picked up his bundle and fled down the nearest alley to saddle his horse who was stabled near by.

"He's mad," said Annette; and she went on, crying: "Hot coffee, piping hot."

Soon, Boufflers was on the high road to Nancy again, having borrowed some money from his aunts. And as he rode, he sang in the sunshine:

I've thrown my cassock overboard,
In spite of my relations.
To Hell, oh send me quickly, Lord,
If I neglect the fashions.
Eh! mais oui-dà
Who dares to say this is a sin?
Eh! mais oui-dà
For all I care, let others win
  The priestly aureole.

CHAPTER X

THE CHEVALIER MEETS THE COMTESSE AT A BALL

On the day that Boufflers' great-aunt, the naughty Maréchale de Luxembourg, reached the age when a woman discards rouge and patches and goes to Daily Mass, she renounced the scandalous flirtations of a lifetime and became supreme arbiter of good taste and polite behaviour.

Nobody raised an eyebrow. Nobody does, when a woman is buttressed by the triple ramparts of riches, blue blood and indifference. After a while, at the sight of this quietly formidable little woman in brown taffeta, society forgot the outrageous songs composed about her at the Court of the Regent, and took her at her own valuation. Every day she could be seen walking with her doctor, the famous Tronchin, distributing gold coins from the knob of her long cane. Could that indeed be the heroine of the ditty:

Men thought of naught else but to please her,
Then queued up in turns to seduce her.

That seemed long ago. Now you were nobody in the social world unless you had first been approved under the scrutiny of her lorgnettes. She ruled by fear, for she was one of the most cruel old ladies of her time. (Had she not sat by the death-bed of a hated daughter-in-law, trying to inspire her with a terror of Death, and even exclaiming as she came into the sickroom: "I will suffocate in here: this room smells of corpses.")

Yes, the century had its macabre side, under all the rouge and spangles.

In 1777, Marie-Antoinette was twenty-one, and had been Queen of France for three years. At Midsummer of that year the Maréchale de Luxembourg opened the doors of her great palace of the Rue de Varennes, in the centre of fashionable Paris, and summoned the élite of the Court to a ball.

Oh, vanished scene of the *dix-huitième*, sparkle of diamonds by candlelight, swaying of panniers and flash of scarlet heels. . . . Madame Brillant, the Maréchale's favourite Siamese cat, who used to push the loto counters on the table with her paw, left the footstool on which she had been reclining, gave a yawn, and glided out of the ballroom with great dignity. At the threshold of a little inner drawing-room, curtained off in Italian damask, she paused, affronted. Her favourite arm-chair was occupied. On looking more closely, however, she saw that it was only the Maréchale's thirty-nine-year-old great-nephew, Stanislas, Chevalier de Boufflers, whiling away a moment by dipping into a pocket edition of his beloved Horace. He had just lost a lot of money at the card table with his mother, the Comtesse de Boufflers.

The Chevalier looked up. His powdered hair had been tied in a bow and arranged in two curls at the side. He had piercing little grey eyes, shrewd, cynical, yet kind. He welcomed his aunt's cat with his long brown hands.

"So you want to sit on my knee? By all means, *chère Madame.* Forgive me for not getting up, I'm dreadfully fatigued. There, are you quite comfortable? Don't claw at my breeches, there's a dear! It's my last pair, and I might even have to pawn *them.*"

The Chevalier stroked his pet and talked aloud, half to her and half to himself.

"Yes, Brillant, I've been gambling, and I've committed a thousand other little follies besides, since we last met. I've had to mortgage the revenues from my abbeys for a year in advance, to pay off my gambling debts. I can only go out at night, for my creditors are always lurking to pounce on me. I might even have to sell my horse, *Le Prince Héréditaire*—that great fellow who carried me through the war. Such a wrench. . . . Nearly as bad as losing Lout, my old sheep-dog in whose kennel I lived as a boy."

As he murmured, he tickled the lady behind the ear. She began to purr; she was very fond of her Chevalier; he brought her rabbits' heads after hunting with the Prince de Conti. Also, like herself, he had a way of falling asleep very suddenly in company, even in the midst of the most entertaining conversation. A bad habit for which he always made up by his sparkling witticisms when he woke.

The Chevalier was silent for a while, as if he were thinking hard. Then he took out a piece of pencil from his pocket and started scribbling a poem about the cat; he had a great gift for witty silliness:

Throughout the wide-flung earth
Brillant, thy charms are known,
For all do sing thy worth,
Thy praises far be sown.

Thou art the Queen of Love
The Venus of all pussies,
Whose charming grace doth move
The hearts of lesser hussies.

The name thy Mistress bears
Is Luxembourg—fair Queen.
My eyes now fill with tears:
(Would she were mine, I mean!)

The Chevalier was very tired; he'd only had an hour's sleep the night before. During the early part of the night he had gone to visit Madame X, and was just beginning supper by her bedside when an ex-admirer appeared unannounced. The situation was fraught with embarrassment, if not with danger, but Stanislas laughingly said that it would be *too* vulgar to cut one another's throats: why not a card-game instead, with the condition that the winner would remain with Madame X? He had won. After that, he'd left her to join his friend Charlot, Prince de Ligne, at the house of a famous actress who had entertained them till daybreak with her conversation. Those actresses! They knew life and men. So he was glad of a moment's rest at this ball.

A quarter of an hour later, lulled by the purring of the little cat and the sweet viols of the orchestra, the Chevalier had fallen asleep, his head flung back on the cushion of the arm-chair. Madame Brillant blinked at her patron drowsily.

What a pity that the Queen feared Bouffler's jesting tongue and did not invite him to Court. Or was he neglected because rumour had it that his father had been the late King Stanislas of Poland, the father-in-law of the late Louis XV? In spite of the likeness, his intimates never agreed with the popular opinion spread by the envious Talleyrand, that the Chevalier de Boufflers was ugly. That was a calumny bred of literary jealousy. Yes, his features were not regular, his teeth not too good, his nose was long—much too intelligent and cynical—his lips were rather full. But oh! what was all that compared with his supreme elegance? In that century, when a man became fashionable, one could forgive him anything. However shabby Bouffler's clothes, however ungainly and noisy his way of coming into a room, and then standing by the fireplace looking deceptively vacant, twiddling his thumbs and turning out his toes, there was always something distinguished and original about him which compelled attention from the first moment. Why was he adored by all the *salons*, his poems on all lips? Why did so many women flirt with him, and end by having affairs with him? It was not *chic* alone. Perhaps because under all the mocking wit, and in spite of all the ungainliness, he concealed a heart of gold, and his tongue would never wound—a rare thing with wits.

"What? Ugly?" had exclaimed Madame de Créquy, on hearing Talleyrand's slander about Bouffler's looks. "Monsieur de Boufflers has nothing in his face that is not distinguished and noble, intelligent and witty, and this is all that can be required of a man's appearance." Another contemporary of his said that: "Women revelled in him. He adored them as they wished to be adored, with fury but without fidelity, for fear of boredom. He swore them eternal passion for a fortnight and he kept his word faithfully." He was endowed with marvellous gaiety and vivacity, had a huge appetite, often lost his temper in an argument, appeared gruff and casual, and was altogether unpredictable, unusual and irresponsible.

So, at this Midsummer ball the Chevalier dozed and his friend Madame Brillant purred softly on his lap. Suddenly a beautiful fragile little woman in Parma-violet satin slipped through the draperies of the door. Eléonore, Comtesse de Sabran, had come into this room to roll up an unruly side-curl before the mirror. She did not notice the sleeping Chevalier with his copy of Horace nearly falling out of his hand, and the cat on his knee.

Her high-swept golden hair contrasted with plaintive dark brows and sad viola-blue eyes. Her rather wide mouth was expressive and whimsical, her pale cheeks touched up with *rouge de Portugal en tasse*. (Only courtesans were unpainted.)

Her *toilette* betokened exquisite taste. Under her panniers far-spreading like an open flower-calyx, could be glimpsed tiny feet shod in kid with diamond heels, those little feet which had been famous in the minuets of *Louis Quinze*.

Pamard's artificial scented white roses were pinned to her shoulder, and large bows of silver ribbon covered the front of her low-cut, tight-fitting bodice.

Many years later the Chevalier wrote a story called *Ah, if only*, and no doubt recollecting that first meeting, he described Eléonore in the person of his heroine:

"Picture to yourself not the most striking, but, what is infinitely more precious, the most fascinating creature that you have ever seen. A soul made visible rather than mere beauty. . . . None could be indifferent to those lovely tresses whose silvery fairness contrasts so deliciously with the colour of her eyebrows and her eyes . . . that expressive mouth which seems to have spoken before the lips have parted; those eyes, as blue as pansies, that shed more light than they reflect; her nose which by its shape and delicacy, a subtlety of contour all its own, seems to concentrate in itself all the charms of her countenance. . . ."

He goes on to speak of "*an indefinable something, a quality of the Court and of the country, an elegant simplicity*, a restrained animation which is the characteristic of her demeanour, an almost aerial body in which Nature has only made use of matter to show forth grace and to house a soul."

She was wearing mauve, because she was in half-mourning for her husband who had died three years ago. She had come to-night in answer to the Maréchale's invitation, to gossip with her many friends. They had persuaded her to return to Paris instead of languishing at the country seat of her brother-in-law the Bishop of Laon. After wrinkling her nose into the mirror concealed in her fan, Madame de Sabran began to draw off her long kid gloves and ruffle the lace frills at her elbows.

Just then Madame Brillant dug her claw into the Chevalier's satin breeches. He gave a start and half-opened his eyes; he was just going to stretch when he saw the Comtesse: he was so intrigued, that, after gazing for a moment, he decided to shut his eyes again and pretend to be asleep. At that moment, Eléonore caught sight of the glint of the Chevalier's sword, resting in its scabbard by the side of his feathered hat.

"I wonder who he is? Perhaps he is ill." She rustled up to him and put her hand on his brow. No, he did not seem feverish. Asleep? What was that book slipping out of his hand? Deftly she drew it away. Horace! Her favourite author. Only this morning she had been translating some of his Odes, with her tutor the Abbé Delille. At random she read a passage half aloud, beginning:

"Mater saeva Cupidinum . . ."

While she knit her intelligent brows and paused to find the exact translation for the word *saeva*, the Chevalier opened one eye and said:

"Will this do?—

'I thought my day of love was done
But cruel Venus with her Cherubin'"

She gave a little start and dropped the book. Madame Brillant leaped off the Chevalier's knee. He jumped up and, hand on heart, bowed very low, with several elaborate flourishes.

"The Chevalier de Boufflers, at your service, Madame."

Eléonore swept a perfect curtsey, and said: "I am Madame de Sabran, your humble servant."

They confronted one another and were mute for rather longer than was necessary.

"The first look of a true passion involves a whole existence." Thus wrote the Chevalier many years later, probably recalling that unique moment of his life which was to decide his destiny. Eléonore was puzzled by the seriousness which she felt was hidden behind the flippancy. He was a man with a mask. And woman has always wanted to discover what lies behind a mask.

At last she broke a silence which threatened to become a little too significant. "I hope I did not wake you? It is pleasant for me to meet a fellow Latin scholar."

"Do you know my friend the Abbé Delille?"

"Is he your friend too? I am his pupil. I had a lesson only this morning. What a charming person he is."

"I always go to him when I am in difficulties with Horace or Virgil. You see, I carry these little volumes about with me when I'm with my regiment; they have helped me to wile away many tedious hours of travelling and camp life. But you are too beautiful to be a blue-stocking. You should be sharpening arrows instead of quills, for those fingers are too delicate to be stained with ink."

"Oh, you should see my fingers in the morning when I am painting. I get them covered with paint."

"O peerless one! The Muse of Poetry and the Muse of Painting. . . . But beware. While you charm my ear with your conversation, you are missing the ball. Let me lead you to the little gallery overlooking the ballroom. We will sit and chatter in comfort. Or may I crave the honour of a dance?"

"I am in mourning, Monsieur, so I do not dance, but I'd like to sit down for a few moments in the gallery. It is just like a box at the Opera, don't you think? Quite as comfortable. Let us view the human scene from a height, like the Gods of Olympus."

The Chevalier was tall and powerfully built; the Comtesse had to look up to him as they talked, and he bent down slightly. This gave him a paternal air, as if he were cherishing her. He led her away on his arm.

At length they were in the tiny *loge* overlooking the ballroom. The scene that met their eyes is best portrayed by the de Goncourts, describing an engraving by Augustin de Saint-Aubin.

"Here is the drawing-room of the second period of the century, murmurous with sound, glittering, brilliant. Brocade curtains are looped up at the entrance. Cupids frolic and sport above the doors. Medallions of women smile in the wall-spaces between the windows. From the stucco roses of the ceiling hang long chandeliers of Bohemian crystal—each branch bearing a candle. The sparkling crystals are reflected in the mirrors. China made by Sermain, and pyramids of fruit can be glimpsed on the buffet, through the open door. Here is Pleasure in all its liveliness. Here is the Ball. The tambourine, the flute, the double-bass, and the violin, in a sprinkling of different notes, mingle on the musician's platform. Satin slippers glide on the parquet; necklaces sway on fair bosoms; dresses are strewn with bouquets of flowers; watches tick at belts; diamonds sparkle in the hair. In the middle of the drawing-room, ungloved hands are linked in the measures of the dance. Lovely partners spring towards svelt cavaliers, light as thistledown, laces are ruffled against the fur sleeves which Lauzun cuts out of the coats of Polish princesses. The air is full of light, smiling gossip.

"Men decórated with the *Cordon Bleu*, and Knights of the Order of Malta, leaning over the arm-chairs, pay their court to the young brides. Near the fireplace, the old people find one another again and enjoy talking about the past as they hold up the sole of a slipper to the fire, and drop oranges into the hands of the children. Joyousness and pleasure! Intoxicating and delicate feast. The painter who has left us its delicious image seems to have crowded into one corner of a bit of paper, Dance, Love, the Springtime of the Age, its noble elegance, the flower of its aristocracy at the moment of its perfect flowering, at the very zenith of its triumph."

The dance which was the rage of the evening was *l'Allemande*, popularized after the Seven Years War, but refined in the crucible of French taste; it has the supreme honour of being portrayed in Saint-Aubin's famous engraving of this ball which the de Goncourt brothers described. Delightful dance—composed entirely of graceful twinings, of ladies tripping under the bridge of Love formed by the arms of their partners; then back to back with hands joined. The *Allemande* brought into play all the coquettish attitudes of a woman's body, all the varied expressions of her face.

After watching for a few minutes, the Chevalier turned to the Comtesse and said, laughingly:

"What a dangerous dance that is!"

"Dangerous? Why?" she asked naïvely.

"Well, look at the rather unreserved movements, the interlacing of arms, the clasping of hands, the glance seeking the partner's eyes and seeming to smile or blow a kiss over the shoulder. Never before has a dance brought man and woman together so agreeably and so languidly, don't you think?"

"Yes, I suppose it is different from the very correct minuets I used to dance at the balls of his late Majesty; don't you remember?"

"Madame, I am no courtier; I am in semi-official disgrace at Versailles, for I write epigrams and little poems and make fun of everything and everybody. I cannot take life seriously. My excessive gaiety has been the chief cause of all my troubles. The Queen dislikes verse and versifiers, so my friend de Ligne tells me."

Eléonore was too loyal to the Queen, whom she loved, to say, "Oh, what a mistake", so she tapped the Chevalier's sleeve lightly with her fan and said, with a smile—"Now, now! Do you know, I am dreadfully hungry; could you fetch me something from the buffet?"

In a few minutes the Chevalier returned with a plate of preserved peaches and apricots, sliced up on a bed of ice, powdered with sugar and soaked in liqueur.

"Look what I've prepared for you! I was playing cards at Madame du Deffand's the other night and she gave me the recipe: it's her own invention."

"But it is delicious . . . delicious. And how was Madame du Deffand?"

"Racked by insomnia, but still very witty. She was telling me that supper was one of the four ends of existence, but she forgot what the other three were. She said she hated solitude so much that she'd rather spend an evening in company with the sacristan of the Minims than be left alone. How awful to be blind!"

"I wonder whether she is beginning to realize that she is a very lonely, unloved woman, and also whether she misses the companionship of Mademoiselle de Lespinasse?"

"Never! Why, do you know what she said about her when she heard of her death? It was the cruellest epitaph that one jealous woman could devise for another. She said: 'The Blessed Virgin had better look out, as Mademoiselle de Lespinasse will steal the affections of the Blessed Trinity from her.' But I confess I share something of the impatience of Madame du Deffand. I have no use for women who allow themselves to be consumed by the fever of a great passion in the way that Mademoiselle de Lespinasse did for two men whose names I could whisper in your ear. It's all this tiresome Rousseau who set the fashion, with his *Nouvelle Héloïse*. Love is *not* a thing to be taken seriously. It is a game to be played with consummate artistry; over-great earnestness spoils all games and turns them into tasks.

When tender fires
Are too constant,
They become
A great bore.

A chain, however gentle,
Chafes in the long run.
What pleases at dawn
By nightfall is
A great bore.

Without liberty
The delights of love
Soon become . . .
A great bore.

Don't you think so?"

Eléonore fanned herself; she was not listening very intently to this agreeable banter, fashionable among the young men of her day. She was so used to it. Instead, she looked at the animated scene in the ballroom below.

The most richly dressed of all the women were perhaps the dowagers of the Court of the late Louis Quinze. A long reign sets a fashion in old ladies which is socially very pleasant. They clung to their purples and golds, so beloved of the dead Queen Marie Leczinska, those stiff brocades which had all the glitter of a cuirass, the ample skirts sprinkled with full-blossomed peonies and poppies. And if a petticoat were raised a trifle, one got a glimpse of a black silk stocking with a silver thread at the side.

"Look!" cried the Chevalier suddenly, "that imbecile of a footman is snuffing candles in the bracket just above my aunt's head, and the wax is dripping all over her *pouf*. I only pray that she won't notice it."

The old Maréchale had let herself go that night, under the influence of the Queen's mad hairdresser Léonard. She had indulged in a *Pouf au sentiment,* in imitation of the Duchesse de Chartres, whose headdress had been the talk of Paris for a whole season, for it had contained effigies of her baby in its Nanny's arms, a parrot eating a cherry, a little nigger, and many meshes of hair belonging to other members of the family.

The footman stopped snuffing candles above the Maréchale's head.

"No, your aunt has noticed nothing," said Eléonore, laughing. "But look over to her left; there is Mademoiselle So-and-so: I hear she is so overcome by *ennui,* so hard-up for a hobby that she has taken to the study of anatomy, and carries a corpse about everywhere in a trunk at the back of her travelling coach."

"*Quelle horreur!* Now I could *never* fall in love with a woman who did that."

"Couldn't you?" said Eléonore vaguely.

The Chevalier was rather provoked, if not to say piqued, that Eléonore seemed much more interested in looking at the dancers than in talking to him. In reality she was not being provocative at all, but as she had only very recently returned to Paris from her retirement in the country, this social scene filled her with pleasure and absorbed all her attention. What fun it was to see everyone again. There was the Duc de Nivernais who had fallen out of love with his wife because of her rouge, that violent carmine that was his despair; and over there was the Vicomte de X who had given his mistress a carriage by Francine, horses and livery exactly like his wife's, and the two women had met one day driving in Paris. And here, oh, here was her friend, that versatile Madame Vigée Lebrun whose husband pounced on every *sou* she earned as a society portrait-painter. She had recently been invited to paint the Queen at Versailles, and she sang her praises at every turn. She was talking to a group composed of the Comte de Caraman, who had been appointed by Her Majesty to superintend the building of the new English garden at Petit Trianon, the old Duc de Croÿ, the greatest connoisseur of gardens during the last reign, and their mutual friend, the Prince de Ligne, a specialist in modern English gardens and a devotee of Marie-Antoinette's. Charlot de Ligne was a boon companion of Boufflers, a handsome, wealthy Austrian, much too fond of women, but very entertaining.

"Hi, Stanislas!" cried Charlot as he glanced up in their direction and caught sight of his friend. "We'll come and talk to you up there; it looks very inviting." And he led his little group towards the Chevalier's private nook.

"What a pity," sighed Stanislas, turning to Eléonore. "I was enjoying myself so much in your company. Not that you've taken any notice of me the whole evening, but then, you haven't yet learnt to appreciate me at my full worth. But you will. It takes time: I am an acquired taste."

Eléonore laughed. "Yes," she thought, "he's an original person, and I daresay he knows how to keep one amused." However, she began to recall vague rumours of his bad reputation with women, and his wild gambling, so she made a mental reservation not to encourage him to call on her. A young widow alone in the world, unchaperoned, with a large fortune, and two delicate children to look after, could not be too careful.

Just then the door of the little enclosed gallery opened, and the Prince de Ligne and the Duc de Croÿ came in with Madame Vigée Lebrun, who was arguing with the Comte de Caraman.

Before long the friends were all seated in a circle, drinking iced champagne which the Maréchale sent up to them, and talking in animated fashion about the Temple of Love planned for the Queen's new garden at Petit Trianon, the little country estate which the King had given her quite near Versailles. The Prince de Ligne had seen the wooden model of the Temple in miniature that same afternoon.

"Charming! charming!" he exclaimed. "I wish I could have brought the model to you in my pocket. It was all complete on a piece of mirror representing the lake, with moss for the trees and lawns. What peerless taste Mique has shown this time. The real thing will be built on a hillock in the middle of a lake surrounded by a few weeping willows. The round cupola of the Temple is to house a statue of the God of Love sharpening his arrow. The island itself will be planted with roses and apple-trees. Her Majesty told me that she will give midnight parties on the island; her guests will be rowed on the lake and the stream by the light of Chinese lanterns, to the sound of hidden pipes. Can't you picture the little boats gliding along?"

"On *that* muddy little stream!" exclaimed the old Duc de Croÿ testily. "It's so sluggish that no boats will ever be able to *glide* on it, as you say,—they'll get bogged in the weeds."

"Ah," retorted the Comte de Caraman, "I'm afraid you can never really forgive the Queen for making an English garden. Anyway, the course of the waters will be livened up; I will see to it personally. For myself, I'd rather have a simple stream, than those great marble basins of Versailles, either full of stagnant water or else empty and overgrown with grass; they create an impression of decadence."

"Decadence!" At this point the Duc de Croÿ rolled his eyes to heaven and threw up his hands in despair. His friends tried to look sympathetic as they listened to this staunch old friend of the *Roi Soleil.* "Decadence indeed. All because some misguided gardener went to England in search of novelty and then started raving about Kew and Stowe with their so-called natural prairies. And as a result we've got to run down poor Lenôtre, the designer of the stateliest gardens in the world. We must now put up with this unbelievable hotch-potch of winding alleys, interspersed with Chinese pagodas and classical temples which are the rage in England. A wave of folly has passed over this century: the *poufs* on the heads of our women seem to have affected their reasons when it comes to garden-planning!"

"Versailles is *so* boring," said the Prince de Ligne, rather naughtily.

"Boring! Ah, my good Charlot, what would our late King have said if he'd heard you?"

"Now don't cast such a halo of glory round the past. Confess that those endless walks at Versailles in the boiling sun by the side of His Majesty's push-chair were both exhausting and tedious. Not a spot of shade anywhere, dazzling sand, miles and miles of lozenge-shaped flower-beds trimly edged with box, and at regular intervals those rows of gods and goddesses expressing in their blank faces a little of the boredom which etiquette forced us to conceal. It was all very well for His Majesty, but quite different for us, his courtiers."

The Duc de Croÿ smiled wistfully. "How his late Majesty loved showing us his creations. *I* personally never felt weary."

"I suppose," said Madame Vigée Lebrun elfishly, "you enjoyed his little baskets filled with the different kinds of strawberries he introduced into France?"

"Yes, the good Richard was always bringing me strawberries. That poor Richard! His heart will break when he has to pull down his beloved hothouses and scatter the collection of some of the world's rarest plants. Her Majesty is more interested in the immediate effect of having decorative flower-beds, renewed almost daily, than in the tender science of botany. I must bring myself to go and visit Richard. I've not been to Trianon for three years. It was there that I said good-bye to His Majesty, a few days before he caught that fatal smallpox."

Eléonore felt that the talk was taking too sadly reminiscent a turn. The widow of a very charming old man herself, she understood how it hurts members of the older generation to watch their cherished traditions crumbling, and how they bewail the seeming heedlessness of the young to all the beauties of a bygone generation. So with great deftness she deflected the course of the conversation and persuaded the Comte de Caraman to tell them all how he'd put his own garden to rights in twenty-four hours, before a sudden visit of the Queen's. In the meantime the Chevalier ordered some wood-strawberries for the Duc, and prepared them in the way he had done Eléonore's apricots. Very soon the Duc de Croÿ had forgotten his nostalgia and was thinking that the modern young could be quite delightful. Had not someone compared all that *savoir-vivre*, all those delicate refinements of eighteenth-century courtesy, to the spirit of Charity itself?

The Chevalier, who had already heard about Caraman's dilemma, was the loudest to protest that he wanted to know all about it. "Please tell us everything."

Caraman began:

"Her Majesty had graciously approved my design for her garden, and given me the direction of Petit Trianon. Soon after, Monsieur de Noailles came to me in the country to tell me that Her Majesty would visit me on the morrow in my Paris house, at five o'clock. I was very put out, for the scorching heat had withered all my lawns and yellowed the leaves of the chestnuts and willows. You see, I do not live there in the summer, and everything gets neglected. I left the country immediately and, as I don't believe in the word impossible, I got all my friends, neighbours and servants to help me. We rolled and watered my lawns, swept away the dead leaves, arranged pots of flowers which I had fetched from the florists' and from neighbours, in the middle of thick shrubs, so that they looked as if they were growing out of them; there were gilliflowers springing from lilac bushes, and trailing roses from a mass of syringas! I put up a fine tent on the lawn, and the cords were twined with garlands of real flowers. I surrounded the tent with orange trees, laurels, roses and Spanish jasmine, and inside I arranged a round table with a basket of flowers, a little collation and some ices. Many of the hired plants I had just stuck into the ground without taking them out of their pots, I was so pressed for time. The sand in the alleys was raked with the greatest of care. We were watering in relays all day, up to an hour of the Queen's arrival; everybody helped, and at last the lawns looked green. You can imagine my relief."

"Was her Majesty very gracious to your wife?" asked the Chevalier curiously.

"She was quite charming to her. She seemed delighted with everything, and particularly with a little impromptu orchestra of flutes and violins. I had arranged for it to play in the far distance, as the Queen was in mourning."

The Duc de Croÿ was by now thoroughly restored. He said: "That far-away concert must have been effective and surprising."

The Comte de Caraman continued:

"Finally, I gave refreshments in the entrance yard, to the grooms and coachmen. There was quite a crowd, for the Queen had brought the Princesses Clothilde and Elizabeth. My pretty little girls, with flowers on their hair, presented a bouquet to the Queen and sang a couplet from *Zémire*. They were invited to the royal collation. Everybody said that the ices were delicious. The Queen stayed for nearly two hours, walking, eating ices, and talking to my wife."

After a while, the little circle in the gallery broke up into pairs; they gossiped about more personal matters. One could see the Duc de Croÿ listening intently as the Prince de Ligne talked in a low voice about the incognito visit of Marie-Antoinette's brother, the future Emperor. They shared hopes, entertained by many in the know, that the Queen would soon settle down to the business of giving a Dauphin to the nation. Her brother, stressing that it was a medical matter which concerned His Majesty, said that they should not delay in putting a stop to the filthy libels sung in the Paris streets, which avowed that the King was a poor sire.

The Duc de Croÿ sighed. "Can you imagine us talking so freely about the private life of our late Queen?"

As he gossiped, Charlot noticed that the Chevalier could not stop gazing at Eléonore, who was talking at that moment in a low voice to Madame Vigée Lebrun.

"When are you going to let me paint you?" enquired the artist. "I have already sketched you in a characteristic pose."

"With my hair coming down? But, Madame, what am I to do? My hair reaches nearly to my ankles, it's quite beyond control." Then, in a whisper, like the others—"I wonder what the result of this visit of the Queen's brother will be. Have you heard the latest rumour?"

Madame Vigée Lebrun spoke behind her fan. "Yes, indeed, they say that he has talked to her very seriously, and to the King, also. I shouldn't be surprised if the result were a Dauphin within a year. How pleasant that would be. I want to paint the Queen surrounded by a large family. It might put an end to all this scandalous chatter caused by Her Majesty's little follies."

"Such as, Madame?"

"Oh, talking to strangers at the Opera ball, for example."

At this point the Prince de Ligne, who had overheard, intervened. "Quite harmless, I assure you. The King was there. The handsome Swede of the ball is a noble character—very different from some other young men in the Queen's circle. Besides, Her Majesty is not one to encourage undesirable relationships."

"You're a little in love with her yourself, Charlot," teased Boufflers.

De Ligne did not reply at once. Some time ago he had forced himself to leave France and travel, in order to escape from the spell of Marie-Antionette, of whom Walpole had written after watching her at a Court ball that: "It was impossible to see anything but the Queen; Hebes and Floras, Helens and Graces are street-walkers to her. She is a statue of beauty when sitting or standing, grace itself when she moves."

De Ligne changed the subject. "The Queen is charming to tease and trap in conversation, and I like laying embarrassing snares for her. If one puts a naughty or malicious interpretation on her words she gets cross, she laughs and blushes and is still more delightful."

The Ball drew to a close. Pages hurried forward with capes and furs, footmen called illustrious names to announce waiting carriages, the orchestra stopped playing. The last good-byes were said. The Maréchale removed her *pouf* and summoned her nigger-boy to scratch her head with an ivory hand on a long stick. The dancers melted away like a dream. One by one the candles were snuffed in the great ballroom. Madame Brillant sought her basket at the foot of the Maréchale's bed with its draperies and tufted plumes. Outside, there was the clatter of hooves and crunch of wheels on cobble-stones as the last guest drove away.

Alone in the street, the Chevalier walked home. He had no carriage, and he almost knocked into the night-watchman on his way. The dawn was near. In another hour the girls would be in the roadway selling hot coffee. The lanterns slung across the street on cords were flickering out, though the torches outside the great private houses still gave a good light. Boufflers walked close to the wall, in order to avoid his friends in their coaches. He wanted to be alone with his thoughts. A pair of wonderful violet-blue eyes, irised in brown, haunted his imagination. He recalled her beauty, and all her graciousness to the old Duc de Croÿ, and he groaned.

"*Dieu!* Why have I been such a spendthrift? And now, and now, when I want above all. . . . Fool that I have been! What have I done with my life until now? Oh, cruel Heavens, only uniting those destined to bore one another, always sundering those who could have known the delights of mutual passion! Why have she and I not met till to-night!"

END OF PART II

Part III

THE PURSUIT

CHAPTER XI

THE CYNIC LOSES HIS HEART

"A wit who but for his subtlety might have been simply a buffoon, a rake who but for his fastidiousness might have been a debauchee."

Mrs. Webster.

On that midsummer night in 1777, when Stanislas de Boufflers had met Eléonore de Sabran for the first time, he came home to his house, all in a turmoil. At the age of thirty-nine, after many years spent in mocking the tender passion and in pointing out the folly of constancy, to have become a victim oneself! In his ample taffeta dressing-gown, he sat in his arm-chair by the window. His little bedroom was very untidy, and crowded with mementoes of the journeyings of these last fifteen years, since he had left the seminary that April morning. What years! Penniless though he was, his days had been crammed with interest and adventure.

On one wall he'd hung the sword he'd carried in the army of the Prince de Soubise, and the spurs of his two splendid chargers, *Le Prince Ferdinand* and *Le Prince Héréditaire*. Grand days! Soldiering was in his blood. In the life of camps he found what he had vainly sought at the seminary of Saint Sulpice: "a fine confidence, a frank courtesy, a touching humanity which are nearly always allied with true gallantry, and purify and adorn it with all the marks of generosity."[1] At the end of the campaign, in 1763, he had returned with a brilliant record for valour.

On the same wall was his sword as Knight of Malta. King Stanislas had arranged that Boufflers still drew his revenues from the livings he'd conferred on him, whilst renouncing all his vows save celibacy. "A detail," muttered Stanislas at the time; but now suddenly his face fell, he turned pale. He realized the implications of the vow. "*Mon Dieu*—so I'm caught this time. I can never ask her to marry me, for if I do I lose every penny of my revenues, and she's rich. Better if I induced her to be my mistress. But *ciel et tonnerre*, suppose she refuses? Bah, why should she? No woman has refused me yet."

[1] From *Ah, if only*, by the Chevalier de Boufflers.

The problem rankled in his mind. He recalled the Comtesse de Sabran as he had seen her that night—her beauty, distinction and charm, enhanced by her wonderful *toilette*. If only she were some poor shepherd girl, like Aline in that tale he had written as a young man! Then he could have carried her off to Malgrange, his small country estate which, though devoid of grandeur, was clean and fresh. The delicious idyll of winning her would have unfolded in that pastoral setting which he had always loved. Strange how the nebulous dreamings of his youth should foretell the anguished longings of his manhood, for in *Aline* he had written: "It is only at the end of my days that I learnt to be wise." Ah, he sometimes felt parched in the ballrooms and *boudoirs* of the day. How he longed for flocks of spotless sheep beribboned in blue, guarded by pretty shepherdesses, for summer walks by the riverside, in the cool of evening, watching the sedge-warblers and dragon-flies among the meadow-sweet: "The kindly peace of the countryside, the solitude that loves a lover." Not till to-night had he envied those country squires who were enjoying the pleasures of family life on their estates. What had they done to deserve it? He had been obliged to let half his beloved Malgrange. These other men had merely inherited wealth, and sometimes took no interest in the cultivation of their property or the well-being of their folk; while *he* had fought, gone on foreign embassies, painted, composed, all on a slender purse. He almost lived on his wit, for if that dried up, would he always have been so welcome at all the country-houses which he visited, and where he arrived on his "great devil of a horse",[1] in the shabbiest of clothes? Who was to blame? Why, a social structure which arranged things in such a way that a man of energy and determination should not be able to secure a livelihood by work, or share in the common blessings of mankind. There are solemn moments in life when a man takes stock of his experiences, usually before beginning an entirely new chapter in his career. Boufflers thought with envy of social conditions in Switzerland, which he had visited in 1764, and of the year he had stayed with Voltaire at Ferney. He leaned back and recalled his travels there, after the Seven Years War. Boufflers, in the manner of many of his contemporaries, was fond of building Utopias. Yes, Switzerland was the ideal country. He wrote home: "The land is tilled by free hands. Men sow for themselves, and don't reap for others. Swiss laws are austere, but they have the pleasure of making them themselves."[2] In contrast the French peasants paid taxes while the nobles and clergy were exempt. Ideas of democracy had surged up in his mind during

[1] Letters of Duchesse de Choiseul. She had a great weakness for him.
[2] Letters to his mother.

those travels, though he was so naturally a humanitarian that it did not really need any outside influences to make him realize the injustices of human life. Boufflers, the most violently energetic man of his time, had been condemned by the circumstances of his birth to a roving, aimless life. And he believed in work! From Switzerland he had written home to Lunéville: "Here men are industrious, because work is a pleasure, for they are certain to secure the profit. . . . The golden age still exists for these people. It is not worth while to be a noble lord in order to associate with them; it is enough to be a man."

In Switzerland he had flirted a great deal. He'd written that even in that country "Woman is still woman. Not only that, but she is beautiful". Tired, perhaps, of French women who gave themselves too easily, he tasted the joys of difficult conquest, for he wrote: "Out of thirty or forty girls or women, there are not four ugly ones, and not one wanton. Oh, the good and the bad country."

Stanislas looked up at the portraits on the walls again, as he thought of those days. He had travelled incognito, or rather under the name of Monsieur Charles, and painted portraits as he went. He had sung:

> In the Springtime,
> I was guided by folly,
> Blinded by my desires. . . .

He recalled: "Twenty beauties deceived at one go." He regretted the futility of the little verses he'd composed for them, and the "twenty good horses" he'd nearly killed, galloping over hills and through valleys to pay his court. His heart had never been touched. In fact he had written:

> I was concerned only with the physical side of love:
> True that is an essential ingredient,
> But it is not the only one.
> There are a thousand different ways of loving.

Yes, and he had loved in a thousand different ways. Once or twice, when, contrary to his custom, he thought that he had really lost his heart, he wrote that he had gone to courtesans who might:

> Wipe away the tears of love with pleasure's hand.

Two things he had steadfastly tried to avoid: First, being caught in the tangles of matrimony.

No marriage for me,
I'm not so silly.
The marriage tie
Was always a chain.

And secondly he had a terror of the woman who gave herself too easily, for later on in the relationship she clung feverishly and menaced his love of freedom. Of such he had written a poem:

To a young woman
(Who threatened to make me happy)

Good Heavens! I am lost! What! Favours already!
When I promised to be faithful,
When I vowed that I was filled with the tenderest ardours,
I expected that you would be cruel;
I had planned to find coldness;
Ah if I am dear to you, be more unkind;
Allow my love to experience the charm of desires:
To make it last, prolong its suffering;
I cannot swear that it will outlive pleasure.

For him the hazards of the chase superseded all the pleasures of conquest: the rose he had so eagerly grasped, faded in his hand.

On the wall, next to the portraits of some of these beauties whom he had painted, made love to, and then forsaken or been forsaken by, there was a little sketch he had made of Voltaire losing at chess during his stay at Ferney. "I did it in a hurry, and in spite of the faces he makes whenever one wants to paint him. . . . You cannot imagine how agreeable this man's society is . . . he is a gift from nature to the whole earth." How he'd enjoyed himself there! He wrote to his mother: "Whatever his printers may do, he will always be himself the best edition of his works." The liking was reciprocal, for the philosopher had written about him to his mother: "You have reason, indeed, to love this young man, he portrays marvellously well the absurdities of this world, and he has none himself." And again: "The Chevalier de Boufflers is one of the most original creatures in the world. He paints in pastels charmingly. He will ride off all alone at five o'clock in the morning to go and paint women in Lausanne and make friends with his models; from there he rushes off to do the same at Geneva, and then comes back to me to rest from his labours among the Huguenots." In the evening Voltaire and Boufflers sang, reminisced, satirized, and wrote brilliant little poems to one another.

Standing in the middle of his room Boufflers glanced at his other possessions. His own poems were scattered here and there, together with volumes of classical poets; his packs of cards, and finally a casket of letters which he had not thrown away, for they had amused him at one time or another. In that casket he also kept replies to invitations for his wild supper-parties, sometimes simply scribbled on the back of playing cards, in the elegant fashion of the day. Those supper-parties of his, devised somehow with the aid of his devoted man-servant, in spite of creditors and angry tradespeople! For what mattered such trivial details? Walpole had written: "You have supped with the Chevalier de Boufflers. Did he act everything in the world, and sing everything in the world, and laugh at everything in the world? . . ." Tossed in, *pêle-pêle*, with some of these cards were invitations to supper parties from the Sophie Arnault who was immortalized by Greuze, and Mademoiselle Quinault, now in retirement and adored by Porquet; there was one from Madame du Deffand, written by Wiart, her man-servant and secretary. He remembered how, on that night, he and his mother and the Abbé Porquet had gambled till five in the morning. Madame du Deffand disapproved of the "birds' frenzy of gambling", and though she did not like the Chevalier's verses, she liked his mother.

Lastly, in the casket were two documents connected with his attempts to create a diplomatic career. The first effort had been a failure, for his wit had been too ready. He had been sent to congratulate the Princess Christine of Saxony, sister of the Dauphine, on being made Abbess of the Convent of Remiremont, one of the most fashionable convents of the day. Unfortunately, he'd caught a chill on the way—his wretched teeth gave him trouble throughout his life—and he arrived looking hideous, with a swollen cheek. The Princess, herself a German and no beauty, received him with marked coldness. Nothing daunted, Boufflers wrote a poem in which he said that the "puffy-faced princess" was jealous because his own face had half the attractions of her own! Madame du Deffand was so enchanted with this piece of impertinence that when she was quite old she used to sing it at her own supper-parties, much to the surprise of Horace Walpole. Boufflers had read this poem to the little group at Lunéville, and unfortunately it reached the ears of the Dauphine's brother. From that moment onwards Boufflers was in disgrace at Court, and his diplomatic career at an end. His sense of the absurdities of people was bound to peep out at the wrong moment, and that is no asset in a diplomat. No wonder that, many years later, in 1770, his great friend, the Duc de Choiseul, declined his offer to go as Envoy-Extraordinary to the Infanta of Parma, to congratulate her on her impending confinement! Boufflers had written his request to Choiseul with characteristic frankness: ". . . Envoy Extraordinary? You certainly could not find one more extraordinary than myself . . . but what will please me most will be to go all over Italy afterwards on the profits of my embassy and to travel on velvet. I think my plan will be much appreciated by my creditors."

Boufflers had proved quite decisively that he lacked the smooth tongue, the capacity for fawning flattery and the ability to tell lies—in fact all the qualities which make a successful courtier.

Unfortunately his career as a soldier had also disillusioned him. Like Byron later on with the Greeks, he offered the services of his sword to oppressed nations. He threw himself into the fray with generous enthusiasm, imagining that all the other combatants felt as he did. The bitter truth was soon revealed to him: they were out for gain: they did not burn with the authentic fire. Throughout his life, Boufflers was doomed, by the nature of his temperament, to suffer disappointment about the human race, for he always endowed men with his own altruistic motives. He had taken part in Corsica's struggle for liberty under Paoli, then he offered his services to the oppressed Poles, much to the irritation of the Empress Catharine the Second, who commented drily to Voltaire on "dandies without a vocation who leave Paris to act as preceptors to brigands". Finally, quite recently, there had been months of travel in Hungarian châteaux. About the Hungarians he wrote: ". . . they are the sorriest soldiers in Europe—lazy, mean, selfish, vain and silly. Add to that they are dirty, coarse and rascally—and then love them."

He had now just returned to Paris from this final stage in his travels. At thirty-nine years of age, soldiering was still his only career, he was riddled with debts, disillusioned about men and women, though not embittered or intolerant; outwardly as gay and happy-go-lucky as ever. The range of his experiences had been very wide; for he had tried his hand at everything in turn: theology, novel-writing, diplomacy, painting, versifying, classical studies, and the writing of epigrams, hunting, amateur theatricals, soldiering, and the study of social theories. Yes, *everything*.

And one thing alone was lacking; a purpose, a fiery resolve to weld together all these scattered elements into a working philosophy. Debarred from marriage, not only by his own cynical and restless temperament, but by his vow of celibacy as Knight of Malta, Boufflers' life until that night had not been truly held or rooted in Woman, and therefore his nature had not come to full flowering. What pain in this sudden invasion of his inner citadel! Was there no retreat before it was too late? Even as he planned some means of escape, pacing his room in the June dawn, Boufflers knew that it would be useless. At every turn he would be haunted by the memory of those eyes, half-tender, half-mocking, under the over-arching, expressive brows of the young Comtesse de

Sabran, and everything else in life which he had hitherto found enthralling would lose its savour. He would fall a victim to that malady of his century, *ennui*, and he might just as well be dead.

The sun rose, and with it Boufflers' courage. No, he could never ask her to marry him; it was completely against ingrained tradition to live on the woman you loved. He must win her by years of noble deeds, by all the pleasures of friendship, by making himself indispensable to her. He was by nature a gambler. He would, in the face of great odds, stake all he had in one desperate bid for happiness, and if that failed . . . then nothing remained.

He decided to sleep till mid-morning, then bathe in cold water, drink lemon-juice—an infallible restorer—dress with care, and then persuade Charlot to come with him to pay his first call at her house.

CHAPTER XII

THE CHEVALIER DE BOUFFLERS CALLS ON MADAME DE SABRAN

When Boufflers woke, later that morning, he decided that it was fantastic to dream of winning Eléonore. Point by point, with merciless realism and logic, he went over all the reasons against doing so. He was penniless and proud. She was rich, and he had nothing to offer her. His contemporaries as well as his conscience would judge him harshly. No, it would be unbearable. He could almost hear people saying: "Ah, ha! Boufflers did well for himself, didn't he? Got all his debts paid by the rich widow, and just in time. Why, I've known him lose five hundred *louis* at cards in one night, when he hadn't got a *sou* in his pocket."

He decided, therefore, not to call on her. He'd been so free from attachments up till last night. Why get entangled suddenly now, even by friendship, for although he hadn't got much of a conscience, he had begun to question his right to seek her friendship.

However, he decided to risk a morning stroll in the Champs Elysées and snatch a passing glance at her house from a safe distance. With a lover's eye, he would pierce the walls and imprison the beloved in the crystal globe of imagination. He would picture her asleep in her bedchamber, resting late after the ball.

Eléonore lived in the Faubourg Saint Honoré which was the

extension of the Rue Saint-Honoré into a more countrified district of fields and gardens. Boufflers decided not to approach the house from the street, but from the garden side. A large grille allowed one to peep through into this garden.

Here is Mrs. Webster's description of the situation of this house: "The Rue Saint-Honoré and its continuation the Faubourg was at this date the most varied street in Paris; here lived many of the most fashionable *marchands de frivolités*, the most brilliant courtesans, and here, too, were some of the great convents, and the houses of the old nobles. But the Faubourg was essentially the aristocratic end of the street, and still to-day on its south side, several of the magnificent historical houses with their huge *portes cochères* remain—the Hôtel de Guébrian, the Hôtel de Charost (now the British Embassy), and the Hôtel d'Aguesseau. Between these and the Hôtel d'Évreux (now the Palais Elysée), where either the number 43 or 45 now stands, was the house of Madame de Sabran. It must have been a perfectly delicious retreat amidst the whirl of Paris life, shut off by its massive entrance from the noise of the street, whilst on the other side were the rooms in which she lived, with their windows looking south over a sea of green, beyond which, on the left, were the Place Louis XV (now the Place de la Concorde), and the great gates of the Tuileries. A sunny terrace ran along this side of the house, from which steps led down into the enormous garden, where smooth green lawns, shaded by splendid old trees, stretched right away to the Champs Elysées. To-day, as one walks along the green alley known as the Avenue Gabriel, bordered by the tall iron railings of these old gardens, one catches for a moment a glimpse of the stately world of eighteenth-century Paris.

"Beneath some of these very trees the women of the reign of Louis XVI walked perhaps in their flowing muslin gowns on summer mornings; through that great gateway Madame de Sabran may often have passed with Delphine and Elzéar into the Champs Elysées. Her house is gone, but those remaining close by give one an idea of its appearance, and in looking out of the south windows of the British Embassy one sees—but for such modern disfigurements as the Eiffel Tower—much the same prospect as she saw from the windows of her salon a hundred and thirty years ago.[1]

"Inside the house was charming, for Bouret (the financier) had decorated it at enormous cost, yet with far from plutocratic floridness of taste, and the exquisite mouldings, carvings, and panellings of that enchanting period formed a perfect back-

[1] Since writing this in 1915, Mrs. Webster has now changed her mind, and told me she thought the house still exists, and that she saw the terrace and garden.

ground to the furniture and bibelots, that Madame de Sabran had collected."

At a safe distance from the grille, feeling incredibly suspect, Boufflers gazed through at the winding green alley of trees leading to a summer pavilion. Suddenly a voice from behind startled him: "Eh, *mon vieux*, what's the matter?" He turned round quickly. It was Charlot de Ligne, dressed in a suit of pale blue face cloth, with a waistcoat *couleur gorge-de-pigeon*. They both burst out laughing. It was no good concocting excuses with an old friend and boon companion like Charlot; he knew Boufflers too well. Putting his arm through his, the prince drew him along the Champs-Elysées.

"I was just going to call on the Comtesse," he said, "now I'll take you with me: we'll go together. I'm sure she'll be charmed. She said yesterday that you were very original."

"I'm not coming with you," said Boufflers, looking grim.

"Now, now. Don't be eccentric. I know exactly how you feel, but it mustn't be encouraged."

Boufflers turned round and smiled enigmatically at him. "You know nothing."

"Is it as bad as that? *Mon pauvre vieux!* What an ironical situation. You've spent your life singing that 'tender fires are a great bore', and now you are in danger of becoming a great bore yourself. Come, come, my Boufflers, courage. Attack the whole situation with the elegant poise that becomes you so well. Are you not much better than many other men who adore her? If it's only money you lack, we will all put our heads together and try to find you some post in which you can win renown, and then you can lay it at her feet. A pity she's so virtuous; pity for your sake, I mean: not a hope of making her listen to frivolous declarations. Now come along with me. Don't be so mock-heroic and out-of-date."

In a few minutes, Charlot and Boufflers were being admitted to Madame de Sabran's house. The footman said that she was out at the bathing establishment, but would be returning soon. As it was such a fine day, he showed them through the house, out on to the terrace, and fetched chairs and footstools. During the half-hour of waiting, Charlot described in greater detail some of the rooms which Boufflers had glimpsed on the way through.

The Chevalier little guessed, that June morning, that for the next twelve to fourteen years, in fact, until the Revolution, this place was to be his Paradise. In his letters to her he wrote: "This house is indeed a Paradise . . ." And: "I love to turn my thoughts towards that house which is so dear to me, to see you amidst all your occupations and diversions, writing, painting, reading, sleeping, arranging and disarranging everything . . . spoiling your children, being spoilt by your friends, always different and yet always the same."

Madame Vigée Lebrun said of Eléonore: "In her presence, one never knew boredom." When Boufflers came to know the house, he saw it only as the background for her who was the sole woman ever to captivate his mind. "Beloved angel of painting and poetry." But that morning, before love had revealed the secret of the house to him—and each old house has its secret—he had taken in at a glance all the external beauties which were the setting of her personality and the expression of her taste.

It is impossible to resist the temptation of reconstructing the exterior *décor* of this love-story, this last smile, as it were, of the eighteenth century. The joys and sufferings of the vanished lovers become more poignant if the mute witnesses of buried passion, the very walls, are allowed to tell their tale.

Madame de Sabran was very wealthy; she had perfect taste, and she loved contemporary works of art. One may assume that she did not cling too feverishly to many of the antiquated Louis XIV and Louis XV possessions which her husband had inherited. It was only châtelaines in the distant provinces, living far from the tempting fashionable cabinet-makers of Paris, who allowed ancestral treasures to accumulate in their châteaux, and rarely put them away in their attics.

The style Louis Seize launched a return to simplicity, the straight line and pastel tints. In the painting of rooms, one saw less gold or scarlet or jade Vernis-Martin, but more pale rose and grey and water-green picked out with thin gold lines. The whole effect, as compared with the old, was one of elegant sobriety, restraint in fantasy, harmony in proportions.

Some of the stucco decorations of the walls, around the panels and the chimney-pieces, betokened the new Greek and Pompeian influence on artists; this began soon after the Pompadour had sent her brother, Monsieur de Marigny, on his art-tour around Italy, to prepare him for his position of superintendent of the King's buildings. There were garlands of foliage, acanthus leaves, interlacings of olive and laurel. And then, delicately and lightly painted on the walls with a thin brush, beautifully spaced so that they showed up well and looked delicate and airy, there were the rustic emblems beloved of those times—osier baskets, beehives, gardening implements such as beribboned sickles, rakes and watering cans. Or there were the sentimental emblems—pierced hearts, quivers, flaming torches, superimposed crowns of roses hanging by three cords.

Eléonore loved music. She played the guitar and the harpsichord. It is probable that she had a music-room, and that musical instruments, such as flutes, violins and rustic bagpipes, were painted on the walls. There might also be perfume burners distilling clouds of smoke, ribbons interlaced above oval medallions showing those groups of frolicking babies which have always been such a distinguishing feature of French decoration, even before the days of Boucher. . . . Oh, sportive little cupids, as sweet as Tiepolo's coral-cheeked rogues, attendant sprites of the *dix-huitième*, tumbling over clouds, mischievously spilling cornucopias of nebulous dream-roses, playing with bows and arrows, being whipped with rose-branches by their mother, Venus. Soon these cherubs would give place to paintings of human children—when Marie-Antoinette and Rousseau's *Emile* make motherhood all the rage.

Boufflers walked up and down with his hands in his pockets as Charlot talked of Eléonore's house. He refused to go in with him. He could not say why, but he did not want to see more of this Elysium until his hostess was there to show him. From the terrace he could catch sight of some of the red and blue *toile-de-Jouy* curtains at the bedroom windows, for these printed linens had become fashionable, and in many houses were replacing the heavy silk brocades of Lyons and Italy. Even in the designs stamped on her curtains, a woman can betray her personal tastes, for Eléonore had chosen a rustic scene of Huet's which reminded her of country pleasures. Here were picturesque urchins fishing and playing on their pipes near a ruined tower overlooking a crumbling bridge overgrown with honeysuckle. There were ducks sporting in the water, fine cocks crowing, a little lamb resting on his mother's back, and a country lass with looped skirts and bare feet was feeding some hens. Boufflers always loved sheep. He had plenty at his own little estate of Malgrange, and he had given some away to his friends. They reminded him of Lunéville, and of *Aline, reine de Golconde*—his pastoral tale which the Pompadour had raved about. On one set of long french windows the blinds had been half-drawn against the sun, and they were as green as water-lily leaves, made of ruched taffeta, with tassels on the end.[1]

De Ligne, who loved beautiful houses just as much as he did gardens, continued telling his friend about the interior of that house. Could anything have been better calculated, first to intrigue Boufflers, and then to dishearten him by emphasizing the disparity between his fortune and that of the Comtesse? His face became overcast as he recalled sofas covered with Beauvais and Aubusson tapestries, little chairs with lyre-shaped

[1] See the curtains in the engraving of *Le Concert*, by Augustin de Saint Aubin.

backs, arm-chairs with low backs to make room for the enormous hats in vogue, Riesener's marqueterie tables and chests with their carved bronzes, door plaques and handles by that de Gouthière who had made du Barry's place at Louveciennes such a dream, a new desk called *bonheur-du-jour*, bookcases with light iron grilles, perhaps a marble bust by Houdon, a group by Clodion. As she loved pictures, did she have a painting of the later Fragonard, full of light and impetuosity; a Greuze, both sentimental and sensuous, appealing to all the sensibility of the declining century; an early Hubert Robert or two, the decorative grandeur of his arches inspired by the Roman ruins of France and Italy; a seascape of Vernet's in honour of her sailor husband . . .?

Charlot said: "I daresay, when the time comes, you won't look with the eye of a connoisseur at all."

Through a half-open window the Chevalier noticed a profusion of feminine trinkets . . . a harp which he fancied was still vibrating from her touch, a music-stand laden with the pieces she had played, an open harpsichord, a marqueterie table strewn with Chinese knick-knacks and with flowers carelessly arranged in Venetian and Sèvres vases. Eléonore was very untidy; she could never find anything; her paintings were littered about everywhere, and on the writing tables the quills were not cut, and the inkstands were always empty.[1]

"And yet," said Charlot, "she doesn't carry this charming disorder too far. Now she has a blue bedroom which is a dream.[2] What a pity you will never see it; she rises so early that she does not receive at her *toilette*. Everything is blue, picked out with thin lines of misty gold and swags of gilded leaves on the walls. The day I saw it she had one of her famous colds—for she is rather delicate you know—the floor was so crowded with things that I had to pick my way on tiptoe; the children's toys, a container full of perfume bottles, a washing bowl shaped like a shell, masses of little cretonne boxes with posies and ribbons spilling out of them, her tiny slippers, her little dogs. There are birds and bulrushes painted on the mirror above her basin.[3] I'm surprised she hasn't got one of the modern baths yet. The Queen will insist on having one at Petit Trianon. It's so tiresome for Eléonore, always being obliged to go out to this bathing establishment. Why doesn't she hurry up and come back."

As if in answer to his wish, they heard the garden grille open. The bunch of baby spaniels in their basket all started barking

[1] He teased her about this in his letters.

[2] Boufflers refers to her blue bed in one of his letters.

[3] See Baudouin's engraving, *Le Coucher*, and Janinet, *La Comparaison*. My description is a blend of both these.

D

at once, and then leaped out flippetty-floppetty, silken ears streaming in the wind, to greet their mistress. Madame de Sabran was gliding towards them through the patterned sunlight of the garden, under the chestnut trees with their magical pink candles.

She looked much more fragile and plaintive than at the ball, when her tall head-dress and wide panniers had lent her a fictitious grandeur. Now she was very simply gowned in a white muslin dress with a cross-over fichu and tight blue sash, and a floppy hat tied with blue velvet ribbons under the chin. She carried a mauve lace-frilled parasol. She wore no jewels save very large sapphire ear-rings. She seemed to float through the air. She had been in a day-dream, entranced by the drowsy perfume of a bee-murmuring lime-tree. When she glanced up at the terrace and saw Boufflers looking at her with his rather teasing, ironic smile, she was not startled; since their meeting last night she felt that he would be there quite soon, waiting for her on the terrace. She forgot all her qualms about his reputation and, giving him her hand to kiss, she smiled up at him with welcoming grace.

"I hope you've both come to gossip," she said. "After a ball, I think it is a necessity. Let us go into the house, it is so hot outside."

She went into the drawing-room through the open window, threw down her parasol and her hat, gave an order to a servant, and then turned to Charlot and Boufflers.

"Come to my studio, I want to show you my picture of Delphine and Elzéar—it's *nearly* finished."

"And I am sure it will remain unfinished," said Charlot. "Oh, those portraits of yours which are begun with such fervour, completely forgotten after a while, and allowed to litter the chairs all over the house!"

She laughed, and led them swiftly through a suite of rooms until she reached the *sanctum*—a room which combined the offices of boudoir, studio, music-room and library, carelessly arranged, in pretty disorder as Charlot had prophesied. The place looked lived in. Some brightly-coloured green birds with coral breasts were quarrelling in a huge gilded cage by the window. She went straight to her easel and started touching up the figures of her two children with their little dog. Charlot mixed some paints for her at her bidding, and Boufflers, after admiring the portrait, turned to glance at the titles of the books on the shelves. There were various long, romantic novels of the seventeenth century, the *Nouvelle Héloïse*, the letters of Héloïse and Abelard in the original Latin, Horace, Virgil, a French translation of *Pamela*, volumes of French history, the Confessions of Saint Augustine and, wonder of wonders, a copy of *Aline, Queen of Golconda*. Boufflers could not restrain an exclamation of surprise when he saw that.

"What is it, Chevalier?" asked Eléonore.

"I see you've got a little book called *Aline, Reine de Golconde.*"

"I adored it," said Eléonore. "I've often wanted to know who wrote it, because the author and I have exactly the same feeling for Nature."

Charlot and Boufflers looked at one another and burst out laughing. Eléonore turned to them with smiling enquiry. Then suddenly she said to Boufflers, suspiciously:

"*You* didn't write it, did you?"

"Yes, long ago," he said, looking gawkish, and laughing with his shy, good-humoured laugh.

Eléonore dropped her paint brushes and impulsively clasped her hands together. She looked charmingly excited and happy. He could not help smiling, for she had a paint smudge on her cheek, and her hair was rather wild.

"What a delightful imagination you have, Chevalier! Why have I never met you till now? I love *Aline* ! I know several passages by heart, which is wonderful for me, because I have such a bad memory. Listen," and she wrinkled her brow and quoted a little hesitatingly:

"'And the sun sinking in the West, recalled the shepherds to their huts and the flocks to their stables: the air echoed with the sound of bagpipes and the songs of workers as they returned to rest.' How nostalgic that is! It makes me pine to own some tiny country place far away from Paris, some small but exquisite *folie* where I should be quite alone with my children, and where I could pick wild flowers in the fields and woods all day, and dream by the side of rippling brooks and watch the pretty shepherdesses. In the turmoil of Paris I sometimes long for the simplicity of country life. I wish Charlot could find me something."

They both turned to where Charlot had been standing, but he had vanished on to the terrace. However, far from feeling surprised, Madame de Sabran and the Chevalier found they had so much to say to one another that his absence was unnoticed.

Boufflers felt happy; at last the ice was broken: they could drop all the conventional ritual of small-talk and be natural, and explore each others' personal tastes. He said:

"I am glad to have made a friend by *Aline.* I once made an enemy of the Abbé Talleyrand because of her."

"How is that?"

"When *Aline* was published, anonymously, as you know, the *Abbé* pretended that he was the author. I heard of this, but I said nothing: I bided my time. I waited till I met him in the *salon* of the Choiseuls, who are great friends of mine, and then I broke a pause in the conversation by asking him genially if he happened to know the works of Rabelais. 'Obviously,' replied

Talleyrand, drily. I said, 'Obviously, yet not well!' to which Talleyrand replied, 'Dare I ask you why?' I said with a bow, '*Monsieur l'Abbé*, I asked you whether you knew the works of Rabelais because I had omitted to tell you that it is I who wrote them.' As a revenge he had spread the slander that I am ugly. Isn't that an *outrage*!"

They both laughed. Eléonore said, "Do you make many enemies?"

"Unfortunately yes, particularly among fellow-authors. Not that it worries me much, I have a lot of friends. It never disturbed my sleep, for instance, when Monsieur Rousseau started telling everyone that I have 'many half talents and make little verses and write little letters very well, play the timbrel and daub a little in pastel'."

"Whatever did you do to deserve *that*?"

"When I was a seminarist . . ."

"What!" exclaimed Eléonore in amazement, for she had forgotten this.

"Yes, I was at Saint-Sulpice for a year or two, but I left just in time. They discovered that I had no vocation. Well, anyway, when I was a seminarist, on one of my holidays, I went to see my great-aunt de Luxembourg, at Montmorency. There I met Rousseau. I took an instant dislike to him, for he seemed so conceited, always longing to be the centre of attention; and then I did not trust him: here was a man who was always satirizing society, and yet he was luxuriating in all its amenities at Montmorency. I tried the trick of taking absolutely no notice of him. Unfortunately, quite against my will, whenever I appeared in the drawing-room, everybody else ignored him, and joked and laughed with me instead. That must have annoyed him. One day, however, I put an end to any semblance of polite conversation between us by playing a practical joke on him."

"What was that?"

"I painted a hideous picture of my great-aunt—yes, I paint, too, you know—and I forced him to give me his opinion of it. Being rather afraid of my tongue, he was silly enough to fall straight into the trap and tried to please me by saying that the picture was a good likeness. Of course my aunt put him in her black books, and I made fun of him for the rest of my time there."

"I think you are a cruel and dangerous young man; I should be afraid to have you as my enemy."

"Have no fear. I shall always be at your feet: I am already your devoted slave."

"Really? Will you prove it to me by granting me a favour?"

"Anything!"

"Will you sit patiently as my model while I paint you? None

of the men I know, who come and disturb my working hours in the morning, can ever spare time for this. I'm tired of painting my women friends. Will you come and sit for me?"

"Nothing would please me more. I am on leave from my regiment for some time, and my days are entirely at your disposal. I will sit very still and I won't make you laugh by any impromptu verses."

"The only trouble is that, most mornings, I get so many callers. You will have to remain in the same pose while the room is full of babble, and you will be longing to give vent to one of your witty sallies."

"I will padlock my tongue, and cast a veil over my eyes: have no fear, O Goddess of Painting, I will become as motionless as if I had looked at Medusa's head. One glance at you and . . ."

"Fie!" she laughed. "I am not Medusa."

"No, you are Apelles! Instead of adders, I will see the darts of the cruel little god, and I will be transfixed."

CHAPTER XIII

IN WHICH THE CHEVALIER IS REBUFFED FOR THE FIRST TIME IN HIS CAREER

AND thus, without having planned anything, Boufflers found himself dropping in most mornings to call on the young Comtesse, as she painted in her studio.

And each day, in spite of his resolutions, he fell more in love with her. He had known many beautiful women, but here, for the first time, was that naturalness of which he had dreamed and which he had never found. She was the first woman whom he had reverenced, for she was goodness incarnate. When he was with her, all the old incrustations of his mind, all the cynicism and mockery seemed to drop from him, and he became simple and happy. He ceased putting up any façade of scintillating wit, and was just glad to exist, glad to bathe in the clear atmosphere that she created around her.

So here was a woman who was good and who could still fascinate by her infinite variety. He began to realize that the charm of the unexpected was not the prerogative of actresses or women who loved lightly. Her conversation was never the same, for it touched delicately on one subject and then another, "like a magic lantern of ideas". And then, he grew to adore all those moods of the artistic temperament, the vagueness, the elusiveness and casual ways which matched his own, the delicious disorder and carelessness of her rooms, where he was always helping her in frantic searches for various objects she had lost, and then finding them in the most unexpected places. For example, she had a way of hiding pastel portraits between two mattresses and then forgetting all about them! Her house was quite unlike the houses of other women, for it was a home, not a series of reception-rooms. The two delightful children Delphine and Elzéar were not relegated to their tutors in the attics, but shared in the life and joys of the household. The rooms echoed with their laughter as they played hide-and-seek, and their songs mingled with the sound of monkeys chattering, parakeets squawking on perches, lovebirds twittering in their cages, and puppies chasing one another from room to room . . . And everywhere, sunlight, beautiful colours, loose pages of music, guitars, children's toys, a profusion of casually arranged field flowers plucked on a picnic with the children, books heaped on every chair, unfinished portraits, half-empty tubes of paint. . . . Boufflers felt completely in his element. After a little while he, too, came to be looked on as one of the household. If Eléonore heard someone coming in the distance, making a great deal of noise, she knew it was the Chevalier: from her easel she would half turn and smile at him; then he would sharpen her quills or tell adventure stories to the children, and the morning flew by. She began to depend on him for advice. Under his abrupt, absent-minded ways, she discovered a heart of gold. Even his scoffing was not rooted in cynicism, but grew out of his hatred of hypocrisy which she shared with him. She heard her friends say that he mocked the tender passion; but Eléonore sensed that even here unsounded depths of feeling lay concealed beneath the frivolity. Eléonore was sublimely unaware that she was the first woman to awaken these depths. As Charlot once said: "Good women run the greatest risks—they are the least prepared for what may happen." What did it matter that he had the reputation of a libertine? Surely his past escapades, she thought, must be due to hot-blood and recklessness rather than to the cold-hearted calculations of the seducer.

And then, he had so many gifts! One day, after composing some verses in her honour, he accompanied her on the harpsichord and sang them, while she picked out the tune on her guitar. Anyone stepping unobserved through the long window would have seen a picturesque *dix-huitième* scene and heard the prettiest of rhymes, tinkling like the notes of a spinet.

To be pretty, to be fair,
'Tis of no avail

If you lack the air
Of this lady frail.

Carnations, roses fair,
Are of no avail,
For they don't compare
With this lady frail.

Glory and wondrous fame
Do not on me prevail.
Whate'er be the blame,
I'll live with this Fair Frail.

A tender heart and true
Can be of no avail,
If in vain I sue
The heart of its Fair Frail.

Boufflers continued to sit for his portrait. All that time, Eléonore, unbeknown to herself, was learning the lineaments of his face, so that in after years, when she recalled those early days which vanished so quickly, she said she had loved him from the first. Who can tell? Without knowing it, she may have been growing very fond of him; love that begins in friendship is a tenacious thing: one may securely bolt all the doors and windows against it, but it has a sly way of filtering in through some unexpected cranny and completely invading the domain before the victim has had a chance of arming himself or declaring a state of siege.

Wishing to be free from financial troubles at this time, Boufflers, with the aid of his sister, Madame de Boisgelin, made a great effort, and succeeded in putting his affairs temporarily in order. He paid his card debts, sold another small piece of land, and thus got rid of some pressing creditors, reduced his personal expenses to the minimum and, above all, kept away from gambling. In this way he was able to meet Eléonore socially on a more equal footing, do her little services, buy bouquets for her from the flower girls who always besieged the coach on their way to balls, and also lend her his own horses when hers had gone sick.[1] Not only was Boufflers a magnificent horseman, but he loved his horses, and looked after them well. However shabby his clothes, whenever he rode up to any house for his country visits, his horse, so beautifully trained and cared-for, was the admiration of all the grooms and stable boys, who came hurtling *pêle-mêle* from the stables to attend him. (Once, after losing all at cards, he

[1] His letters contain references to the loan of horses.

turned up on an old nag at Chanteloup, much to the amusement of the Choiseuls.)

Eléonore, a wealthy woman living alone, very vague in directing her business affairs and much too inexperienced to deal with trickery of any sort, was naturally at the mercy of many people of her household. It is quite possible that her head groom was a rascal who falsified his accounts, bought inferior horses at a great profit to himself, was often drunk, and, worst of all—and this is mentioned in her letters—killed off a mare by driving her to and from Versailles on a very hot day at a terrible speed. It is more than probable that Boufflers, with his knowledge of horses and grooms, should have helped her in the management of her stables. This took a great load off Eléonore's mind, and she began to attend to this aspect of her household affairs more carefully, as now she was a little in dread of a good scolding from Boufflers, if she became too flippant.

One day in July, she asked him to drive back with her from a party they had both been to, outside Paris, though he always said he preferred to ride back. She said she wanted his opinion on the new mare. It was the hour before the dawn. Later, in his letters, referring to that mare, Boufflers said the only fault he found with her, was that she galloped home too quickly when they were together. However, they had an hour's *tête-à-tête* before they got to the Faubourg Saint-Honoré. The coachman, who had enjoyed himself hugely at the party, tippling with compatriots, had to prevent himself from bursting into song several times.

The Chevalier was wearing the blue cloth of a Knight of Malta, and Eléonore a lovely heliotrope slipper-satin ball-gown, flounced with black lace.

"How fatigued I am," murmured Eléonore.

"Take off your plumes," said the Chevalier sensibly. And he started plucking all the ornaments from her *coiffure* and strewing them on to the floor of the carriage. Too weary to protest, she sank back into the downy cushions. The coach was lined with blue velvet, as cosy as a nest. It was a dark summer night: by the soft glow of the carriage lamps they could see the trees in strange relief, the foliage looking artificial and brilliantly green. But oh! how cool and fresh the air, how quiet the dew-laden countryside. The stillness was only broken by the hooting of an owl from a distant wood. Occasionally a rabbit would lope across the road, prick up his ears and dart into the grass of the roadside. Boufflers told Eléonore that he had been born on a high road. She was intrigued and drowsily asked him to tell her about his childhood. They discovered that they had both been very lonely, and had sought comfort in the sympathy of a dog's friendship. He told her about Pataud, she about Zina.

"You know," he said, "I've noticed this about people who love dogs: either they are very nice (like you and me!) or else they are rather unsociable, and turn to dogs because no human being will befriend them. What do you think?"

There was no answer: Eléonore was fast asleep!

Boufflers was in a maze. What was he to do? His perplexities were increased when Eléonore's head gently slipped down on to his shoulder. He was glad that there were not a lot of ostrich feathers to tickle his nose and make him sneeze. Very carefully he made her lie back among the cushions; then he gazed down at her. Any other woman would have expected, on waking, to find that reasonable homage had been paid to her beauty. But with her, never!

A torrent, a torment of love welled up in his heart as he drank in her beauty. She had shed her mask. Now she looked such a girl, defenceless and at his mercy. How tiny she was, and how delicately made. In spite of her heliotrope panniers, she seemed like some elf-creature who would fit beautifully into the hollow of his hand. As for her little feet from which her pale green mules had slipped off, they were a dream in miniature, like two pointed water-lily buds. Her sweet bosom glimpsed in her frothy spangled *decolleté*, he could only compare to a bed of roses, like any hackneyed songster. Lines from Ronsard came to his mind, lines he had never breathed to any woman.

Ma petite colombelle,
Ma mignonne toute belle . . .

What a strange thing it was to fall in love for the first time: Mystery, Silence, Trust, Union and a great Peace. . . .

Yes, he felt at one with her, poor child. So she, too, had known a lonely childhood. But it had all been much more cruel for her, in the way that a girl is at the mercy of older women. How brave she had been in defending her sister against the others; it was this tenderness, this generosity, which he most loved in her. He had never heard her say an unkind word about anyone, and her heart was always brimful of pity for the weak.

"All the seductiveness of woman in repose; the languor, the idleness, the abandonment . . . the little air of nonchalance, the cadence of poses, the pretty profile . . . the fugitive breast . . . the flow, the suppleness of woman's body. . . ."[1]

It is not often, he thought, that a man has the good fortune to see his beloved in all the sweet self-betrayal of sleep. He cursed the fashions of the day, which not only buttressed woman in whale-bone, but also painted her face so that the little defects,

[1] From the de Goncourts, on Watteau's women.

the moles and tiny wrinkles dear to the eye of the lover, were invisible.

When they got to the outskirts of Paris, Boufflers picked up her feathers, and then woke her up very gently. Her complete lack of embarrassment at her behaviour filled him with sadness, for it indicated that her feelings towards him were still too purely sisterly, and full of *bonne camaraderie*: a woman the tiniest bit in love would have been overcome with shyness, or probably would never have fallen asleep at all!

"Come to-morrow for the final sitting of your portrait," she called out to him as she left him outside her door.

As he walked down the Faubourg, he was still in a maze. How hard it was to tear himself away from her at this hour; what an unnatural sundering of leaf from flower. That ride home had been an enchantment. Now he pictured her preparing for rest, in all the foam and froth of lace, attended by her maid. He saw it all: the alabaster shell filled with perfumed water, the heavy jewels flung aside and then put away in a large jewel-chest, the wonderful mauve slipper-satin gown with its flounces of black Alençon lace lying limp in a chair, linen scented with her body, the long gloves unbuttoned and stripped off, the fading rosebuds of the nosegay slipped into a crystal container; trinkets, fan, reticule put away into boxes. At length, Eléonore, in her lace cap, her beribboned night bodice and all the pretty negligence of snowy batiste, closes her eyes under the heavily-looped draperies of her blue bed. The maid takes away the little dog in his basket, in case he wakes his mistress too soon; she draws the folds of the curtains against the intrusion of the dawn now stealing in from the East, behind the Place Louis-Quinze; and then she tiptoes away. Is it a wonder that the engravers of the time loved to portray woman in bed, in a century which turned the ritual of preparing for the night into a work of art?

Late the next morning Boufflers came for his final sitting of the famous portrait. What a trial to his peace of mind these sittings had been! And yet he was sorry now that they were nearly over.

At the end of the morning Eléonore was called away for a moment by Elzéar's nurse. When she came back, Boufflers had vanished. Tiresome man! She went to her easel. A piece of paper was pinned on it; she opened it and inside she found the following couplets—in almost illegible handwriting.

My young Apelles has a trick
As sure as it is new!
Inflames her model's heart, and quick,
It hath a life-like hue.

You take a hundred different hues,
The sombre and the bright.
To paint in all my loving views,
I'd have to rhyme all night.

Secrets proclaim on drum and fife,
Sing to the Heavens above:
When my portrait comes to life,
'Twill tell you of my love.

At first, Eléonore smiled: his versifying was so compact and dexterous. Then she frowned: "I wish he didn't think it necessary to speak of love. It's a little tiresome. He must realize by now that he has no need to pay me conventional compliments. And yet, of course, it *may* be true. No! it can't be. He's loved every pretty woman in Paris in his time. He may be saying the same thing to half a dozen others. He doesn't know what love is." And then she walked up and down, crumpling and then smoothing out the sheet of paper, smiling and frowning in turns. "Do *I* know what love is?" Then she realized in a flash, for the first time, that she had not been in love with her husband. No, this was an agony she had not known from experience. Everything was so pleasant in her life at the moment. She was her own mistress, she adored her house, her children, her days divided between social pleasures and the joys of solitude. Love would mar all by claiming exclusive sovereignty over her: she knew intuitively that at heart she was a passionately loving woman, and if once her heart were awakened she would give herself body, soul and spirit.

Give, to him? To him who had been so used to take, almost negligently, as if love were a ripe fruit which you plucked and tasted when you were hungry and threw away when sated? No! A thousand times no. She decided to make it quite clear to him, firmly and yet lightly, that there must be no talk of love between them. She felt that he valued her friendship sufficiently not to risk her displeasure by disobedience. Yes, she had this hold on him, unshared by other women: the bond of friendship. All their tastes and occupations were the same, and he seemed to fit into her surroundings quite naturally, as if he'd always belonged there.

The next evening she had planned to go to a play in a grilled box, where she could not be seen, and afterwards return to her house to entertain some friends for supper. She decided to speak to Boufflers about his poem after this party; she would do it delicately, banteringly, making him feel that she did not take him seriously, but on the other hand telling him clearly enough that these insincere declarations of love were rather distasteful to her.

To her discomfiture, Boufflers turned up very early, and insisted on accompanying her to the play: he looked serious, and even rather anxious.

"It will not be so easy to put him off, after all," she thought. "What a good thing that it isn't a box at the Opera!" (When a woman wanted to declare that she had a lover, she was seen with him alone in a box at the Opera.)

The theatre was darkened, the curtain rose, the orchestra played music by Glück, now in vogue through the patronage of Marie-Antoinette; the little painted marionettes glittered in the candlelight. Neither the Chevalier nor Eléonore could be seen, hidden in the obscurity of the comfortable little box. They began to talk in whispers; this was tiresome, for it felt intimate, and she wanted to avoid that. She wore voluminous panniers of white lace. Her little powdered head was half-turned from him, and he could just see the outline of cheek-bone and the tiny ears on which hung long ruby ear-rings. Boufflers began:

"I am sad that you won't need me for a model any more."

"And I am not likely to do so if you fluster my Muse by pinning insincere little poems on my easel after the last sitting."

"Insincere? I meant every word I said."

"You've spent your life writing poems of that sort. *I'm* not used to them. If you want our friendship to continue you must not speak of love to me, for that is a word which you and I interpret differently."

"How do *you* interpret it?"

("I am neatly trapped," thought she.) After a moment's hesitation she replied: "To you, love is having an affair, it is something temporary, almost an expedient for the moment. To me, it is the passion for one human being for a lifetime."

"That is what I now know"—in a trembling voice.

This rather shook Eléonore's calm. After a moment, she replied: "I don't believe you."

"Why not?"—rather angrily.

"You forget that I am acquainted with your views on love, for your poems are well known. . . . Don't you remember writing:

I like a prudish waist to span,
For then I should be chidden.
Is aught so tempting to a man
As fruit that is forbidden?

Oh, and a thousand other little couplets, all exactly alike."

Boufflers made a gesture of protest. She silenced him with a cold look. "No, *mon ami*, you and I will remain very good friends, only if you promise me that you will never again mention the word love in my presence."

Boufflers looked upset and bewildered. Glancing sideways at him, Eléonore felt a tiny movement of pity, so she put her hand on his coat-sleeve, impulsively, and said gaily: "Look, not only will we be great friends, but we will be brother and sister; that is such a tender relationship, if you *must* have tenderness."

"I want more than tenderness."

"I'm sorry, then, but you must seek elsewhere. How insatiable you are! I am prepared to give you all that I can—trust, devotion, complete frankness, access to my house, my society, and my children . . ."

"But I never see you alone; you are always besieged by callers. How can friendship prosper with so many interruptions?"

She weakened a moment, then said:

"That is soon remedied. When I go to Anizy to visit my brother-in-law, the Bishop of Laon, we will invite you to stay, if your regiment is stationed near; and then we will all go for rides and picnics together. You can help me with my translations of Horace."

What a bait! Boufflers smiled a little wrily. Is there anything more maddening than to want a woman to give herself to you, and, after being denied, one is offered a little sop in the form of sharing her classical studies? A pest on her; he'd teach her! One day she would do all his bidding; he'd make her pay heavily for the time when she had repelled him. This had never happened to him before. All the unconscious cruelty of a frustrated passion seethed in the wild, hot-tempered Chevalier.

However, knowing that she would be inexorable, he promised, with various mental reservations, to do as she commanded, and peace was restored. They listened to the music in silence, and he never looked at her for the rest of the evening.

They had gone to the theatre at five, and the supper-party was to be at nine. She looked at her watch and gave a little cry: it was already nine. She pulled the bell-cord and told a footman to order the carriage, and then to go ahead quickly and warn her guests that she would be a few minutes late. She went into the little *boudoir* leading out of the box and arranged her curls at the dressing-table. Boufflers wrapped her in those luxurious furs which were the *coquetterie* of theatre-going women in those days, and they both went down to her coach, Boufflers holding her finger-tips and handing her in himself.

CHAPTER XIV

A SUPPER-PARTY

WHEN Eléonore returned, she found, to her relief, that only the Comte de Ségur had arrived. He seemed in a sulky mood. She rang that candles might be lit everywhere, and said how sorry she was not to have been there to receive him. For an answer he pointed dourly to a piece of paper he'd taken from his pocket. As prose portraits of one's friends were then the rage, Eléonore and Boufflers between them had found a fine epigram in Martial suitable for the Comte de Ségur; she'd foolishly left it on her desk. It caught the Comte's eye in her absence, and was not to his liking! He put it in his pocket and refused to return it. All Eléonore's tact and diplomacy were needed before she could soothe his wounded vanity.[1] However, after a little teasing from other friends who were now clustering round, he began to thaw. He said: "I suppose listeners never hear any good of themselves. Just lately I seem fated to be the butt of mockery." He pulled another piece of paper from his pocket. "Now listen to this letter to Maurepas from an officer of distinction in my regiment who had asked me for leave in order to attend to pressing affairs in Paris. He kept applying, and I kept refusing. At length he wrote to Maurepas, asking for leave, and on the same day, he also wrote to his mistress in Paris. Unfortunately, in his turmoil of mind, he addressed the letters wrongly. This is the letter which Maurepas got, and passed on to me:

"'Darling angel, Ségur is cruel enough to refuse me permission to fly to your arms: I would be in despair if I did not expect a more favourable reply from Maurepas; he's an old rip who will guess the object of my request, and will thereby be more disposed to grant it. He will readily understand that, at my age, one prefers to die in the arms of one's mistress, rather than live in a sad garrison. And then, as I seem to lack myrtle, if only I had laurels to pluck! But I vegetate here, while my comrades are fighting elsewhere: it's a f . . . profession, this war in peacetime. I say peace, because it isn't for me that the cannon roars. Good-bye, bitchlet-face; if I held you, you can well imagine what would happen to you. In the meantime, before I come to surprise you, as I hope to do, I kiss you in anticipation . . .'"[2]

There was a ripple of mirth from all the women in the

[1] This anecdote is from the *Journal* of her son, Elzéar de Sabran.
[2] Memoirs of Bachaumont.

drawing-room, and murmurs of "Adorable man", while the men who followed the career of arms smiled slyly, and made inward comments on the eternal union of Mars and Venus.

Eléonore asked: "And what happened?"

"Oh, Maurepas wrote the young man a charming letter, and gave him permission to go on leave."[1]

In the meantime, Boufflers who was more a soldier than anything else, and who enjoyed this kind of story, seemed to have recovered his good spirits, and was regaling the Duc de Nivernais with a feast of mimicry. This time he was imitating an officer from the regiment of Penthièvre whom he'd met at an inn on his way to Ferney: "By Jove! They began by a shower of bullets, just the usual kind, this was followed by four little balls, as fat as eggs, by Jove, and which made a frightful carnage, by Jove!"

Soon the room was filled with the customary côterie of friends —the Duc de Croÿ, Charlot de Ligne, Monseigneur de Sabran, the Comtesse Diane de Polignac, ugly, spiteful, but entertaining, Madame Vigée Lebrun who was received everywhere. Then there were one or two old ladies of the Court of Louis Quinze, every whit as amusing as the younger women, with this added charm, that the years had taught them tolerance, and it was diverting to get them to talk about their young days. In a corner, Monsieur de Vaudreuil was having an argument with the Cardinal de Bernis about Prince Charles Edward.

Supper was announced, and the conversations were continued in new surroundings, where diverging opinions would melt into a golden harmony in the bubbles of champagne. The guests sat where they wanted, they did not go in ceremoniously according to precedence in those days. So they were all happy and at ease, because they chose their supper companion. Boufflers took care to sit where he could see Eléonore. She was not unaware of his stratagems, and gave him a quick glance, in which amusement and despairing reproof were mingled.

The dining-room was round and domed, with festoons and garlands over the doors; there were candles in the wall brackets and in the glass lantern hanging above the large round table. White silk tapestry was looped over the doorway to give a feeling of greater privacy. As there were those new movable side-tables at one's elbow, with three tiers holding the different courses, Madame de Sabran had dispensed with servants, and the men served the women; this was a pleasant fashion which was spreading all over Paris. An alabaster group rose in the middle of the table: the Three Graces supporting a real pineapple on their heads. The gold knives and forks had handles of pale green enamel. A posy of

[1] From a letter to his mother.

summer flowers rested on the Sèvres plate before each guest. Eléonore asked Boufflers to pop the champagne corks. He was in high spirits: she was relieved that he did not seem hurt. Irrepressible creature.[1]

Eléonore wore a priceless gown of white Brussels lace, with little posies of white moss roses strewn on it, and a dazzling necklace of rubies, with pendant and ear-rings to match. Her slippers were green, to tone with the foliage of the moss roses. She felt happy and excited, she could not say why. On her right was Monseigneur de Sabran, her brother-in-law, who was engaged in tossing remarks at Boufflers about Voltaire. "Ah!" sighed Boufflers, "would that Voltaire's spirit might remain on earth and his soul go to Paradise."

The two fading beauties of the Court of Louis XV, one of them rather deaf, were unknowingly causing subdued mirth among the rest of the company by their asides, as they confectioned an omelette of cocks' crests in a small silver pan at a console table: "Ah, *ma chère*, do you remember how His Majesty used to whisk an omelette at one of those intimate little suppers he gave after hunting? How he loved creating new dishes. I believe he was making quite a collection of special saucepans."

"I miss those days, don't you?"

"Oh, I still manage to get some fun."

"Fun! My dear, everything is changing so quickly. Why, even the smells of Versailles are toning down: people are getting squeamish."

"There, *ma bonne*, I am in complete accord: nothing indicates the individuality of a place so much as its so-called bad odours."

"Be careful, you'll lose that egg. Ah, those pestiferous stenches in the corridors and the chimneys and . . . and everywhere, what memories they recall. . . ."

During the next course, which was cold stuffed duck, with a simple lettuce salad dressed by Eléonore herself, the men talked about experiments being made with balloons which would change all the old ideas of travel, while the women chattered about dress. They were all unanimous in condemning the Demoiselle Bertin, the Queen's new dressmaker, who was not only insolent to all her other noble *clientèle*, but was causing quite a minor insurrection among the ladies of the Queen's wardrobe, because she ousted everybody else, occupied far too much of the Queen's time in the mornings, in a private closet where Her Majesty, as if bewitched, accepted every gew-gaw without even asking the price. It was rumoured that the Bertin charged the Queen for things she had never bought. The controllers of the Queen's

[1] See engraving of Moreau, "Le Petit Souper" (though this is a supper for ladies of doubtful virtue).

privy purse were in despair, as her allowance was exhausted long before the allotted time. The Mistress of the Robes, who looked into all the bills, was always threatening to resign, because the Bertin sent in enormous bills for gowns without specifying a single detail, as had been the rule in the times of Queen Marie Leczinska.

In spite of the presence of the Comtesse Diane de Polignac, the talk veered round to veiled criticism of the Queen's conduct. Here, one of the old ladies became voluble in an interval of picking her teeth with an ivory pin.

"Do you know, my cousin was entertaining her nephew Rouget[1] the other day in the Palace, when, hearing sounds of scampering and laughter, she made him hide behind a screen. And what do you think they saw?"

"What?" they all asked, prepared for the worst.

"Her Majesty playing hide-and-seek with Madame Elizabeth!"

Eléonore interposed loyally: "It might be worse! In fact it's rather touching: it only shows that Her Majesty is very young—only twenty-one."

"But a Queen of France must forget her girlhood: she is a figurehead, a symbol, and everyone at Court must have access to her. She must not shut herself off in seclusion with her own coterie of friends."

At that point Eléonore rang the little silver bell and the butler brought in the triumph of the whole supper—a sweetmeat composed by herself. There were cries of "Divine! Miraculous!" as a huge highly-scented cantaloupe melon was placed on the table, resplendent on a bed of vine leaves and sulphur-coloured tea-roses: it had been scooped out and filled with wild strawberries from the woods around Chanteloup. (Choiseul had sent them that morning by a special coach.) The whole was surmounted by stiff whipped cream tinted yellow and flavoured with Kirsch, sprinkled with crystallized rose petals, *marrons glacés*, almonds and pistachio nuts. Nothing more decorative could have been imagined, and the scent was delicious.

Choiseul said to Boufflers: "Come now, Stanislas, stop gobbling, and let your Muse delight us: at this point you should compose some couplets on Eléonore's creative gifts."

"No! no!" cried Eléonore. "Spare me. I'm frightened of his poems: he's always either a little blasphemous or a little licentious: he can't really please me."

Everyone laughed. Stanislas stopped eating and looked like a thundercloud.

"A challenge, a challenge," they cried. "Take it up, Chevalier. Shame her by composing something that is neither blasphemous nor licentious."

[1] Rouget de Lisle, who later wrote the Marseillaise.

There was a little pause. Eléonore rolled up a side curl which had fallen down from her *coiffure.* Boufflers watched her, smiled suddenly, thought a minute, and then, amid the hushed silence which always greeted his poetic efforts at supper parties all over the kingdom, he rose and recited this poem which in the original is a little masterpiece of its kind:

To a lady with ill-combed hair.

To all other fair attractions,
To the beauty most *soignée,*
I prefer, oh! to distraction
Who then, but Lise *la mal-peignée.*

On her Virtue envious girls
Never cast aspersions;
And 'tis only in her curls
Appear wild revolutions.

An iceberg free from stain,
Eschewing Cupid's sinlets.
As he can't turn your brain,
Lise, he attacks your ringlets.

"Bravo, bravo, Chevalier, you have surpassed yourself!"

Eléonore smiled delicately and enigmatically, and did not look at Boufflers. She rather enjoyed feeling that she would never outwit him. It was all pleasantly exciting, this ambiguous situation: both of them flirting against this background of their friends who little knew what either of them felt. In fact neither he nor she were fully aware of what the other felt.

With the coming of coffee and liqueurs, the conversation became more general. It turned on the favourite topic of the day—social reform. The old school held that the peasants on their estates were perfectly happy and would only be fuddled by economic changes and new ideas of equality. The bishop, who was a traditionalist, argued with Boufflers, as he peeled a peach, and then dipped his long ecclesiastical fingers into a finger-bowl:

"Why, even your own Voltaire said 'it was essential that there should be some ignorant clowns—and when the people take to reasoning, there will be an end to everything!' Now at Anizy, I never try out these new ideas, but we all live a very happy social life together. Whenever there's a family celebration, I invite all the shepherds and shepherdesses and the bailiffs and ploughmen to a big supper, and we have fireworks and country dancing, and they devise the most amusing little plays for my enjoyment. My guests from Versailles always dance with the locals. It's all so simple and pleasant. Now my head farmer's father, a dear old man, full of dignity, was chatting with me in a hay field the other day and telling me of patriarchal life in the farmhouse—twenty-two sitting down at table with the master and mistress in perfect order. He used to read the Bible aloud, his wife served everyone with food, so that the maids who had worked all day should have some rest. The next day the subject of which he had been reading formed the staple topic of conversation, especially among the ploughmen, for whom the Bible seemed to hold a personal message. In the winter he used to tell them stories after supper, as they sat round the great hearth, the girls spinning and the men working at some handicraft. His stories were the great, the sole amusement of the peasants and children.[1] Now is it right to upset all this by idiotic notions of equality?"

The Cardinal de Bernis, Pompadour's old friend who was now the Ambassador of France to Rome, a plump, pleasant little cardinal, said:

"You are judging by yourself, for you are a benevolent despot. But think of all the estates, in Brittany for instance, riddled by the evils of absenteeism, where the landlords prefer a tiny garret at Versailles to draining their marshes and pulling up the ling and heather. As a nation we are not interested enough in agriculture—in the way the English are, for example. Also our peasants are not concerned enough with politics. Over here, I notice a singular apathy about the pressing questions of the day, whereas across the Channel, the very grocers and blacksmiths would be discussing the political topic of the moment." [2]

The Duc de Nivernais said: "You are right, Monseigneur, I noticed all that during my embassy in England. Moreover, I came to the conclusion that it was a thousand pities for us to be so terribly individualistic over here. We shall never have a House of Commons like the English, for the simple reason that here the different classes can't easily unite for the common good. Now I quite agree with Monseigneur de Sabran, our ruling classes get on wonderfully well with their peasantry, they've been brought up together, so to speak, on the same estates, they have mutual obligations, the land has brought them together; and there is really something dignified and aristocratic about the old type of peasant. The trouble nowadays comes from *quite* a different direction, from the rising middle classes, the rich financiers who want to ape the landed gentry, build or buy big houses in the country, farm out the collecting of taxes to hard middlemen who don't care about the peasants,

[1] From Restif de la Bretonne's description.
[2] Arthur Young says that.

but only about the money. When these financiers give a ball they never dance with the country-folk, but only amongst themselves, and I've even heard of a certain *parvenu* who gets out of his obligations to be a liberal host with food and drink, by telling the local provision merchant to set up his booth in the grounds! This new class is a menace; I never return their calls. I have a financier a few fields away from me at Saint-Ouen, and I never receive him. No one wants to know him, the upstart."

Eléonore said: "It is dangerous to excite their envy and their spite, for I think we may one day be at their mercy. Money, not breeding is going to be the great power in the new world, I fear. I heard the other day of the Marquis de . . . who married a rich little nobody simply for her money, and then left her on the day of the wedding. Now that sort of thing is disastrous. They will be avenged. If ever there is a surge of popular feeling, it will be excited by these same middle classes, believe me, not by the good peasants who know how naturally interdependent we are. What do you think?" She turned to Diane de Polignac.

"I agree with you, Eléonore. Now at Court I have noticed that when Her Majesty has appeared at a ball—and we must all admit that she then eclipses many women by her beauty . . ."

"Ah! yes," groaned Charlot, and they all laughed.

"Well, it is always the envious little *bourgeoise* from Paris who is overheard making unpleasant remarks about Her Majesty, rather than the members of her own Court, who have no social ambitions."

After a while, the guests drifted into the reception-rooms. The windows opened out on the terrace. Great tubs of tobacco-plant and night-scented stock were on the balustrade. Monseigneur de Sabran was so charmed with Boufflers that he invited him to come and stay at Anizy while Eléonore was there—which was just what Boufflers had secretly hoped for. The two old ladies took out their reticules and began purfling with some gold threads they had snipped from the uniform of the Prince de Ligne. The Cardinal de Bernis stood over their arm-chairs, and they chatted somewhat sadly of the little bygone suppers in the Pompadour's northern attic, in the good old days before the Cardinal had lost her friendship by trying to draw France away from an Austrian alliance. The Empress Maria-Theresa, knowing that the favourite was the power behind the throne, had flattered her by writing to her as "*Ma chère amie*", and the Pompadour then did all in her power to cement an alliance with Austria.

"Well, she got her way in the end," sighed the Cardinal. "I wonder whether Her Majesty knows that she owes her place on the throne to Madame de Pompadour."

"Her Majesty deserves some kind of good from *cette espèce-là*: she suffered enough from Madame du Barry. By the way, how is the du Barry, Charlot?"

"Very well, a little plumper. Louveciennes is a dream. She is now carrying on an intrigue with the Duc de Cossé-Brissac. So hard on his wife. Sh . . . don't let Nivernais hear you—it's his daughter, you know."

Eléonore interrupted the whispered gossip which threatened to become dangerous, by suggesting to them that they might like a game of cards. She settled them in a comfortable green closet near a flame-coloured parrot in a gigantic cage; Boufflers was very mischievous, for he tried to teach the parrot to say: "How beautiful you are!" Eléonore drew him away and told him, in a low voice, to watch the hands of the card players. How expressive they were! They suddenly became terribly alive with the passions of gambling, nails diabolically avid to rake in the spoils, or finger-tips very cautious as they placed a card, or deceptively negligent as they tossed one down, or the whole hand clenched with suppressed anxiety, with the knuckles white, when luck was turning. Eléonore put her hand through Boufflers' arm and pulled him away into the next room, for, with his inborn love of gambling, he was beginning to show signs of restlessness. "I don't like to see you looking like that—come away." They were alone for a moment in the little red library, full of white roses in alabaster vases. He looked down at her and suddenly became serious.

"If you want me to promise never to touch a card again, I will." He drew her out to the terrace for a minute. She realized that he was paying a great tribute to her, and this was a unique opportunity for her to help him: even the tolerant Madame du Deffand had criticized the "birds' frenzy for gambling", which was the besetting vice of his family. So she smiled up at him, half-teasing, half-tender, and said:

"After my sharpness to you at the theatre to-night I don't deserve such sacrifices from you. Can you really promise *that*?"

"Yes, I will. And anything, anything else you care to ask me."

She hesitated a minute, then again trying to ward off intensity she tapped his shoulder lightly with her fan, in that inimitable vanished gesture of the eighteenth century, which said so much in so little.

"Very well, then; and I know that you will never regret your promise. Let us watch my guests for a moment from the window. I am a little fatigued."

Hidden in the obscurity of the July night, they peeped through the draperies of the open French windows. The scent of summer was wafted to them from the garden. Eléonore looked so lovely in her white lace panniers.

In the engravings of Cochin, the Court lords and ladies come alive like this, and almost step out towards one in the bright light of the picture. One can visualize these dapper little personages with their mutinous faces and their glossy, sculptured headdresses, and in a trice the marionettes all start moving: it is the miniature world of the ballet, beribboned, beflowered, sparkling. . . . How well they hold themselves, how courteously they greet each other! One can see the vivacious meetings between the guests, the balloon-like billowings of the curtseys, the ease and nonchalance of the scions of great houses, hand in waistcoat, feathered hat under one arm, sword at side, high red heels in an elegant stance. And the women with wasp waists, like little dolls, their lovely skirts puffing out against the men's white silken legs; they are turning round over their shoulders to give a meaning glance, or else their powdered heads are clustering together to indulge in scandal.

The Chevalier and Madame de Sabran looked on and smiled. Even the social freaks in the groups were rather fun. Here were two inseparable young ladies, bitten with the craze for sentimental friendship; they walked round the drawing-room with their arms encircled, wearing hearts on pendants, calling each other *mon cœur*. Then an affected, mincing young man, looking like a stage shepherd, laden with gold casket, watches, rings, charms and the most marvellous buttons of scented woods.[1]

As Boufflers looked at him, he said dryly he was glad that the English influence in men's fashions was beginning to make itself felt.

Eléonore said: "No, I don't agree that it can be a good thing. The love of personal display was not unmanly during the Renaissance, when men wore drop-pearl earrings. It comes as natural to a man to adorn his person as it does to a woman. When men haven't got taffetas to think of, they'll have more time for mischief, such as planning wars and revolutions."

"Perhaps. But I've always had a fancy for revolutions." And he relapsed into a thoughtful silence.

"Do you know," she said gazing through the window, "I feel sometimes that I am looking at these scenes for the last time."

"How strange. I have often felt like that lately. It's all this talk of change. That is why I sometimes long to get away into the country—far away from people. By-the-by, your brother-in-law, the bishop, has invited me to come to Anizy when you are there. Would you like me to come and help you with your Latin?" He laughed slyly and added: "You see, it might keep

[1] It may not be true, but a memoir-writer of the times tells us that many young men in Paris, from duke to lackey, were infected with sodomy.

me away from the temptations of the gambling table and . . . and a thousand other little follies."

Her eyes flashed angrily. "Oh! you *are* clever and tiresome."

He laughed triumphantly. "Is that the way to speak to a brother? Fie, my sister, where is all that sisterly tenderness which you vowed to me behind the grilled box? Instead, you are behaving in a provoking manner, almost as if you wished to coquette with me."

At this, she lost her temper outright. "This is too much! Coquette! Really, you are impossible! After all my serious speeches to you. No one has such a power of enraging me as you. Very well then: I withdraw my invitation to my children's picnic to-morrow. They will be very disappointed, but I can't help that. Good-night."

And she rustled furiously into her drawing-room, leaving him on the terrace in fits of laughter.

CHAPTER XV

ELÉONORE GOES FOR A PICNIC

THE next afternoon Eléonore took her two children in her carriage to a retired stream in meadow-land, a few miles out of Paris. The pleasant young coachman from Nancy, who incidentally had known Boufflers at the Court of Lunéville and adored him, carried rugs and a hamper of provisions to the little boat moored under the willows, while the footman brought the grave three-year-old Elzéar on his shoulder. Delphine, who was six, and the most exquisite child one could imagine "as fresh as a little narcissus", chased the dog, called Bonne-Amie, which Boufflers had given her, through a field of high grass. Eléonore, in simple white muslin skirt and green bodice, was in a dreamy mood. Hoping to dip into the pages during the intervals of minding the children, she had brought her old copy of *La Nouvelle Héloïse* with her, that book which had frightened her so much as a young girl. She had a great belief in matching a book with its rural setting. With Julie, she saw the flowers strewn by the wind, the thickets of roses and lilac, the tortuous alleys, the climbing plants, the springs, the running water, the solitude, the shade; Julie revealed all these delights to her, and compelled her to feel them more keenly.

However, after Elzéar had nearly fallen into the water trying to catch a dragon-fly, Eléonore put the book away. She took out her ivory spool and her tatting thread from her reticule, while the children burbled happily away among the cushions, and regaled themselves and the dog on new bread and whipped cream from a cool brown jar. Elzéar looked such a little darling in his dark red trousers and white, frilly shirt. He was extremely delicate, and therefore rather serious. He did not frolic as lightheartedly as his sister, but kept toddling insecurely across the boat to his mother, to kiss her with his creamy little mouth. Eléonore wiped him clean again. Then she drew him to her breast, told him to stay quiet a moment or two and not make the boat rock so much. Eléonore lay back among the cushions feeling like a contented thrush. The heat was intense. How pleasant it was to listen to the noise of the water clip-clopping against the boat, to a horse trotting on the distant road, to the swish of a water-rat swimming across the stream with his whiskers well out of the water, to the sudden plomp of a little frog jumping delicately on to a water-lily leaf, to a murmuring wind lifting the leaves of the water willows and the aspens and showing their undersides. Eléonore closed her eyes and enjoyed all those faint rustlings to the full. The din of Paris streets and the noise of crowded drawing-rooms had not made her ears any the less sensitive to country sounds. What a deep, green peace, melodious with the tiny, busy stir of Nature!

A raindrop falling on to the end of her nose startled her. Delphine said rather pompously: "Mama, the swallows are crying and dipping close to the water. That means rain."

Eléonore woke with a start. "Children, children, we're lost! Hide quickly under the rugs and cushions. We'll all catch terrible colds. What *shall* we do? Oh, how silly of me not to foresee that."

Large, ominous drops started falling; the little tree-shaded nook got darker and darker. Supposing it were a thunderstorm! Eléonore flurried and scolded like a water-hen, and brooded over her two babies, in order to keep them dry. But she felt too small in expanse to cover them altogether, and kept going from one to another. Elzéar looked adorable and said: "Mama, if I were a baby water-rat, it wouldn't matter if my little coat got wet, would it? You wouldn't scold me, would you?"

Just then, they heard a rustle in the alder bushes at the riverbank. They all turned to see what it was, and behold, *there* was the Chevalier peeping through, looking as cynical as a faun and as impious as Acteon! But Eléonore could not be cross, for he was holding in his hand—oh, Heaven be praised—a huge oiled-silk umbrella such as Swiss doorkeepers used for guests at big houses. Eléonore gave a cry of relief, and, putting out both hands, helped him into the boat. How reassuring and warm was the clasp of his hands. The children squealed for joy, the little dog barked, and the boat rocked unsteadily. Eléonore made room for him beside her, and they all clustered under the umbrella. It had become very dark now, and the rain was falling steadily.

Boufflers laughed. "The boat is a cosy nest, isn't it, and we are the baby wrens."

Delphine said: "You are the papa bird and we are your babies. You've just been fetching us some worms."

Boufflers looked at Eléonore as if to say: "You see."

By now the rain was pouring down. Boufflers put his hand out into the water. "Do you know, the stream is quite warm. I wonder why it is always like that, with summer rain on a river?"

There was a long silence. Then Eléonore said to him rather sarcastically: "Well, I suppose you are very pleased with yourself?"

"That's gratitude! You don't think I am responsible for the weather, do you? I'm not God."

"I know. But how did you get here?"

"I saw the sky darkening over Paris. I knew you would be at the mercy of a storm, so I saddled my horse and cantered along after your coach. You'd all be sneezing hard if it weren't for me."

"I am very grateful to you."

"What are you reading?" He picked up the Rousseau, glanced at the title, and then, to the dismay of Eléonore and the delight of the children, let it drop into the water with a plop.

Eléonore bit her lips and said nothing. Boufflers was rather disappointed, as he had hoped to provoke one of her pretty little tantrums: this unexpected silence made everything fall flat. Feeling a little silly, he started declaiming to the bulrushes: "The admirers of Rousseau are recruited from the discontented and ambitious middle classes, embittered small gentry, sentimentalists and women with overheated imaginations."

This was so preposterous that Eléonore burst out laughing; the children laughed, too, without understanding. The little boat-load heaved with merriment.

Then followed an enchanted half-hour in the sweet-smelling summer rain, when Boufflers told the children about Bébé, the horrible little pygmy who had teased him so much when he was a boy at Lunéville. They always listened entranced. They adored getting him to describe the tiny house in the woods to which Bébé used to run away, his miniature carriage drawn by four goats, and his various costumes and little hats. Eléonore loved listening to all this just as much as the children.

After a while the rain cleared and the sky brightened. The raindrops sparkled in the level beams of the evening sun and a yellow-hammer, who had bided the storm, now carolled away in the willow trees. Boufflers got out of the boat, and, taking both the children on his shoulders, he carried them through the drenched grass to the carriage. Eléonore was just going to follow him, holding up her skirts, when he made her sit down again with an imperious gesture and said: "Come at your peril; you don't want to stay in the carriage for an hour in soaking clothes, do you?"

After a while he came back, and, without more ado, bent down and picked her up in his arms. She said apologetically, "I'm afraid you'll find me rather heavy."

He laughed: "Would you mind putting your arms around my neck, it would make it easier."

There was no avoiding it: she had to do as she was told. Then he rushed through the meadowsweet and the clover and she felt deliciously insecure. The afternoon had seemed a little blighted until he had appeared on the scene, with his good humour and his mockery, his great big laugh and his vitality. He was striding along by the hedgerows, which were wreathed with honeysuckle. She stole a glance at him. As chance would have it, just then he looked down at her. Their eyes met: for one fleeting moment their souls were naked and defenceless. This was the first time it had happened. She could feel his heart pounding through her body. She broke the spell by saying, "*Mon frère*, you are very kind."

He smiled at her with great sweetness, and said nothing. But for a brief second he closed his eyes and gathered her more closely to him. Then, looking away from her, he carried her the rest of the way to the coach in silence.

One morning in the following Spring, Boufflers spent two hours in a rage, touring all the trinket shops in search of a gift for Eléonore, and finding none that he could possibly afford. Every time he set his heart on something exquisite, the jeweller would say: "Monsieur le Chevalier has impeccable taste: he has chosen my greatest treasure." First, there was a pair of earrings holding bewitching miniature watches which chimed! Entrancing! Just what he wanted, for thus she would be reminded of him at every hour. He asked the price. A King's ransom! He ground his teeth. Oh, and she had forbidden gambling.

Then there was a rosary with beads of different woods, each bead hollowed out to hold various perfumed unguents. Even at her prayers he wanted to be with her, to steal near those delicate little nostrils of hers and turn her from her devotions.

Oh, how he longed to be the only Deity she worshipped. Then there were the thousand and one treasures which a fashionable woman stowed away into her reticule:—needle cases designed by Moreau, gold comfit-boxes with ivory lids painted by Boucher, embroidered gloves perfumed with ambergris, musk, oil of jasmine, orange and lemon flowers, a watch cut out of an emerald, and another watch from a sixteenth-century goldsmith made in the shape of a crucifix. He did not dare to cross the threshold of the Fan-maker's with its painted sign "*à l'Eventail*". Oh! those rococo fans painted in bright colours with woodland feasts and concerts in parkland! Happy the bygone lovers who could whisper of love's delights in the paintings on a fan. Boufflers loved to see Eléonore wield her fan. As a friend of Madame Récamier has said, ". . . the woman of breeding differs from others in her use of the fan. Even the most charming and elegant woman, if she cannot manage her fan, appears ridiculous".

Then there were the little mantles of Brussels lace, and the *engageantes* or ruffles for her sleeves. Thus through his gifts would the lover wish to linger where his lips might not rest, around the fragile shoulders and on her white arms.

In despair, Boufflers went home and scribbled a note to his bailiff at his country place of Malgrange, telling him to send two of his best sheep to the Comtesse de Sabran at the Château d'Anizy, near Laon; also his favourite little mare who had a step as light as a *demoiselle*. Then after buying a good supply of notepaper, quills and sealing wax—for he was soon to leave Paris to join his regiment again—he went to call on some of his old friends to see if they could recommend him for a post of importance. They all said: "*Mon cher*, your epigrams have been your undoing: we can give you nothing ambassadorial." One of them said: "Our relations with England are really breaking up. We might even try an invasion this year. Now you've got soldiering in the blood: I'm sure that you can win glory in the field much better than in the reception rooms of foreign princes. Go to your regiment now, and see what the year will bring."

By the Spring of 1778 everybody was asking for staff appointments in Northern France, in order to invade England. Boufflers, in Brittany, was made second in command to General de Castries. The first batch of his letters to Eléonore was written during these early days of the Platonic friendship, when he was Colonel to the regiment de Chartres.

CHAPTER XVI

LETTER-WRITING BETWEEN PLATONIC FRIENDS

AND so in the Spring of 1778 Boufflers tore himself away from the delights of Eléonore's society, with all the pleasures of shared occupations, and left Paris to join his regiment. He consoled himself by writing to her very often. She, maddeningly elusive or just forgetful, wrote one letter to his four, so he spent a great deal of time scolding her, and she, as much time in protesting that he was the culprit.

These enchanting letters were preserved for us, through all the hazards of the reign of Terror and the wanderings of exile by a mere accident. By the narrowest chance have they been safeguarded for lovers of literature, these documents which are the most elevated and the most impassioned love-letters of the whole century. During the Terror, Delphine was preparing to escape. She suddenly heard bangings at the door; the servants had betrayed her. Swiftly, she kicked all her mother's letters and the Chevalier's under the valance of a sofa. Not a moment too soon, for the armed revolutionaries burst in the next minute. They searched everywhere, but they never thought of looking under that sofa. When, at length, Delphine was taken to the *Prison des Carnes*, the servants went off with the plate and linen, but they could do nothing with the private papers, as the door had been sealed by the *comité de sûreté*. Thus for several months the room with the letters was left totally undisturbed.

Many of Madame de Sabran's letters are lost—as it is to be expected when one thinks of the wanderings of Boufflers. Also, there is a period of two years—1779 to 1781—of which there is hardly any record; probably the letters written during that period were too intimate to be preserved. Perhaps, even, they were not written at all.

A few of these early letters must be allowed to speak for themselves for a while. They are so alive that they almost spring up from the printed page.

For a man who had such a reputation for immorality, Boufflers' letters are astonishingly elevated in tone. What a contrast with Napoleon's early love-letters to Joséphine, in which his passionate absorption confines itself to her body. Towards the end of his life Boufflers aspired to a noble philosophy of love, for he believed in its transforming power on the human personality. One feels that he is discovering all this for himself, he uses no hackneyed phrases, he is absolutely sincere, and he is never coarse. His tender playfulness is delightful. His little scriptural allusions and touches of witty blasphemy betray the pupil of the Abbé Porquet and the ex-seminarist. But even these show that he had been thoughtful about abstract questions. It is pleasant to watch love growing quite naturally out of friendship, for the lovers give glimpses of the tastes they shared together. Boufflers is also revealed in his profession as a soldier—very energetic, kind to his men, and longing to win glory so that he might be less unworthy of Eléonore. Roughly, those early letters before May, 1781, cover a period interspersed by the Chevalier's occasional visits to Anizy, during which Eléonore was growing more and more devoted to him. By the Autumn of 1779 she became ill through trying not to fall in love with him. It is then that she very probably had a frank explanation with him. After this she kept him at bay for another two years, 1779–1781,—and this is the time of which we have almost no record.

The first letter which she kept is ceremonious. Apparently Boufflers had asked his great-aunt the Maréchale de Luxembourg to invite Eléonore to the château de Montmorency while he was staying there.

1777.

I would like to receive good news of your health, Madame la Comtesse, and carry with me to Montmorency the hope of seeing you there. It is very generous of me to point out to you that the weather is very inclement, and that it might be unwise to keep your promise.

If I possessed the talents I envy in you every day, Madame la Comtesse, I would paint myself at your feet.

Mon Dieu, dear sister, when shall I see you again. I am like a miser without his treasure: actually he did not enjoy its possession, but he gazed at it all day. I have neither books nor paints. I have left all my learning and my tastes with you. All that pleases me has remained behind with all I hold dear. . . .

Ce 21. Brest.

I should so like to have news of that chest of yours, for I almost hear the little cough from here. I should so like to have news of these children whose smallest ailment makes their mother ill. I even want to know what is happening to those pictures which are begun with such enthusiasm, planned so intelligently, and completed with such an effort. In a word, I long to know all that is going on in that house where everything interests me, everything charms me, and where, nevertheless, I miss so many things. Write to me, my sister, and remember that it is from your badly cut quill and your ink-well devoid of ink that I draw all my consolation in life. . . .

[This is in '78, when the French were planning to invade England.]

March 2nd. Landerneau.

At last she has remembered me again, that charming sister. She has written to me with that kindness, that grace and that gaiety which so entirely charm her brother. . . .

I would so like to see that charming portrait. If it is set, send it to me. . . . Ah, my dear little profile, if only I had taken you with me into Brittany! I warrant it is left about everywhere as usual, badly framed . . . dragging about on all the tables, on all the chairs, and even in the cinders, while yours is surely placed in the best light, and the greatest care is taken to enhance all its good points. . . .

You laugh a little at our expense about our campaign in Brittany. It's easy to see you aren't on the spot. Do you know that all we lack is the enemy . . . ?

Would you be good enough to send me a box of French pastels. . . . It is a commission I charge you with, not a gift I ask for. I am tired of your presents. I don't want anything which reminds me that you are richer than I. . . .

Remember the need I have of your friendship. It charms me without satisfying me.

[This letter shows how jealous he was becoming of her other friends.]

March 11. Landerneau.

. . . You are quite right when you say that your vigils are killing you, my poor sister. Add to it that you are not the only one to have a destiny linked with yours of which you cannot dispose, for it is the destiny of someone of whom you are not the *mistress*. Recollect that each night which you spend, is a month which you take away from the life of that poor wretch, and all that for the pleasure of gossiping with Madame de Matignon.

So you miss them a little, those friends, those books, those pencils. See to it that your regrets are not fruitless. . . .

I wish I were there to cut your pencils and to sharpen the weapons with which you think to defeat me. . . .

If my vanity were not compromised by such a sentiment, I should be tempted to say that one loves you in proportion to one's intelligence. . . .

[Concerning her translation of Ovid] . . . In the very carelessness about which I reproach you occasionally, there is a grace which always charms me. It is like your hair which I love just as much in disorder as in ringlets.

About your dress, you make out that you looked ridiculous? I refuse to believe it. True, you sometimes lack artifice [*l'art*] but it only makes you prettier. . . .

Mon Dieu, how I love you, my dear sister. Get used to it if you can; as for me I will never lose the habit.

[Why did Eléonore exclaim in one of her early letters: "I love you with all my heart and for my whole life." Difficult to keep up a Platonic friendship under such circumstances!]

March 27, 1778.

. . . You know what end I have in view with this war; glory is not the reward I promise myself, but her who is the only treasure worth pining for.

By the way, my sister, I cherish as the apple of my eye the sword-knot which I was so cross to see you buy. In order not to use it unsuitably, I have given orders to the regiment that golden sword-knots should only be worn with full-dress ceremonial uniform, but I want to supplement this with one of white thread, for everyday use. Would you have some made for me, three or four, according to your taste. They will serve as models for all the officers. This is not a commission I give you but a present I ask from you. . . .

Talk to me about your health, and above all think about it. You are not too strong, you are not ill; it is a regulated life you need, rather than remedies.

Tell me something of what you're reading. I want to be in touch with everything which occupies you. . . . Send me your criticisms, your opinions, your doubts and your observations. Force me to send you mine. I want, not only to be engrossed in you, but to be busied through you.

April 3rd, 1778.

. . . You are better. You are coughing less, but you still cough a little. If you knew, when you cough, how that affects me, and where it affects me [what cord it touches in me]. But you will never know that. . . .

The sixth.

. . . By the way, my sister, send me [a picture of] the façade of your house seen from the garden. I will then feel that I am walking on your terrace, and that I am waiting for you to return from the bath or your lesson.

. . . Remember, my sister, that all the talents in the world count for nothing without perseverance; let us have it in all things, except in certain resolutions.

. . . I've just had such a horrible toothache, raging for three days and three nights, that I couldn't even seal up my letter. I was like a madman. I'm suffering a little less to-day.

Ce 28.

My imagination is draped in mourning. To this have been added for the last few days unbearable headache and toothache, so that mind and body conspire to torment me. Sometimes to distract myself, I imagine I'm in the fraternal house. From here I can see some books, some pictures, some pens, some paints; green trees, a pavilion, big alleys [*de grandes promenades*]; between the trees I catch a glimpse of a sort of little nymph walking with a book in her hand, and I run to meet her. What a joy that she is my sister. What a pity that she is only my sister.

[At Easter time of that year, Eléonore, who was a practising Catholic and went to Confession, had written him the following letter:]

The 25th of April, 1778.

I feel a great need of chatting with you to-day, my brother, to raise my spirits and help me to forget a certain visit I have just paid—and *what* a visit——! A visit that one only makes at a certain time, before the knees of a certain man, to mention certain things that I have no intention of telling you. I am still completely exhausted and covered in blushes. I don't like that ceremony one little bit. We are told it is very wholesome, and I put up with it like the respectable woman I am.

[To which Boufflers wrote this delicious reply:]

What's all this, delightful little Magdalen, you had just emerged from the Confessional, and you said in there a whole lot of things which you won't tell to me, to me who would say so many things which my confessor will never know! *Mon Dieu,* how offended I am at not having figured in your conversations! And what did he say, this man who saw you at his feet? Oh, if only I'd been your confessor! Oh, if only I'd been your transgression! Why am I not your penance?

[Versailles was particularly gay that Summer. The Queen was only twenty-two and she was expecting her first child. Her brothers and sisters-in-law were almost the same age. The Prince de Ligne, speaking of Summer evenings on the terrace of Versailles, says: "I gave my arm to the Queen; her gaiety was charming. Sometimes we had music in the groves of the Orangery, where high up in a niche is the bust of Louis XIV. Monsieur le Comte d'Artois used to say to him: '*Bonjour, grand-papa.*' One evening the Queen and I planned that I should stand behind the statue and answer him, but the fear that they would give me no ladder to get down by, and that I should be left there all night, made me give up the idea . . ."

Eléonore was as popular as ever at Court; she often visited the Comtesse Diane de Polignac at Montreuil. She acted in the amateur theatricals of the Comte d'Artois, and produced *Le Misanthrope* with all the costumes of the time. All this made Boufflers jealous, as the following letter shows:]

You are spoiling yourself, my sister. And the Court, after all the wrongs it has inflicted on me, will now rob me of my sister. Allow me to scold you, my sister. You are not suited to that environment or for those kinds of habits. You have neither health nor wealth, nor patience, and you have too much nobility, kindness and intelligence. . . . But, my sister, it isn't there that you will be happy. It is with your children, your friends, your books, your paints, your garden.

[Boufflers had been visiting his wounded soldiers in hospital:]

24th June, 1778 . . .

The wounded man whom I saw in Hospital did not complain . . . and all talked of nothing else but of how they fought. . . . But what consoles me is to see that there is in brave people an interior balm which sweetens all their misfortunes; it is the vision of glorious deeds, and the feeling that one has done one's duty.

I am still thinking of your translation of Seneca, and I am delighted with it. Why didn't I follow the course of your life from your cradle until this hour, dear sister! We would both have gained thereby; you would have known and cultivated your talents earlier, and I, instead of so many follies, would have been content with one alone, the most reasonable of all, and one from which I would never be cured. My sister understands that I am speaking of poetry . . .

July 13th, 1778 . . .

I was waiting for volumes from Anizy, and not one word has reached me yet. After having spent my life in praising the country, I will curse it. I hope this sad silence will not last; you have nothing to do, and you know how I need to bear you in mind . . .

A translator must not intrude his personality any more than a lackey who goes on an errand. If one gave you the freedom, you would roam at your own sweet will, and you would finish by being the rival of your author instead of his interpreter . . . Good-bye, my sister. I hope the week won't go by without one of your letters.

. . . You are already as good a Latin scholar as I am, you believe yourself to be a better painter, you don't know that you are a hundred times more worthy. I only know one talent in which I excel you, and you have the cunning to prevent me from exercising it. That's why I want to take refuge in philosophy. Just as men who have come to an end of everything become Trappists.

28th Sept., 1778 . . .

. . . Thus, if I were master of my actions, I would not like to go either to Paris or to Paradise without you. The best of all, my sister, would be to go to Hell with you; I am sure that the boredom of one's stay there would be nothing in comparison with the charm of the journey. . . . You are my light, and I your shadow.

[At last Boufflers got leave from his regiment, and he was able to accept the longed-for visit to Anizy.]

Now I am going to paint, write, study, laugh, argue, run or stay still with you. . . . I feel that I am going to live a new life, and return to my native element. It is only with you that time is as precious as they make out. It has the only fault of time, and that is to come to an end. . . .

We saw Delphine yesterday; I was with Madame de Mirepoix and my sister, Lucille, in the Champs-Elysées. Passing by a grille Lucille saw Delphine coming out of the drawing-room. . . . Delphine has been invited to tea by Madame de Mirepoix on Sunday; she glowed like a little narcissus. Her skin, her colouring, her lips, her hair were at their best. I was proud of her on your behalf, for I know what you take a pride in . . .

Good-bye again; I kiss you like a good father, a good brother, but a shady friend.

[This delightful letter shows them both to be children of the times in their passionate love of the country:]

I saw my poor Malgrange estate again: I only own half of it now; I've given the prettier half to Monsieur de Bauffremont, but what remains mine still has the power to please me. My house is simple and poor, but clean and gay. There is in my courtyard a horse-chestnut planted by the sister of Henri IV, under which one could shelter a hundred and fifty men. I have a little garden, at the end of which is a wood of about a hundred feet in circumference, where you can walk for half-an-hour without retracing your steps; I have a fig-house, a hot-house, a quantity of cherry trees in flower. I am going to house three or four sheep under my windows, and they will be enclosed in a wire network, so fine that they won't know it's there. They will be like men who imagine themselves free, for they don't see their chains, and they think they are doing their own will, when they are only following the natural course of things.

If I am in the world when you are no longer young, I would propose that we buy a country house for the two of us, so that you might enjoy for once all the pleasures you have missed till now. You don't realize that one can have *motherly feelings towards trees, towards plants, towards flowers*. You don't know that a garden is a kingdom where the Prince is never hated, and where he enjoys the fruits of all the good he does. Your Paris garden can give you no idea of all that happiness. It is only a pathway, with plants set out on either side, which leads to your pavilion; you don't know any of your trees, and you order that their crowns, branches and trunks be cut without giving the matter another thought. . . .

Douai. June 18th.

. . . But write to me, my dear and gentle and good child; remember that you are a hundred times more loved by me than you think yourself lovable, and that you ought to be a little grateful for this. . . .

Adieu, dear angel of painting and poetry.

July 6th.

. . . When shall I see you again, you whom I love so much? When shall I spend whole months, years, centuries with you? . . .

I've just bought something here which has ruined me, but which will help me to fill the tedium of many moments; it is an anthology of all the Latin poets, either whole or in part, from the times of Plato till the fall of the Roman Empire. . . .

But write to me then, and often, and a lot. If you love me a little you will always find something to say to me; and if you know how much I love you, you will always be sure of your letters being devoured.

Good-bye, my sister; kiss your children on my behalf. Thank your holy[1] nephew for the warm welcome he gave me, and for all the others which he will give me. And ask him if he has remembered my two cases of wine, for I drink water whilst waiting for them.

[1] This nickname refers to the bishop, who was his host at Anizy.

Raismes. 16th July, 1779.

. . . They say, but I'm not inclined to believe it altogether, that with every passing year the heart grows colder and colder. If that is true, beware of your own. Reflect, you who boast of lukewarmness, *you will become an icicle.*

[This was after the visit to Anizy during which Eléonore tried to live up to the idea of Platonic friendship. By then, she was finding the strain unbearable.]

Raismes. Thursday 26th.

. . . Don't accuse me of not thinking of you. I would like to be able to think of something else sometimes, for my brain goes round in circles, and I'm frightened of it exploding like a champagne bottle.

[This letter shows that she had fallen ill with the strain.]

A la Ville d'Eu. 14th Sept., 1779.

You are suffering, dear and beautiful and good child, and I am not there to pity you, look after you and amuse you. I should ask in vain to suffer on your behalf all the pains and all the griefs which might await you, for Heaven would deem me too happy; for if Heaven has eyes to read into the depths of hearts, it would see with what tenderness and what folly I love you. . . .

As a first trial to my patience, I have a grumbling toothache which never leaves me, and which becomes very sharp when I eat, when I laugh and when I give orders to the regiment. Added to this I have frequent migraines, the kind you know I have, and sometimes a temperature. . . .

The hospital is full of my soldiers whom I go to visit every day. . . .

However, as you may well believe, I have less unfortunate moments. Yesterday I was the God of the Ville d'Eu; I gave orders for a camp to be pitched; in my tent I had five or six very beautiful ladies to dinner. We left the table at the sound of a very lively attack; from there, we went to watch target-practice, and we came back to dance until ten o'clock. Your march was played for the first time with the full score. It could not have been more beautiful had it been composed by Glück or Puccini, and it would have given less pleasure if they'd composed it; the ladies had it played three times in succession . . .

[Boufflers had probably guessed the cause of her ill-health, and was, therefore, trying again to break down the barriers of the Platonic agreement.]

Eu. 2nd Sept., 1779.

I expect to spend my Autumn in the same agitations as my Summer. Perhaps it will be the same with the Autumn of my life, unless the one to whom I wish to dedicate all the remainder, changes the influence of my stars with a word. *But that prayer has always been so frowned upon*, that I hardly dare to think of it, and if sometimes I give way to this sweet illusion, it is followed by a depression and sadness which I cannot conquer. . . .

Nov. 5.

I detest Paris until I see it again, dear sister. It seems to me that Paris separates you from me more thoroughly than the distance which divides us. There is everything there to hold your attention, everything to amuse and distract you, everything conspires to blot out from your mind the slight impression I might have left there, and when I return I shall have become a stranger to you. [In this letter he calls her "*Ma Sabran*".]

[About some verses she had composed.] They are pretty and good, like you; they have that charming negligence which lays itself open to criticism, but which delights one's taste. The theologians all agree in saying that God has only left in His creation the imperfection which is inseparable from matter; you are a little god in your handiworks, and whoever tried to remove some faults would, at the same time, deprive them of many charms.

[The barriers are falling fast.]

How touched I am by your last letter, *ma Sabran*! How I thank you for believing yourself loved! . . .

Let us talk of your health, my dear child. It seems to me that your medicines are not prescribed for the evening, and the horrible nightmares they give you are an indication that you must take them in the morning. If that goes on, dear love [*cher amour*] change the time, or anyhow, let there be an interim, to give you a little respite. . . .

Ma Sabran, you had wanted to hide from me all that occupies you and gives you black moods. . . . Some other time I will reproach you in the way you deserve. In the meantime I kiss you and press your heart against mine. I hope you will never see again two [hearts] more united. . . .

[At this point Eléonore was feeling really ill with the effort not to fall in love with Boufflers, and when she tells him of the medicines she is taking, he wrote to her in the following maddening, blind way.]

. . . I find it very difficult to believe that health, gaiety, happiness, are contained in little bottles. It is, however, in these that you seek it.

Good-bye, all that I hold most dear; I imagine I am holding you in my arms and kissing you in a fashion far more to my liking than to yours.

July 1.

I kiss you in imagination; it's a sorry way of doing things, but it's always better than nothing.

July 29.

I rejoice in being loved by you, it seems to me that it is by this means that I lay hold on perfection; for I am a little like the ancients who clothed all intellectual ideas in human form, and I adore virtue in your person. . . .

It must be agreed that my soul was well guided to give itself entirely to yours. You combine all that is most touching with all that charms, and I've never thought of you for any length of time without smiling and at the same time having my eyes filled with tears. . . .

. . . You have written the address with the same hand which paints your pictures, which writes your verses, and which I kiss rapturously, however inky it is. . . .

Here is the second letter in which I forgot to ask you to send my mare to my sister [where she will stay] until she has recovered. I could only allow her to remain on in your stables if she could pay for her oats in gambols. . . . I've just added up how much I've cost you since I knew you; it's prodigious. For the same amount of money you could pay for the upkeep for the jolliest little lover in the world. . . . Adieu, *ange*.

Boulogne; 29th July.

If you dated your letters I would know when all mine had reached you; but like all fishy people, you like to shroud yourself in the mists of time.

Your verses are simple and pretty, like yourself; full of that gentleness, that grace, which goes so surely to my heart and which almost brings tears to my eyes. It is odd that I, who have not at all got the reputation of pious Aeneas, *never* read anything you write without being moved. There is in the depths of my heart and even in my mind, a string attuned to all you think; it vibrates every time I hear you, or read what you write, or see you, for to see you is again to hear you and read you. . . .

Good-bye, my well-beloved; [*ma bien-aimée*].

Aug. 3rd.

Here is about the fourth or fifth day that I go to bed late and get up at five in the morning, first because I am showing Mme de Gontaut and M. de Ségur round the town, and then because I don't want to interrupt instructing my regiment.

At this very hour, not only do I believe that you really love me, but I think I sense it, and it is the most delicious sensation I have ever experienced.

I wish I could give you some measure of the impression which that charming way from Lille to Saint-Omer made on my imagination. It helped me to realize that there are other pleasures than those I sought till I was thirty, to the exclusion of all others. For I have to confess it to you, my pretty sister, we [men] are all great libertines. I only know two remedies to that affliction; retirement from the world, and love. . . .

Love, whether happy or unhappy, provided it is sincere, is, moreover, a good antidote to loose living, because it concentrates all our affections, in turning them to the real or supposed perfections of the beloved being; in persuading us that pleasure and happiness are not always to be found where we sought them formerly, and stirs up a great upheaval in one's inmost heart. Don't despise this love, *ma bonne fille*, and by this man among all other men, conclude that the more one loves, the better one becomes. . . .

In the evening . . .

. . . A man reveals himself much more in the faults he commits than in those he amends, and I have the ambition to please you with my faults . . .

. . . [About a mare], I require your word of honour that you won't mount her unless I'm there. You must not be alarmed at the scars with which she is covered, even on her knees; she has been horribly ill-treated when she was young. I have begun to console her, and I hope that the quiet, peaceful life of Anizy will complete her cure. You will soon see that she deserves all the interest I take in her, and that her movements show her up to advantage, that she is as attractive as a *petite demoiselle*, that she is light without being capricious, and gentle without being too tame. . . .

You must really agree that I love you madly and continuously, my sister Sabran. You are the Divinity who watches over all I do, from morning till night. Whether I paint, or read, or write, or walk, or even if I'm just bored, I'm always thinking of you . . .

. . . M. de Gand arranges the exterior of his old château most charmingly, after having made the inside more than habitable. I cannot see a squire on his estate without being jealous; I feel I would be so happy on yours or on mine; happier, however, on yours, for I would see more of you. Life's only fault would then be that it was too short, instead of being too long, as I sometimes find it.

16th.

[She had apparently decided to stay at Anizy, to avoid him when he came to Paris. He threatens to return to gambling.]

17th.

I can't answer for my actions if I don't see you. . . .

Good-bye, once again; either I see you in a week or you will hear ill news of me. . . .

[In the end, he insists on her telling him all.]

It is to me that you must tell all; for I know the very thing you are most anxious to conceal. If reason has any sway over you, I will be able to communicate some to you, although I don't always have enough for myself. If I have to wrestle with you, I feel armed with the courage of a lion; if I have to yield, I feel endowed with the gentleness of a lamb; and if all that is required of me is to pity you, I will shower upon you the tenderness of a mother and a woman friend; and all that will be sincere, for I love you with every conceivable kind of love and every imaginable manner of friendship.

The Abbé de Bonneval spoke to me yesterday of the letter you wrote to him, dear child; I am dumbfounded by it. What is the cause of this sudden profound sadness, and this awful depression, of which you showed no signs to me when I was near you. . . .

But *what* is the cause of your depression? For one fleeting moment I dared to flatter myself that it might be partly caused by the departure of him who lives only for you . . . Why spend the winter far from me? Let me believe for a moment what I heard from your very lips. If you spoke truth, then I am essential to you; why do you want to flee me, *ma Sabran*? . . .

CHAPTER XVII

WOMAN PROPOSES, BUT STANISLAS DISPOSES

"Why do you want to flee me, *ma Sabran*?"

Why, indeed!

For two years after Eléonore and Stanislas had first met at the ball, they had written to one another, seen one another during the winters in Paris and in short periods during the summers at Anizy. By then, Stanislas was forty-one, still only a lieutenant-colonel, and all hopes of winning glory in the war had vanished when the French saw that it was hopeless to think of invading England. The Channel, "that ditch", seemed daily more and more impassable; it was quite futile, all this peering across with glasses and planning to pitch a camp at Dover. Worse still, Boufflers was now more hopelessly in debt than ever, and had been obliged to write to his sister, Lucille, now Madame de Boisgelin, and beg her to do something about it. Now less than ever could he dream of asking Eléonore to be his wife. But he still protested his undying devotion.

One late autumn evening, probably in 1779, perhaps later, Boufflers rode to Anizy in a storm of wind and rain. Not only did he feel very oppressed by his own lack of good fortune, but he had been growing extremely worried by the tone of Eléonore's letters. For no apparent reason she had been steadily losing her health. "Languor. Depression. Thinness." Even a visit to Switzerland with the Polignacs, and consultations with Tronchin had failed to restore her. He came to the conclusion that it was mostly imagination, and warned her not to relapse into invalidism. Naturally she had been furious, and had written to him in no measured terms:

"I am cured for life of telling you of my troubles or of my sufferings. I dread more than anything that you should regard me as hysterical. . . . I can think of nothing more revolting."

And now he had heard from a mutual friend, the Abbé de Bonneval, that she had fallen into a condition of "sudden profound sadness" and did not intend to return to Paris that winter. He had written imploring her to tell him the trouble, saying that he knew, anyway; and at length she had promised to do so. That was why he was on his way to Anizy, this Autumn evening.

Boufflers paused on the brow of a hill which was crowned with a magnificent beech-grove. The leaves had turned from the pale gold colours of the September mists, to all the fiery splendour of approaching decay. It was Halloween. The twilight was deepening. A wan streak of yellow died out in the West. The wind shrieked and whistled, rose in volume and then sank again. Myriads of wet leaves blew frenziedly across the path, like lost souls driven to Judgement. It began to pour, torrential Autumn rain, and everything in Nature seemed to call out: "No hope. No hope."

Very soon Boufflers was soaked to the skin and his horse kept sliding on the slippery clay. In another quarter of an hour it would be quite dark. In the distance he could see the delicate white turrets and the terrace of the little Renaissance château of Anizy. He dismounted and muttered to his mare: "Don't let us lose our path; you ought to know the way by now." Just then, as if by magic, a light appeared at the window of a turret. Half an hour later Boufflers arrived, completely drenched.

She had been waiting for him for two days. With every passing hour she had grown more terrified, for she knew that he would wrest her secret from her. Years later she referred to that time in two of her letters.

"I particularly recalled your last apparition, when, like a second Leander, you arrived soaked and drenched from head to foot. Like Hero I wanted to dry your clothes and to warm you, but I hardly dared look at you, I was so frightened in case I, too, would be looked at, and that others could read in my face all that was in my heart."

And again, writing in her *Journal* to him, one November night:

"I spent an awful night in thinking only of you; there was a storm just like the one on a certain day when I was waiting for you, more dead than alive, and when you only arrived the next day. Recall that moment, my child (it is the moment which decided my life's destiny), (recall) that letter which terror had forced me to write, and which told you my heart's secret. How far away is that time now. . . . Every blast of wind shook me in my bed. I wept, I prayed, to which God? I don't know; but instinctively my soul rose up and looked for help in a being more powerful than myself."

So often had she waited for him in that turret room, when he had come on summer visits. In her *Journal* she speaks of all the kindness he showed to her then, and all the patience he displayed with her caprices and little fears on horseback. The bishop and the children, too, had delighted in him: he was always in high spirits—he himself deplored his "over-great gaiety"—and they loved his large appetite, his huge laugh and his extraordinary way of suddenly falling asleep in the middle of a conversation, as if he had to catch up on arrears of sleep after his strenuous days of soldiering.

Eléonore threw some more logs on to the fire of her little *boudoir* and put away his letters in a casket. She had spent the afternoon re-reading them, and some of the endearments made her wildly happy.

"*Ma bien-aimée, ma fille, ma Sabran.*"

Surely no man wrote these things unless he really loved a woman? Or was she reading more into his letters than he had ever meant her to? Ah, no! She knew, beyond any shadow of doubt, that he loved her, for he had proved it by the devotion of two long years, his tenderness to her in a thousand little ways, caring for her when she was ill, sending her his favourite horses, writing so regularly to her though she felt that he was not naturally an assiduous letter writer, coming to see her every day in Paris and even twice a day, and visiting her in the country as often as he could get leave from his regiment. And always, always, assuring her of his love.

And she, did she love him? Alas, yes, she could hide it from herself no longer. She adored him with all the passion of her nature. She could see to the depths of him, and she saw only good. She pierced through the fiery temper to the warm heart which could never hurt another, through the flippancy to the seriousness, through the ungainliness of manner to the exquisite courtesy beneath. Their contemporaries, who only knew Boufflers as "*le plus aimable des fous*" (the most charming of jesters), would have laughed if she had told them: "But this man is noble, is spiritually-minded, he is striving towards perfection". He himself said that his love for her was his means of laying hold on perfection.

What! Boufflers who had made love to every pretty woman in society! Sometimes she was assailed by a faint misgiving. Was he so persistent just because she was the first woman to elude him? In that declining century, as Laclos soon showed in his famous *Liaisons Dangereuses*, the pure woman who said "no" and must be vanquished at the price of her tears and her adorable hesitations, this rare woman was the seducer's choice.

She dismissed the suggestion. No, in spite of everything, in her heart, she gave him the only gift of any value to the lover—her complete and unbounded trust.

At that moment she heard a commotion in the courtyard and knew that he had arrived. And he had written: "It is to me that you must tell all, for I know the very thing which you wish to conceal." She turned very pale.

In the candle-lit hall, standing in a miniature lake formed by the drippings of his clothes, Boufflers was welcomed by the bishop, the two children and their dog, Bonne Amie. He was laughing and shaking himself and splashing everybody around. Servants were rushing to and fro with candles and logs and mulled wine. His host was saying:

"Darnaud, my valet, will look after you. He has stacked up a big fire in your room. It is very unfortunate, Chevalier, but I have to go to Laon to-night, to a Chapter meeting. I have ordered dinner to be served in Eléonore's *boudoir*. You will be warmer there."

Just then *she* came down the stairs in her ivory velvet *polonaise*, looking so white, so frightened. At a glance, he knew that she was ill. And the thought that she had promised to tell him her secret, this secret which he already knew, overwhelmed him with happiness.

After they had dined by candle-light, Eléonore's maid put more logs on the fire, and then left them alone together at last. Eléonore's *boudoir* was a white panelled room with cream-coloured satin curtains sprigged over with tiny posies of rosebuds tied by blue lovers'-knots. Two white porcelain Cupids supported an ormolu clock on the mantelpiece, between two pearl-tinted alabaster vases holding sprigs of roses fashioned of gilded bronze. On the walls under the candle-brackets were some of the latest engravings of Moreau le Jeune from the series depicting the joys of happy marriage and family life. The Savonnerie carpet was so misted over with roses, peonies and convolvulus that it brought all the illusion of a summer garden to the room. There were little corner wall-brackets holding rare pieces of china and several favourite books, a gilt console table with one scarlet hothouse Amaryllis in a narrow Venetian bottle, a miniature desk littered with her writing materials, and downy chairs piled with small, heart-shaped cushions covered in Valenciennes lace.

The wind howled around the turret. The lovers felt as though they were alone in the world. Eléonore, reclining in her *chaise-longue*, turned her head away from Boufflers, who was standing by the fire. She felt so much in his power that she could not bear to break the spell by making conversation. At the very least she owed him the sincerity of her silence. He would see through all her defences. Oh! how terrible that, soon, she would have to speak! After a while, as if compelled by an irresistible power, she turned to look up at him. To her amazement she saw that his face was buried in his hands. In a hushed voice she said "Stanislas". He did not answer. She had never expected him to be so moved. "Come to me," she whispered, holding out her hands.

Swiftly he knelt by her side and seized her hands. She made no movement of withdrawal. How natural it felt, just as if it had always been so. Then he took her in his arms and, without looking at her, pressed her head down against his shoulder. He spoke quickly and vehemently.

"My dearest child, I will make everything easy for you, and you needn't even look at me. I'm going to say it all for you. To-night you promised to tell me your secret. I already know it. No, don't try to escape. Don't be frightened of me. I know you love me. Tell me you do."

A muffled "Yes".

"Ah!" A long silence. Then he continued: "We love each other, terribly, terribly."

"Yes."

"And I will always love you and never love another."

"And I too."

"Ah, my sweet child. No, don't look at me yet. I might drop tears of happiness on you. It's a very wet evening, what with the rain and all."

Eléonore laughed.

"Ah, that's better, now we can talk reasonably. I could do nothing with you when you looked so tragic. Now I will continue. We've both agreed to love one another madly, for ever. But, alas, my sweet, dear love, I have nothing to offer you."

"I only want yourself."

"I know, but I can't insult you by asking you to marry me. I should make you the laughing-stock of all our friends. Oh, I had dreamed to lay valorous deeds and military renown at your feet. But Fortune has turned her face away from my ambitions: the campaign against England was a failure. I have a lot of debts. You would come to despise me when you heard people whispering: 'Well, Boufflers did well for himself, marrying the rich widow.'"

Eléonore put away her pride—for no woman in love can afford to be proud—and pleaded with him. But as she looked with dread at the stern lines of his face, she knew it would be in vain.

"The gossip will die down in time, we can live apart from society, in a château in the country, and we would look after the people on our estates together and ignore the rest of the world, we . . ."

He interrupted her. "I'm not only thinking of society. *They* might forget. *I* would never forget that I had come to you as a beggar and was living on your money. Besides, there are your children to consider: I haven't got the right to take money which is rightfully theirs. Oh, if only you were a shepherdess in a tattered kirtle and a crown of cornflowers, that would be quite a different matter."

She groaned. "You will make me hate my possessions. If it weren't for the children I would throw my riches into the Seine and then you'd have to take me!"

"And we would go and live on my poor old estate at Malgrange. We wouldn't starve: there is always country fare and I've got a lot of fruit trees." He seemed to be relenting.

They laughed and he buried his face against her neck.

Then she suddenly flared up. "You are sacrificing me to your pride. You can't bear to hear people laughing at you, and you don't want to lose your liberty. Oh, you are so cruel to me! It is I who will have to suffer in all this."

For all answer he looked at her very sorrowfully. Tears would have welled up in his eyes if he had not mastered himself. She turned penitent and flung her arms around him, and cried wildly: "Oh, forgive me."

Then he was whispering in her ear, mad, sweet words of supplication, telling her that they might still belong to one another, and the world be no wiser, and that he would defend her good name with his very life. She felt as if she were going to faint, her whole universe was tottering and swaying. He said:

"I love you with every kind of love—like a child, like a father, like a friend, like a lover, like a madman. *A la folie.* Ah, say that we will be lovers!"

Then he was silent and cast his head down on her breast. Timidly she caressed him. After a long time she said to him quietly:

"You said it would be unfair to deprive the children of their heritage: it would be still more unfair to rob them of the mother they worship. And if we became lovers we would be doing that."

"They need never know. You could slip into my house at night, thickly veiled, and you would not be recognized. You must never come in your coach."

"It is true, the children would not actually know, but they would feel that something had gone out of their lives. And then, as Delphine grew up, how could I possibly guide her by the principles I have always kept, unless I followed them myself? If I were living for love alone, the whole atmosphere of her home life might change. I would be a woman in a continual ecstasy, remote from her simple joys; sooner or later, the fever, the restlessness, would communicate itself to the children, and when they grew older they might suffer from this unrest in their childhood. They are both so sensitive, so delicate, and up till now we have all three been so united: don't ask me to spoil all that. You have your standard of honour, which you impose upon me, I have my standard as a mother—respect it."

And so the night wore on, in agonized wrestlings and pleadings, each seeing the other's point of view, both captives of the social system of their century. He whispered his love-making, a flood of tenderness and folly: "I love you madly and continuously, dear love, my little nymph. How delicious it feels to be loved by thee. Ah, the power of love to change a man utterly! But still, my beloved, I would have you love my faults. I want to give myself to you as I am." And he wooed her, with all that playfulness which had always delighted her, enchanting her by that complete absorption in herself and all that concerned her, which he had displayed in those cherished early letters.

But still she withstood him. After a while, she closed her eyes and turned away. He felt that she had withdrawn into an inner citadel, and he had to acknowledge defeat. He fell silent.

At length, as if by a sudden inspiration, Boufflers regained a little courage and he said to her: "I will leave no stone unturned to secure some good post; sooner or later, something is sure to be found: I have many influential friends. Will you marry me when I've made a position for myself? Until then, will you wait for me?"

"Yes, oh yes!"

"Even if it means waiting for some time?"

"Yes, I can bear anything, now that I know how much you love me. I have only to go to my secret mind and say to myself: 'Yes, in heart and spirit, we belong to one another,' and I can bear it all. Oh, I don't know . . . it's too hard to endure being away from you. In Paris, I am so rarely alone when you come to see me: there are always too many callers to interrupt us. We can never talk."

"Do you love me as much as that?" he teased.

"Yes, with all my heart. I'm only alive when you are there. Oh, if only I were a shepherdess, what sweet hours we could spend together." And she dreamily caressed his brow.

"Shall I ask Longus to tell us?" And stretching out a long arm he took her copy of *Daphnis and Chloe.*

He read at random: "But Chloe fits the chaplet to his head, and then kisses his locks as fair and sweeter than the violets, and out of her kirtle she gave him of her cakes and simnels to eat, and snatcht it by stealth from his mouth again as he was eating and fed like a wanton, harmless bird. While thus they eat and take more kisses than bites they saw a fisherman's boat come by. . . . But now when the Sun was grown more burning, the Spring going out and the Summer coming in, they were invited to new and Summer pleasure. Daphnis he swome in the Rivers; Chloe she bathed in the Springs: he with his Pipe contended with the Pines, she with her voice strove with the Nightingales. Sometimes they catcht the chirping grasshoppers, they gathered flowers, they shak't the trees for mellow fruits."[1]

Eléonore closed her eyes; Boufflers glanced at her and found the passage where Daphnis gazes at Chloe asleep, for it reminded him of a certain coach ride.

[1] George Thornley's translation is used here, though the French version is by Amyot.

"What sweet eyes are those that sleep? How sweetly breathes that rosie mouth? The Apples smell not like to it, nor the flowery lannes and thickets. But I am afraid to kisse her. For her kisse stings to my heart, and makes me mad, like new honey. Besides I fear, lest a kisse should chance to wake her."

Just then the wind rose to a climax of fury and the whole house shook. Eléonore opened her eyes and snatched the book from him. "It's all so picturesque and artificial; he says nothing about the wind and I want him to, because it's on a night when the west wind was raging that you have told me of your love." She threw back her head and laughed, and as she did so, she was no longer a fragile porcelain lady in an ivory-velvet *polonaise*, but a little fire sprite, a spirit of flame and air and passion, with brilliant blue eyes and golden hair. In that instant the startled Boufflers discovered a new woman. She cried: "This wind makes me exultant and terror-stricken and exhilarated. All to-day when I was waiting for you, and for the terrible moment when I knew I must either lay my heart bare to you, or die from keeping silence, this wind filled me with joy and a deep sense of security, although the terror was in the house, was part of the crumbling stone, was part of me. It was as if I was uttering these wild shrieks up and down the turret stairway and making the old holly tree groan and creak. Yesterday, on the last night when I was to keep my secret from you, as I lay in bed on the brink of a new and terrible life, the wonder, the joy of the wind was beyond description. Yesterday evening at twilight I was compelled to escape from my children and fling myself headlong into the arms of the gale. I am a small woman and the gale would hold me and save me in spite of the mad risks I took. I felt that long, long ago the wind must have meant life and death to us, so that all our deepest emotions are carried by it. It spoke to me of the fear of chaos and the hunger nevertheless to return to it. I went about untamed and untouched all day."

He was spellbound. She sprang up, ran to the long window and opened it. All the candles blew out at one gust. She turned to Boufflers with a gesture of appeal. "Come and drink in the wildness with me; the rain had ceased." He went to her and, sheltering her in his arms, they leaned from the balcony and gazed at the tormented black branches of the oaks and elms in the park, the eddies of wet leaves scurrying round in circles. Like a great orchestra, the beeches in the distant grove sang in the Autumn gale and were answered by the trees in the park. They felt so secure, together against the elements.

The stable clock struck midnight. He drew her in again and shut the window. Without letting her go, Stanislas bent down and threw another log on the fire.

The sparks shot up the chimney. In the glow, a great pot of late scarlet dahlias was aflame against the white panelling. Eléonore stood looking down at the fire, sometimes appearing very happy, sometimes wistful. As for Stanislas, he seemed a changed creature: the mockery and the dissipation of years had been washed away and a kind of radiance was in his face. Such is the transforming power of love.

Looking up to meet his intent gaze, she whispered. "It is my soul that loves you."

And he said: "Ah, my sweet love, why have you and I not met till now?"

Then clasping both her hands in a gesture of inexpressible fervour which she was never to forget, he cried: "Let us love life and not fear death, for souls do not die, but live on for ever."[1]

Two years passed. Of these two years there is almost no record. The Chevalier did not get the promotion he sought so feverishly; Madame de Sabran, in spite of his ardent love-making, still kept him at bay, and refused to become his mistress. And the months were slipping by. . . .

Very often, decisions have a way of forming overnight. At Eastertide of 1781, as she left her parish church after performing her Easter duties, Madame de Sabran felt that she would not keep Easter again for many years to come. The letters of Stanislas had become more and more daring. Fearing that he was slipping into the intimacy of lovers, she had written to him, reproving him for calling her by the familiar "thou" or "*tu*", instead of "*Vous*" or "you", and he had replied:

14th April, 1781 . . .

And why do you forbid me to call you "*tu*"? Because, thou dost say, dear love, of the fear that my letters are too like others. I would rather never write any more letters at all than to be cramped in this one I'm writing to thee. That "*Vous*" freezes me; it doesn't seem to be in keeping with any of the feelings with which you inspire me. It is as if one always had to bow to you instead of embracing you. Remove your prohibition, *chère* Sabran: if you insist on my being ceremonious, you will make me insincere and cold, and above all, *gauche*. Love is a badly-brought-up child. . . . I would hate any state of life which prevented me from being your lover (*amant*).

With these words ringing in her ears, Eléonore drove with the children to Anizy in her travelling coach. In answer to the bishop's invitation, Boufflers came to stay on the first of May.

[1] He wrote thus to her.

On the day after his arrival, Eléonore and Stanislas decided to go out riding together for the day, taking provisions with them in their saddlebags. The prevailing fashion lent the horsewoman a free and saucy air, and a thousand tricks of coquetry. Madame du Barry knew so well that disguise has its charm and its own provocation, when she chose to be painted in riding-costume. Eléonore looked bewitching in her fashionable puce-coloured jacket with its three-tiered collar, her pink skin shoes peeping from under the long skirt, her apple-green waistcoat topped by a large cravat of white gauze, and her enormous hat with its streaming feathers of green and white. Her hair was disciplined into a large *catagon*, like a man's wig. Waving to the bishop smiling on the terrace, Eléonore and the Chevalier mounted and rode off.

Soon the château was out of sight. There were cascades of pink and white blossoms everywhere. In the orchards, the pear-trees in bloom had a matt brilliance like the powdered heads of worldly abbés. In the distance were groves of tall chestnut trees, as majestic as Louis the Fourteenth's periwigs. "This is my wedding-day," thought Eléonore; "these bouquets are to deck my way." After a while, they had left the fields and the hamlets behind and were riding uphill to the wide over-arching beech-grove through which Boufflers had ridden two years ago in the storm. He kept singing snatches of song.

Years later, Eléonore was to write to Stanislas: "I could almost hear and see you, laughing with those great shouts of laughter that I love so much, and saying in a flash a thousand charming things, one more piquant than the other, inspired by the mountain air, the freedom and simplicity of the surroundings." And the man who loved her wrote in a story: "If any two acquaintances of mine . . . were afraid of going any further . . . I should forbid them to take walks together in certain sylvan spots, and especially on a beautiful Spring evening, because this is exactly the season . . . that the invisible enemy chooses by preference to lay his most deadly traps . . . You must be afraid even of those birds who would not sing if they were not in love, and which under the leaves that hide them, are sirens for your destruction . . . even of those flowers whose perfume so benumbs your senses and entices you to pluck them, give them away or pin them in your bosom. Then those lovely trees that protect you with their shade, those hillocks whose mossy surface is so inviting, and those streams, whose murmur seems to say to you 'Do like us; follow your inclination'. You smell, you taste, you savour that sparkling light air which is to the air of towns like spring water to stagnant pools. It seems to penetrate your very soul and banish all the fancies that were besieging you. You are only too glad to surrender yourself to the kindly peace of the countryside, to solitude that loves a lover, to solitude that veils your eyes to all else but your companion and delivers you into one another's arms; to Nature herself, who is present in all her power, and there alone achieves her fulfilment, who speaks to you unceasingly, and if you listen carefully, speaks of nothing else but Love. What will it be like at the close of the day when everything that might distract you gradually fades away, and, as the minutes pass, yields to your contemplation the object that dominates your thoughts."[1]

Towards evening they came to a mossy glade with a wide cavern opening up in some rocks. A great carpet of bluebells and swaying wood anemones misted the ground right into the far distance. They dismounted. Boufflers tethered the horses and got a rug from his saddle-bag. "Hush," said Eléonore in a whisper, "don't move. Look at those two birds under the larch tree." The prettiest sight imaginable met their eyes; two redshanks were courting, late in the season. The cock-bird advanced towards the hen with his graceful pointed wings raised above his back, showing their pure white under-surface. He lifted his scarlet legs alternately in a delicate way and uttered all the while a clear, far-carrying trill, full of wildness, charged with desire, piercing and exciting.

Stanislas and Eléonore watched them until they flew out of sight. They turned to smile at one another. He said: "I always knew that birds in Springtime were sirens appointed for the destruction of lovers." He took both her hands in his and whispered in her ear.

She did not answer, but let him lead her into the cave.

Many years after the anniversary of this day, Eléonore wrote in her *Journal* for Stanislas: "I don't want to go to bed without reminding you of that cavern which we discovered one day on our way as we were riding, and we went in from simple curiosity; just now it comes back to me—guess why if you can, though for my part I won't tell you, but I will go to sleep dreaming of it."

[1] *Ah! if only.*

END OF PART III

Part IV

THE CAPTURE

CHAPTER XVIII

MARTYRDOM

"... I look beyond the space of time that separates us and think only of the moment when I shall see you again, which will be for me, I believe, the only true resurrection. Good-bye, my husband, my lover, my friend, my universe, my soul, my God."

Journal of the Comtesse de Sabran kept for the Chevalier de Boufflers.

1783. Two more years had passed. The lover and the contemplative have this in common: the rest of the world ceases to exist for them, all their former interests fade away, and their souls are focused entirely on the beloved. Oh, surrender, full of suffering and delight.

Two more years. Stanislas was completely under Eléonore's spell. She was always a creature of infinite variety. As Madame Vigée Lebrun had said, "one never knew boredom in her society". She was teasing, capricious, elusive, profoundly feminine; he could only be sure of her in their moments of passion together; and then, indeed, he gloried in the wealth of tenderness which she lavished on him. It was the first time in her life that she had loved, and she gave herself to him with all the abandonment of a woman of mature judgement and deep feeling.

In society, the lovers had to behave with very great reserve, and indeed no one guessed their secret. But when they were alone together, usually in his house in Paris, where they were sure of being undisturbed, then heart spoke to heart. At those times she was not afraid to tell him all that he was to her. No more need for concealment: they were one.

She would probably go thickly veiled in the evening, on foot, or by cab. He would let her in quickly. Then for a while she was no longer the great lady of fashion, a friend of the Queen and the leader of a *salon*, but simply a beautiful woman with her lover. In the winter he would put some fruit and wine on a table by the fire, and she would come in with a little sigh of contentment. Over and over again she looked at the treasures in his room, the trophies of his adventures and journeyings, with murmurs of wonder and interest. Her absorption in his young days always touched him. Then, brimming over with the sweetest gaiety, she would take him in her arms and say: "And to think that the wanderer is now mine." And so, for a few hours they would forget the world and live in each other's hearts. Years later, he wrote to her: "I kiss you as if you were in my little room; think well about this."

In her letters her expressions of love towards him at about this time are most moving:

"I feel every variety of tenderness for you: I love you as if I were your brother, your sister, your daughter, your friend, your wife, better still as your mistress."

". . . Our souls are united to each other, how would we ever be able to live alone? . . . You are more essential to me than the air I breathe."

"Good-bye, my friend, good-bye, my lover. I love you as if I were only fifteen and we were living in the golden age."

"I feel towards you as I did on the first day. Only death can separate soul and body. You are my soul, I can't exist without you . . ."

"What are the riches of the world in comparison with that close union of two souls who are made for one another and who become purified in the fire of love, like gold in the crucible? . . . However, up till now, I have loved you so much that I have loved enough for two."

"The soul does not grow old. I have in mine a furnace of love that will last for eternity."

"Good-bye, my dear and too dear husband; do not weary of being greatly loved; it is more rare than one thinks, and it is a source of great sweetness, amid all the cares of life, this certainty of having a good ally to help one bear the burden."

"Good-bye, delight and torment of my life."

It was the first time in his life that Boufflers had been loved so constantly and so passionately, and it was as joyous to him as the sunlight. He placed Eléonore in a shrine high above every other woman he had ever known: these had merely captivated his senses, while to her he gave his inmost soul. She was the first woman who had tried to understand him: she seemed even to delight in his faults.

Yes, she soon discovered that he was not perfect, and they had violent quarrels about some of his misdemeanours. In fact they often quarrelled, for they were both hot-tempered and impetuous. But the reconciliations were sweet, particularly at Anizy, where the memories of that first Springtime as lovers remained ever-present.

Indeed, he had his faults. For one thing he was desperately casual. This was partly due to his life of vagabondage on the high roads, without any fixed abode, travelling about all over

Europe, a soldier's life, staying at stray inns and never for long. Once, in Paris, he promised to come and have lunch with her one day before going off to his regiment. She waited for him all the morning, not daring to send word to find out what had happened, and he never arrived! She was desperately sensitive, and lived only for her moments alone with him. Even her children could not distract her from her absorption in him. She was at his mercy. Being of her century, she was the slave of her moods; on this occasion, she wept and stormed and planned to leave him. When, lo and behold, the heedless Chevalier sends her a note full of good spirits, from an inn on the way to his regiment, telling her of a good meal he'd just enjoyed! Maddening will-of-the-wisp. . . . He never mentioned the broken appointment.

They both had explosive tempers; in fact, once at a friend's house party, during an argument with his friends on the art of letter-writing, Boufflers gave great shouts of fury, and went out of the room slamming the door. So these two stormed at one another, and Eléonore behaved like a little termagant. Indeed, but for the physical bond, which in some mysterious way settled many differences, and but for Boufflers' enormous fund of high spirits, the quarrels might have been serious. But at the remembrance of his unvarying tenderness to her when they were together, of the way he bore with all her caprices and follies, and his care for her when she was ill, she always melted, and gave in at the end. She even tried to forgive his patchy and infrequent letter-writing, she who now lived for the post, and who had written one letter to his four in the old days.

It was impossible to resist a man who had the sublime impertinence to write after a quarrel: "Content yourself with being sure that all the faults are on your side, and all the perfections on mine." He was witty even when he was being most tiresome.

One day, in 1783, two years after they had become lovers, Boufflers, who was going to Brussels, had arranged to meet Eléonore at an inn at Valenciennes. They had planned to be there by nightfall. However, Eléonore suddenly decided to appear by midday, so that she could have a good rest in the afternoon, and be looking her loveliest by the time he arrived. She could rely on the discretion of her young coachman from Nancy, who would not gossip when he saw Boufflers. She sat back in her great travelling coach which was lined with blue Utrecht velvet, and as large and downy as a little *boudoir*. However simple her dress, she could never really disguise the fact that she was a great lady of the Court, for she had an aristocratic air of carrying her head, her manners had grace and distinction, and all her movements expressed that combination of ease and dignity which were so characteristic of a woman of the time. Her dress, down to the smallest detail, was very *soignée*. In an enormous box at her feet was her travelling beauty-case, with all its manifold bottles of lotions, including one for killing bad odours and quenching insects at the inn! Then there was her mirror, lace coverlets for the table, pillows for the bed, unguents and perfumes without which no lady of the century would travel.

When, at length, she got to the inn at Valenciennes, the proprietor, his wife and all the maids and scullions came rushing to the door, curtseying and bobbing. As her room was not quite ready, she said she would go for a walk in the kitchen garden. The *chef* must be sent to her there to take her orders, for meals were eaten privately in one's room.

Eléonore lifted her veil and picked her way delicately between the beds of spring onions, artichokes and asparagus. She stopped in front of a bed of cabbages. Yes, she must order *sauerkraut* for him to-night, or would it give him one of his famous colics? He had acquired from King Stanislas at Lunéville a positive passion for that dish. Enchanting being, so full of *joie-de-vivre*, so like a child in his likes and dislikes. She smiled and sighed for sheer happiness.

Just then a young woman in a travelling cloak crossed by the cabbage-patch and stopped in her turn to gaze at the cabbages. Eléonore glanced up at her: she looked as if she were simply some rather pretentious provincial *belle*, sentimental and full-bosomed. (To modern eyes, a kind of Madame Bovary of the eighteenth century.) In her dress, she had, as she thought, aped the elegance of the Court, and the effect was rather mannered: the patches were all wrong, she tried to look languishing, after the new mode introduced with cross-over neckerchiefs, but she only managed to appear simpering and affected, and, above all, thoroughly provincial. Eléonore wondered what she was doing there, but of course did not venture to address her. The *belle* turned away and, meeting the *chef* on her path, she said to him: "Remember to give us some *sauerkraut*, the Chevalier adores it." Eléonore heard this quite distinctly.

A cock crew on a distant dungheap. The sunlight suddenly became full of mockery. Eléonore clenched her hands in an effort to regain self-command, and, dismissing the *chef*, she went up to her room. In the passage she saw one of the room maids, without shoes or stockings and said to her as casually as possible: "Do you know if a certain Chevalier de Boufflers is expected soon?"

"For the midday meal, *Madame*," replied the girl.

Eléonore went to her room and closed the door. No, it couldn't possibly be true. There must be some mistake. She must give him the benefit of the doubt.

After a while she heard the *belle* in the passage outside saying to the room-maid: "Tell me at once when the Chevalier de Boufflers comes." Then she went downstairs again to another wing of the house.

Nothing could have been clearer. The shock was so great that she felt stupefied, almost unable to think. Mechanically she sat down in a chair and stared vacantly into space. At intervals she kept repeating in a whisper: "I must go. I'll have to go now." After a while she pulled the bell-rope and told the maid to give orders to her coachman to be ready in half an hour. She had not unpacked, so there was nothing to prepare. She sat on in her chair without moving. Her world lay about her in ruins.

Suddenly, for the first time since she had become Boufflers' mistress, she was overcome with a sense of the shame of her situation. Here she was, trundling about the high roads of France, making secret assignations at inns with her paramour, exactly like that trollop in the cabbage-patch. In the eighteenth century, when a Court lady broke the seventh commandment, she spoke in a high-flown way of having lost her honour. The woman of the people had a crude, more realistic word than this: she said she had lost her "*honnêteté*"—her integrity or *decency*. At that moment Eléonore felt that she had lost honour, integrity and decency. And to think that she had given up all the consolations of her Faith, all the peace of a clear conscience, all the spiritual joy of guiding Delphine and Elzéar, for this, for this, for this. She had committed herself to this horrible life of subterfuge and constant play-acting, just to satisfy the passing lust of an adventurer who had other affairs with common women. How he must have laughed at her! Possibly the woman had ridiculed her, too, and they had laughed together. Perhaps he was unfaithful to her with other women in Paris. So that was why he did not want to get married. He'd written some couplets once:

Matrimony always
Was a chain.

So it wasn't a question of disparity in their fortunes at all: he just wanted to be free to live his own life, and he'd sacrificed her for this.

"What a fool I have been! So easily trapped by his soft words, his tears. Of *course* he wooed me for a long time: a libertine's appetites are always whetted by resistance." Of course he was a libertine: she had known about his past when they had first met, and his reputation was deplorable. And yet, in spite of it, she had trusted him. She had the vanity to imagine that she alone had pierced below the surface, that she alone understood and appreciated this contradictory being. In turns, she felt humiliated, angry, deceived, revengeful. If Boufflers had succumbed to the spell of some wondrous Circe, some woman of their own world, Madame de Sabran could perhaps have understood a little. But that it should be this overdressed, vulgar creature. . . . Eléonore felt intolerably smirched by the association. And so it was to a man of this sort that she had given up six years of her life, years during which her health had slowly been breaking up in her effort to master herself. He had simply played cat and mouse with her, made himself indispensable in a thousand different ways, seized hold of her entire nature as a woman, spiritually and bodily, just . . . to satisfy his lust. She was simply an episode in his life, like the other woman, and he would soon be discarding them both.

Just then Boufflers arrived at the inn, and, on hearing that the Comtesse de Sabran had come earlier than was expected, but was leaving again at once, rushed up the stairs towards her room. History will never disclose whether he had been merely flirting with the woman whom Eléonore was later to nickname Dulcinea di Tobosa, or whether he had enjoyed more tangible favours. (She was possibly an old flame.) But one fact remains beyond any doubt: he had never ceased to love Eléonore. She was the only woman in France who had complete dominion over his heart, and his love had grown with every passing month. That day he was feeling extraordinarily ill, and when he suddenly appeared in Eléonore's room, his extreme pallor and his haggard eyes gave her a shock. Indeed, it was only his iron constitution which carried him through the feverishly active life he led, for he was always being stricken by various ills, not the least being those pitiless, raging headaches, toothaches and colics for which that century had no cure, and to which he is always referring in his letters. On seeing him, Eléonore's first instinct was to run to him and try to comfort and tend him. But she remembered that he had betrayed her, that he had desecrated their love, and ruined her life. If Boufflers imagined that she was the kind of woman to acquiesce tamely to infidelity, he was mistaken. She told him all that had been in her mind, as she sat alone. As she spoke, her eyes flashed and her body quivered with rage. She listened to none of his interruptions.

"This is the last time I will ever speak to you, I shall go home now. I shall return all your letters, and I don't want to see you again." Then, without waiting to listen to a word of explanation, she wrenched herself free from him when he tried to force her to stay, and went hurriedly downstairs. In a few minutes he heard her coach rumbling away in the distance. He knew it was no good to follow her on horseback, for it might attract too much attention at the inn, and endanger her reputation.

Lost in the blackest thoughts, feeling sick with misery and a splitting headache, Boufflers was just going downstairs when he was waylaid by the chambermaid, who told him that "The lady in the next wing, Madame X, sent a message to him that the meal was laid in her room, and she had ordered *sauerkraut.*" Boufflers swore a thousand oaths, told the girl to go to perdition, then went downstairs to write a letter to Eléonore.

CHAPTER XIX

AFTER THE QUARREL

Correspondence between the two lovers after the quarrel:

From the Chevalier de Boufflers to the Comtesse de Sabran, as he was on his way to Brussels.

". . . You left me with Death in my heart. I see no hope of future happiness; all my illusions are falling from me, like leaves in the chill winds of Autumn, when each day brings a more gloomy morrow. Courage has utterly left me; my strength and my age are unequal to the burden of this grief, for at the age of five and forty, love should have almost lost its special character, and melted into a sweet and tranquil friendship. We are very far from that, aren't we!

"I do not want to overwhelm you with reproaches, but my heart is shattered. This kind of anguish is too poignant for it. You have treated me as unjustly as a child of fifteen. You never saw the situation as it really was, you did not hear a single word I said to you, and I exist in perpetual fear of reliving those horrible moments, and it is impossible to prevent a thing from happening, if it has no cause. Nevertheless, dear child, you are more necessary to me than the peace and happiness of which you deprive me. And so, I give you plenary absolution for your causing my griefs, past, present and to come, and I go as far as to crave your pardon for exposing them to you.

"Good-bye, *ma fille*; unless I fall seriously ill, I shall see you at Anizy on the fifth. I place my trust in your children: the pleasure of seeing them will have dispelled a little of the black mood that overshadowed you; love, or at least your kind heart, will do the rest. . . ."

Reply from the Comtesse de Sabran.

"Do not hate me, my child, because I love you too much. Have pity on my weakness, laugh at my folly, and may it never trouble the peace of your heart. . . . Go, be free as air, abuse your liberty if you will, and I would rather have it so than make you feel the bondage of a chain too heavy. . . . Good-bye, dear heart, love me if you can, or rather if you will; only remember that no one in this world loves and cherishes you as I do, and that I care for life only as long as I can spend it with you."

Reply to this from the Chevalier de Boufflers.

"Let me tell you, dear and naughty child, that I am beginning to feel a little better in body and spirit. I have been making wise reflections, and realized that I was mad and you were mad, but that I love you and you love me, and so for both of us, more good will come of this than evil. Let us say no more about it; you should have kissed me as much as you scolded me. I should have laughed as much as I was hurt by it, but the past will return no more, and sorrow will remain with it. . . . I take up my pen again to ask you to kiss your two darlings for me. . . . Content yourself with the thought that all the faults are on your side and all perfections on mine! . . ."

Reply to the above from the Comtesse de Sabran.

"Yes, my child, I forgive you all your tempers, past, present and future. I suffer too much when I have to be cross with you, and so I find it better to love you, and tell you so. Whatever you do we always come back to that, and so, once and for all, I make a resolution to abide by it. I give you full indulgence for all your amusements, and I feel more than ever that the best way to keep you is to give you perfect freedom. There is in man a vague restlessness that makes him seek happiness only where he is not. You will no sooner be far away from me than you will want to come back, and I promise you beforehand that you will always be welcomed. . . . This letter is our treaty of peace that nothing can ever break—not even time. After this I kiss you and love you more than ever."

Extract from a letter of the Comtesse de Sabran. (In reply to a complaint from Boufflers about his eyes, which did not prove to be serious.)

". . . I could not read without emotion what you say about your coming blindness. . . . I think it must be due to your white and delicate skin [*ta peau blanche et fine*]. All that you have to do, and that would certainly cure you, is to put a bandage over your eyes—at night, I mean, for you are cunning enough to suspect that I have reason to dread your piercing little eyes. No, my child, why should I have recourse to illusion? Our love has no need of it, it was born without it and will endure without it. For it was certainly not the effect of my charms—which had ceased to exist when you first knew me—that kept you to me, nor was it your Huron-like manners, your gruff and absent-minded air, your true and pithy sallies, your large appetite and your deep slumber whenever one wants to talk to you, that made me love you to distraction; it was a certain something that set our souls in tune, a certain sympathy that makes me think and feel like you. For beneath that rough exterior you conceal the mind of an angel and the heart of a woman. You combine all contrasts, and there is no being in Heaven or on Earth more lovable or more loved than you. Come to me then as soon as possible. . . . Good-bye, my child; good-bye, my friend; good-bye, my lover; never have I said this word with greater pleasure, never felt so much the happiness of living only for the one I love."

CHAPTER XX

FIRST RUMBLINGS OF THE STORM, AND A PARTING

After the reconciliation, Eléonore went to take the waters at Spa. Boufflers came to her there, and they spent some delicious hours together, going for walks in the country around. As usual, she was greatly fêted wherever she went, and the attentions of a certain admirer made Boufflers furiously jealous. When he left again to rejoin his regiment, she made great friends with an English family named Buller, whom she found very entertaining; her letters about them reveal an understanding of the English temperament and a tender teasing appreciation of their foibles. Then she went for a journey to Holland, travelling incognito by coach with her friend, Madame d'Andlau, and being treated very lavishly to beer by an unknown English commercial traveller. Later in the year, she and her children went to stay at the Prince of Ligne's at Bel Oeil where they all acted in a private performance of Beaumarchais' startling new play *Le Mariage de Figaro.* Eléonore took the part of the Comtesse, Elzéar was Chérubin and Boufflers a raging success as Figaro. Mrs. Webster has said: "Boufflers, ever at war with Courts and courtiers, at heart a democrat, threw himself into the role of Figaro with all the ardour of conviction, and, as he declaimed the famous monologue, he was far from foreseeing that the words he spoke would go to swell the mighty tide of insurrection that was soon to sweep away the misguided world that applauded them."

No wonder Louis XVI had banned the performance at Court.

It was the first time the great had ever been publicly criticized: "Because you are a noble lord, you think yourself a great genius. . . . What have you done for so many good things?"

Far away, and yet stealthily drawing nearer every day, the distant rumblings of a great storm could be heard. If only Boufflers could have foreseen that, only six years later, one Autumn day, the Queen, sitting sadly by her grotto at Petit Trianon, would be summoned by a footman to return immediately to the Palace: the mob from Paris was howling at the gates: pikes and pitchforks, red bonnets, dishevelled hair, furies and galley-slaves; and at their head a Belgian courtesan, Théroigne de Méricourt, who finished her days in a madhouse, stark naked.

No, he could not have guessed. In Eléonore's company, he gave himself up entirely to the pleasure of living. The Prince de Ligne was a marvellous host, and wanted everyone to be happy at Bel Oeil: "The mornings were given up to study; music, literature, drawing occupied every one in turn . . . The Prince, as soon as he was dressed, went down to his island of Flore with a book in his hand, worked in his library, and looked at his gardens. The guests walked, rode, drove, or sailed on the great lake . . . and spent fine evenings on the water with music and moonlight. . . . The garden paths were well laid, so as not to wet the ladies' feet, and bowers of roses, jasmine, orange blossom, and honeysuckle led to where they went to bathe. Here and there in quiet corners were shady seats and rustic shelters where each one could find her knitting, her netting, her writing things and a raven's quill."[1] What happy hours Stanislas must have spent with his mistress. The Prince de Ligne himself, the most devoted and enlightened of her admirers, has written about the charms of her conversation: "Eléonore knows so well how to pass from one subject to another! She seems to lead you through an English garden, where one never goes along the same path twice, and where one always sees fresh objects of interest, her simple and lively imagination shows them to one as in a moving picture; one sees them, they live, they walk about. She conveys her impressions as vividly as she receives them, for to relate well, one must be able to feel keenly. . . . She never knows what she ought to say, and one lets oneself be carried away by the unpremeditated charm of her gentle talk [*sa douce causerie*] as if in a light skiff along the course of a beautiful river. One no more knows where one is going than she knows where she is taking one. She interrupts herself, she goes wrong, she corrects herself. Her want of memory adds to the originality of her discourse, she never repeats herself, just as a bird never sings the same song over again. The right and piquant expression always comes to her lips. She writes, and her

[1] From *Histoire de la Princesse Hélène de Ligne,* by Lucien Percy.

pen, even in verse, seems to fly all by itself. The greatest charm of Eléonore is, above all things, naturalness . . ."

After the visit to Bel Oeil, Madame de Sabran returned to Paris with her children. The winter of 1783–4 was a severe one. The Queen deprived the royal children of toys on New Year's Day in order to set them an example of abnegation, and instead she sent blankets, clothes and bread to the poor. Though it is true that no human creature should be dependent on the charitable sensibilities of the rich for security during a bad winter, on the other hand one fails to see that the Revolution improved things in any way. As far as the poor were concerned, it made matters worse, for when the Republic was declared, the destitute, entirely deprived of the ministrations of religious institutions and private charity, had absolutely nowhere to turn to. The Revolutionary leaders never relieved want: they only thought of their own stomachs.

In the middle of that dreadful winter, when great fires for the poor had been lit in all the courtyards, the year 1784 dawned. Both the Chevalier and Madame de Sabran were often at Court that year. The Chevalier was received by the Queen, probably because of his friendship with Eléonore. At the request of the Queen, he composed some couplets on her supposed faults, but she was not subtle enough to discover the wise advice deftly woven into the compliments. She foolishly sang the verses to her friends. Marie-Antoinette, who loved children as much as Eléonore, and who had heard of their success as actors, received Elzéar and Delphine at Petit Trianon, where they acted before her, and they were given a collation afterwards. The King and Queen waited at table on the children.

(In 1785, when the Queen's heart was very heavy about the affair of the necklace, she saw little Elzéar in the Galerie des Glaces one morning and stopped to kiss him "on both his rosy little cheeks". The next day, when she saw his mother, she said, laughingly, that she had kissed a gentleman. Eléonore replied: "Yes, and he is boasting about it." Elzéar never forgot that kiss, and to the end of his life he spoke of the wonderful grace and beauty of Marie-Antoinette.)

In 1784, after the cruel winter, the Hameau, or little rustic village of Petit Trianon, was being built; Madame de la Motte was hatching the affair of the diamond necklace, which was going to bring the Queen into such disrepute; Cagliostro and other sorcerers were troubling the public imagination so that the powers of darkness held greater sway when the hour of doom eventually struck. A libertine of Spanish origin named Laclos wrote *Les Liaisons Dangereuses*, which is the story of how a nobleman callously achieved the seduction of a virtuous woman, and then, at the instigation of a former mistress, the Marquise de Merteuil who was a fiend incarnate, he cynically threw her over just as she was beginning to love him, thus eventually causing her death. It is one of the most corrupt books of the whole century: there is neither love nor passion in it, but just the slow tracking down of a defenceless woman, followed by a sadistic gloating over her writhings. The Prince de Ligne tells us that the portrait of the wicked Marquise de Merteuil was drawn from life. None of the people in this book break the seventh commandment because they are swept off their feet by desire, but merely in order to shame and outwit someone else. The reading public in our century, deluged with perverse books and by now thoroughly innoculated against their poisons, can hardly realize the influence of such a publication on the middle classes, whose reading up till then had been so carefully censored. "So that is how the nobility behave!" they would exclaim. And the so-called enlightened intellectuals among them would make disparaging comparisons between the upper and middle classes: already the high-flown classical jargon of the subversives was creeping into their speech, heralding the day when thieves and homicidal maniacs would talk quite glibly about their "virtue" and their "incorruptible souls".

In 1785, when the Queen was thirty, the disgraceful Necklace scandal burst upon the nation. In grief and bitterness, she took refuge in the little village of Petit Trianon, which had just been completed for her. She neglected to entertain the leading families of France, whose smiles concealed such malice; when they came to pay court at Versailles they found the Queen was not in residence, so they went off in disloyal huffs, and created little courts of their own, both in Paris and in their country-houses in the provinces, and spent their time gossiping malevolently about the Queen and her intimate friends. The women of bad reputation who had not been received at Court, and the little *nouveaux-riches* upstarts from Paris who had only slipped in through marrying above them, fiercely jealous of the Queen's beauty, and angry that they were only admitted on official occasions, vented their spite by repeating scandalous gossip, and humming the filthy songs now circulating in the streets of Paris. (The Marquise de la Tour du Pin tells us how she and her friends used to laugh behind their fans at these "*bourgeoises de Paris*"; they were nicknamed "*Traineuses*" or "draggle-tails": you could tell them a mile off, for they had not yet mastered the art of sliding their high-heeled shoes along the dangerous polished floors of Versailles.)

It was in that year, in 1785, that Boufflers faced another financial crisis. He found he could no longer escape his creditors, so he sought the advice of his old friend the duc de Nivernais. The duc told him that the Governorship of the new French colony of Senegal was vacant. The French had just seized it from the English. In the hope that, at last, he would distinguish himself, he applied for the post. He was then forty-six years old, and in spite of his wonderful energy, and in spite of being one of the most brilliant men of his day, he had not yet made a position for himself. He still had nothing to offer Eléonore.

November 22nd, 1785. Eléonore had come to Boufflers' house for the last time before he set sail for Senegal, on the West Coast of Africa. She had been with him since morning, and there was death in her heart. It had been a terrible day, for the spectacle of her grief was enough to shake Boufflers' determination. She made efforts to be valiant. In their last moments of passion, he had longed to communicate some of his courage to her, and inspire her with fortitude by welding her into himself. In those moments, she promised wildly to believe that he had done all for the best, and, exhausted by her tears, she rested awhile on his breast. But after a little time, she would rouse herself, look at him who had become her god, her universe, and was again overcome with anguish at the thought of so terrible a parting.

"You can't do this. Oh, why don't you take me with you? It isn't too late. There's still time. You know I would follow you to the ends of the earth. And now you are leaving me, perhaps for ever. I shall never know when to expect news of you. I shall be racked with anxiety about your safety, about your health in that horrible climate. And then, at the end, what position will you have made for yourself? You are not a colonizer, like the rest. You don't grab for yourself, you don't believe in slaves, and you won't bleed the place white. You are a humanitarian, and you are simply going to spend yourself, ruin your spirits and your health and come back poorer than before. They threw this thankless task out to you in order to keep you quiet. The Government won't provide you with a single necessity, whatever their promises."

She ran her fingers through his hair, which was now streaked with silver: "And you will come back to me with your hair all white!"

Her lovely golden hair was lying all about her on the bed, almost reaching to her feet. Stanislas seized a long strand of it and twined it round his wrist. He had so loved that wealth, that cloud of silvery fairness, long before the day he had written his famous couplets on "Sabran, the Ill-combed One". It was anguish to know that now he would not play with it, and grasp it, and be mingled in its perfumed mantle for many, many months.

"When you speak like that," he said, "you make me feel I'm your torturer."

"You are my torment as well as my delight. If I had known when I first met you what suffering you were going to bring on me . . ."

He groaned, and buried his face in his hands. "Yes, I know. Why do you continue to have pity on me? I'm getting old, I've nothing to offer you. I feel quite unworthy of you. I can only tell you again and again, my beloved one, that I love you as I did on the first day, nay, even more; I love you so ardently that I feel my love will continue after death. It is no longer you and I. We are one."

The pitiless hours sped by. It was he who urged her at length to return to her own house, for she was so stricken, that time had ceased to exist for her. When she was ready he made her sit by the fire for a moment, and kneeling before her, he held her hands very firmly and made her listen to him for the last time:

"You *must* be brave. When you feel you are losing your self-command, sit down for a moment and think of Delphine. She is leaving school, you must bring her out into society and then arrange her marriage. This is, therefore, the best moment for me to be away, so that you can devote your mind to her entirely. She is getting old enough, now, to notice any intimacy between us. Also it would be a crime if a good match for her were ruined by people gossiping about us. You know we have been lucky up till now, because of our great discretion. But you must admit that we've lived on the brink of a precipice all this time. When I return, everything will be settled. Remember Delphine, repeat her name to yourself, again and again, and you will find strength to bear this. I feel full of hope, as if the end of our troubles were in sight. And above all, remember that in everything but name you are my wife."

The last farewell: "You will send me a lock of your hair," and "You will look at that portrait." "Write to me, I shall have nothing else to live for." One last embrace. She lowered her veil. Then the door shut behind her. Eléonore was alone in the street, in the cold November twilight. She tried to rouse herself to the reality that she must reach the Faubourg-Saint-Honoré somehow without attracting attention.

And Boufflers, listening in his room, heard the little halting footsteps die away in the distance. . . .

They were parted for about six months, and during the whole of that first journey to Senegal,—during which his mother died—for some reason that has not been satisfactorily explained,

Eléonore never heard from her lover. She knew that he was alive, for he had written to others: but never a word to her. There were moments when she felt that he had ceased to love her, and had taken this opportunity to go out of her life for ever. His letters were written to her during the second journey, which took place soon after.

CHAPTER XXI

A DAY WITH THE CHEVALIER IN AFRICA

"How greatly do I need courage, particularly as I think of the last moments we spent together! But I will see you come back again, sweet moments that I have lost."

From Bouffler's Journal.

Two o'clock after midnight. . . . Two hours previously, the Chevalier, now Governor of Senegal, had fallen into his rather dilapidated camp bed, completely worn out, hoping for a good night's rest. He went to bed with the thought of Eléonore in his mind, like greedy little children go to sleep with a sugar-plum in their mouths. But at two o'clock he was still tossing and turning, his mind filled with the worries of the past day, and his body suffering from a multitude of ills.

First of all, he had burnt his leg, trying to put out a fire which had broken out in the Colony during High Mass. Then he had the remains of a headache and a colic which he traced to *vert-de-gris* in his salt-cellars, for they had not been properly cleaned by those idle natives. Or was it also the bad flour and the unfiltered water?

At length, in despair, he lit a candle, got up, and drank some barley water mixed with Hoffmann drops. He murmured incoherently to the picture of Eléonore . . . "to spend the night in the arms of Morpheus, to make up for being unable to spend it in yours".

He tumbled back into bed and gazed at her portrait: "I've got an awful headache; all this would be unbearable if it were not for the beacon of hope held out to me all the time by your pretty portrait, which shows you to me in all your joyousness, in all your enthusiasms, in your moods, in your attacks of injustice, in your whimsies, in your charm and in all your faults, which I have the stupidity to love also."

He groaned aloud, then wished he hadn't, for he knew he might be heard by his staff through the ill-fitting boards of his room.

What a hovel was this house of the Governor of Senegal, the representative of the King of France in West Africa! All the tables and chairs were broken. In his own words, it was "the poorest, the dirtiest, the most degraded of all hovels" . . . or again . . . "my hideous house, dilapidated, none of the doors close, none of the floors are solid, all the walls are crumbling, all the rooms are furnished with dusty rags. . . . All I lack is money, labour, and wood, but if there is the slightest opportunity I will do all that, for if man's spirit is really the breath of God, he must prove it by being creative."

Stanislas blew out the candle, and resolutely shut his eyes again. But various unpleasing sounds and odours assailed him through the window, and again the healing balm eluded him. In the far distance he could hear the howling of hyenas around the outskirts of the town: he shuddered with anxiety, for he knew that these wild beasts would try and dig up the corpses of prisoners he had buried out there, for, until then, the merchants, from economy, had thrown them into the sea, and they stank the place out. And then, the geese in his farmyard were making an unwonted cackling, and Boufflers wondered whether someone was going to steal them. Ah, well, whatever thefts were committed under his rule, he would not hand over the culprits to the Admiralty, which was responsible for the execution of justice, because it inflicted atrocious punishments. Boufflers, inspired by the humane ideals of Eléonore, and by his own generous belief in mankind, was content to let the culprits restore their ill-gotten gains, little by little, furtively.

"At this rate," he thought, "I daresay I shall never make a fortune, like my predecessors, and I shall return to France poorer than I came, and thus defeat the principal object of this cruel separation. But what can I do? That is the way I am made. Mercy and belief in human goodness are worth nothing in administrative work." Even those who benefited from his kindness did not profit by it: he was coming to the conclusion that one must do good to men by stealth.

Towards the hour of dawn Boufflers fell into a troubled sleep. The sun rose, and dusty sunbeams flickered on his bronzed face and his hair, which was fast turning white. At about six o'clock, his servant, a worthy negress, came to wake him, and said in deplorable French: "How are you this morning?" He replied: "Fairly well, but I did not sleep."

"You haven't slept? No, that's because your thoughts are far away."

But Boufflers' courage and gaiety were hard to extinguish. Yes, in all his trials he was more courageous than Eléonore; man-like, he did not realize how much harder it is for the woman, waiting and hoping, while the man forges ahead, and shapes his own destiny by action. He rose quickly, swallowed his coffee and sang military songs as he performed his toilet. The last thing he did was to put all her letters in a pocket against his heart. "They are angels coming to console Adam, but they are not God." The thought of this great love of theirs would support him throughout the difficult day ahead of him: ". . . Real happiness consists in loving, because we see, speak, and hear one another even in absence; and though we complain a lot, we are less to be pitied than those who do not love at all." Yes, their love, the thought of their marriage, and the union of their souls would restrain his impatient outbursts all day.

It was already getting very hot—hot enough to boil an egg in the sand, or to bake his riding boots until they were as hard as iron. And mosquitoes were buzzing everywhere. With the clatter which was characteristic of his walk, the Chevalier strode noisily into his office, where he knew his desk would be covered with reports and inventories which he could hardly attend to, for all his colleagues would be in the room at the same time. That was the only place they had as yet. At the door he paused and gave an exclamation of amusement: thirty black faces were gazing up in admiration at Eléonore's white portrait, and his French colleagues, who were rather afraid of Boufflers' abounding energy and the enormous demands he made upon them, were smiling in the background.

"*Bonjour, messieurs, bonjour, mes enfants.* Come now, come now quickly, let's settle down to the business of the day. Now what have we here?"

He glanced round expectantly at his subordinates. He scanned them with his shrewd piercing little grey eyes. He'd written to his uncle, the Maréchal of Beauvau, describing them: "Each and all, they are the most agreeable, the most honest, the best fellows in the world." M. Blanchet, "firm and measured," M. Daigremont, "who had several faults which revolted me at first; but in the end I had to recognize his uprightness and frankness; he is a good worker, good at figures, very keen on order, very firm (perhaps a little hard) with his subordinates. And then he is very gay and witty. . . ." M. Marcel, the *greffier*, who had "all the intelligence, all the kindness, and all the nobility that you can imagine". The Director of the Company, "agreeable enough, but too elegant for the country we are living in and for the subordinate position he occupies." M. de Golberry, "full of intelligence, but he reserves it for his conversation; he makes no use of it in his behaviour". M. Thirion, the secretary, not yet twenty years of age, "a charming subject for intelligence, order, exactitude and activity". M. de Cruzel, who commands the battalion, "one of the bravest and worthiest fellows I've ever met".

In short, one gathered that Boufflers enjoyed their company at meals,—for they sat down about twenty to table; but they were not as efficient and untiringly energetic as himself.

Throughout his crowded morning, amid all the noise and hubbub, Boufflers refused admission to none, kept nobody waiting, never exploded like a champagne bottle, and attended to a great deal of affairs. First, there was trouble brewing among the prisoners thrown into jail for looting ships wrecked nearby. Although Boufflers wanted to spare these men, if they restored their spoils, they were being incited to revolt by a nasty little merchant's clerk who stirred them up even against the mercy he tried to show them. Then there was a man whom Boufflers had reinstated as overseer . . . "Corrupt to the very marrow of his bones, touchy, avid for gain, ill-tempered, hard, impertinent, and I'm very much afraid that in a short time I shall be obliged to have it out with him, which would upset me, for this man, whom I have dragged out of the pit, will sink down again into it without any resources. . . ." The others were all for dismissing him, as they thought it had been a great mistake, in the first place, to expect a leopard to change his spots, but Boufflers persuaded them to give him one last chance.

Then there were the repairs to the barracks and the hospital to be seen to: nothing had been done yet. Why not? *Mon Dieu*, the slipperiness and idleness of those natives, only working under the strictest supervision, and then getting through a third of what a French labourer would do in the time. And the hospital, flooded out with men afflicted with tropical ills, with venereal diseases, scurvy and worms. Impossible to do all these repairs without materials, the ship bringing supplies from France was over a month late, and everybody and everything were held up.

Before his midday meal Boufflers had to give orders for his caravan excursion into Goree, ordering the necessary camels, horses and provisions, and making allowances for all that the native servants would pilfer on the way. He was greatly looking forward to this journey as it would be a change from the *tristes sables de Sénégal*. Goree was a land almost beautiful enough for Eléonore, with its "delicious freshness, green meadows, limpid waters, multi-coloured flowers, trees of a thousand shapes, birds of a thousand kinds . . ." How good if, after making a treaty with the local King, he could found a colony of French families there. . . . Boufflers shook himself out of a momentary day-dream and welcomed his secretary who came in to make arrangements about the dinner to be given to the King of Podor. The others did not want the Government plate and silver to be used, and swore it would be stolen; but here again the Chevalier was in favour of treating the King with becoming courtesy and hoping for the best. He even gave orders that the trunks from France be opened, and various gifts selected for him—a scarlet coat braided with gold, ten pieces of blue stuff, a beautifully made gun, a fine pair of pistols, twenty big amber beads, a lovely coral necklace. . . . "And what about the Queen?" "Oh," said Boufflers, "we will give her mirrors, scissors and combs. The ladies and gentlemen of the Court will receive presents according to their rank, and will return the compliment with fleas."

The men in the room burst out laughing. "And they will all stink like a herd of goats," added Boufflers, with a guffaw of boisterous merriment.

(This dinner went off beautifully. Boufflers wrote that the King . . . "was overcome with the order, the magnificence, the politeness and the nobility of the French. . . . He said a thousand times that he'd never seen a white man like myself; and that all his life I would be his best friend . . . and that he would always look on me as his own son.") There was not a coffee-spoon missing!

As the trunks were being searched that morning, Boufflers looked out various gifts for exchange and barter with the natives —little mirrors, little tobacco-boxes full of cloves, gun-powder, red handkerchiefs and faulty guns.

At length, the hour for the noon-day meal appeared. The officers were preparing to add brandy to their water, for it was not too good. Boufflers' entrails were now lacerated by his colic, sweat was pouring down his face, but still he forced himself to add to the gaiety of this meal taken in common. However, he felt very thirsty, and wished he and Eléonore were together, drinking some of the palm-tree wine which he had tasted the other day, but it was only good on the first day. "It is like pleasure, but not the pleasure of which you have the source and the secret. Oh, my pretty palm-tree! When will I drink thy wine?"

He was silent for a moment. In the rush of affairs that morning, he had forgotten "the ejaculatory prayer of one-fifteen", the lovers' Angelus which he and Eléonore had arranged to say at a fixed time together.

After the meal came a short siesta, because of the heat. Boufflers went to his garret, summoned his negress and ordered milk for his colic and a hot foot-bath because it might cure his fever. By late afternoon he washed again, and went out in a canoe on the river, with two horses following in case he wanted to go inland. On the banks the natives were delighted to see him, they did not know how best to entertain him, and what presents to give him: after a while, the canoe was loaded with hens, ducks sheep, and even oxen. The women begged him to come and watch their dance. "A man played on an instrument, the whole assembly clapped its hands, and in turns a dancer would come out, mimicking all the contortions of Mesmer. . . . She came towards me, rolling her eyes, twisting her arms, imitating a thousand little movements which my chaste pen dares not describe to you. . . ." After the ball, Boufflers rewarded them with various presents, and one of the women came up and apologized for not having danced better, but explained that she had just had a baby a fortnight ago. She begged his permission to call the child Boufflers; it was readily given. "It will injure my reputation when I've left the colony," said Boufflers laughingly to one of his men.

When he returned, he had various things to see to before dinner: buying an ostrich for the Duc de Niverna is, a green parrot with a red head for Elzéar, and a yellow parrot for Eléonore, unique among his kind in Africa—a worthy gift to her who was unique amongst her kind. Then followed an uncomfortable half-hour in which he had to threaten an officer with severe penalties for having trafficked in slaves. Boufflers was determined to prevent that kind of thing under his governorship. He did not want to leave to England the glory of the abolition of slavery, and in districts outside his jurisdiction, he bought ransomed slaves himself to give them their freedom. He did not care if, by doing this, he were more out of pocket than ever, but he wished, above all things, to carry out his humane principles, and give bountifully to the colony instead of despoiling it to enrich himself. He dismissed the erring officer with disgust and contempt: "Faugh! All have commercial hearts under an officer's uniform." What an uncomfortable situation. In weariness, his heart turned to Eléonore. "Here I am not so much at my ease as with you:" (he wrote to her) "I have not the same authority over the people around me as I have over you. Here I only represent the King, and with you I *am* the King. *Dieu*! When will I see my pretty kingdom again, my pretty little subject; far away from you I am dethroned; but that won't last long, and the month of September will not go by without our seeing one another again." He scribbled this little note to Eléonore, and ordered a native to take it in his canoe, and, if he had to swim, to put it safely in a bladder tied round his neck. "I wonder whether it will ever reach her?" he sighed wistfully, as he watched the man disappear.

During dinner, Boufflers had an unexpected visitor, who caused universal commotion. "I have just received one of the important local queens who came with a numerous train, which was composed of men only—the queen is as fat as Madame de Clermont. She has two boar's tusks for teeth, and her eyes are shadowed by nasty black grease. I gave her sweetened water, wine, brandy, biscuits; she swallowed everything, and if I'd offered myself, for two pins she'd have swallowed me too." This queen wanted to stay for the night, but this was impossible. After settling her elsewhere, the Chevalier, with a sigh of relief, turned in for the night. He lit his little oil lamp, sharpened his quill, called for more ink—for the heat had dried up the contents of his ink-pot—and, bringing out some of the supply of note-paper which Eléonore had given him before this voyage, he poured out his heart to her in his *Journal*.

What moving love-letters these are! The expressions of his tenderness, his little farewells are never hackneyed: "*Adieu toi*, for thou art prettier and more tender than love itself." . . . "*Adieu* friendship, love, marriage." . . . *chère moitié* . . . *ma tant-aimée*. My Paradise. *Pur amour*. . . .

Here, taken at random, are some extracts from this impassioned *Journal* which travelled in so many lands before it was given to posterity.

"What does it matter whether one is young or old, provided I can live with you; that I see you quite freely; and that at the hour of death I can hold your hand."

"I love you like a father, like a child, like a madman."

"*Adieu*; I kiss you as if you were in my little room; think well about this."

"*Adieu*, love; *adieu*, angel; *adieu*. I kiss you in a way that no angel had ever been kissed, unless there are women angels, and that they are as charming as you."

"When I think of your beautiful soul, of your kind heart, of your frankness, of that lofty spirit . . . and when at the same time, I remember your mischievousness, your follies, your attacks of obstinacy, your fits of temper, I feel I see Hésiode's Venus surrounded by frolicsome naughty little Cupids, but all pretty enough to eat."

"Our life was perhaps empty in the eyes of others, but it was full for us. What other people call affairs, occupations, business, all these are less than nothing. Leisure, and mutual trust and love, and detachment from all things are what really fill the heart."

"Our union, right up to the moment of departure, has been like a delicious season in the year of life. Here is a stormy Summer which will be followed by a rich and bounteous Autumn."

"Let us love life and not fear death, for souls do not die but love for Eternity."

And so, in the quietness of a tropical night, broken by the howling of hyenas, permeated with the smell of the prisoners' corpses in the bay, Stanislas de Boufflers, Governor of Senegal, afflicted with colic and fever, prepared himself for yet more broken sleep in his squalid attic room, by writing to the woman who was his wife in all but name.

CHAPTER XXII

THE ABBÉ BERNARD AND A VISIT TO TRIANON

"It seems to me as if I had chased the devil from my house, I see nothing but laughing faces around me, my children have returned to their natural gaiety, and we feel we are unhappy people who have escaped from a shipwreck."

From a letter of Madame de Sabran.

In the winter of 1786, soon after Boufflers had sailed to Senegal for the second time, Eléonore discovered a terrible plot in her household. No doubt the criminals waited till the Chevalier was safely out of the way. Delphine, aged fifteen, had just returned for good from her convent, but Elzéar, aged twelve, was still studying with his tutor, the quiet and reliable Abbé Bernard, who had been with them now for seven years.

On the morning when Boufflers left France, and she knew now that she would be alone again for many long months, Eléonore lay in her blue bed and tried to muster all her fortitude. She rang for Darnaud her maid and told her to have her children sent up to her. She had engaged an actor to coach them for those amateur theatricals in which they excelled, and which had won such praise from the Queen; she decided to hear them recite their parts. Elzéar always took it all so seriously! He was the more grown-up of the two. Delphine, one of those beautiful little creatures which the Creator sometimes bestows on the world—as the Duchesse d'Abrantès put it—was very frivolous and inconsequent. At Anizy, when Eléonore had held a kind of little academy and given lessons to the children herself, it was always Elzéar who learnt with application. How she had loved asking the advice of Stanislas on their education! Once Delphine had surpassed herself by writing the following delightful letter to him:

"Monsieur le Chevalier,

"It seems a very long while since I have seen you. We are at Anizy where I am enjoying myself very much, 'Bonne Amie',[1]

[1] A dog he had given the children.

ugly as she is, knows how to make everyone love her; all Anizy adores her, including myself, for I love her very much. She is very nice but not nicer than you; I think it would be difficult to be as nice as that. Elzéar is now a big boy; he is with his tutor. He was very sad at being parted from his wife,[1] it made him very ill, but now he is better. I am reading Corneille's tragedies with Mama now. I have read *Polyeucte* and *Cinna*. They amuse me a great deal, because I think them very ridiculous, especially when Émilie says:

"'*Tout beau, ma passion devient un peu moins forte,*'

"And when Polyeucte says to Pauline:

"'*Tout beau, Pauline!*'

"I admit to you that I prefer Voltaire and Racine to Corneille. I hope you will agree with me. Your letter pleased me so much. I hope you will write to me sometimes. My brother sends you his love. Mama has been very ill and has stayed in bed. She sends you her compliments, and is very annoyed because you do not write to her.

"Delphine de Sabran."

Eléonore felt so proud of this little girl, this rose-tree "whose roots held in her heart", as she said. She had taken her to an evening reception at the Polignacs, at Montreuil, and when the Archduke Ferdinand of Austria had spoken to her, she had rushed to the other end of the room like a little wild thing, and everybody had laughed and teased her. And then there was nothing so adorable as Elzéar, particularly when he was telling everyone with grave pride of how the Queen had stood behind his chair at Trianon and served him herself with brioche and cakes after watching him act. And of course he never let you forget that the Queen had said he was the best actor in the world, not excepting Mademoiselle de St. Huberty.

Eléonore sometimes thought it was a pity that she had been obliged to entrust Elzéar's education entirely to the Abbé Bernard. However, that was better than sending him away to the Jesuits. Many noblemen of the day deemed that the Jesuits were too harsh in their discipline, and therefore had their boys educated at home. But many of the tutors were no better than uncouth lackeys who vented on their pupils the *chagrin* of their own failure in life. It was a thankless task. If their pupils did not succeed, the tutors were blamed, if they were brilliant, it was put down to inherited brains.

The abbé was a mysterious being, neither priest nor layman, and Eléonore sometimes wondered uncomfortably whether he felt envious of the ordinary human pleasures which he saw others

[1] His Nanny.

enjoying. Here he was, an ecclesiastic, apparently lacking a vocation for the cure of souls, and yet precluded from taking any part in the life of a normal man, debarred from marriage, ambition, or the possession of a house or land. Was he soured by jealousy of all the gay people who flocked continually into her house? He never showed it, for his manner towards herself was full of discreet deference. Still waters run deep.

The children came in and stood by her bedside; she held out her arms to them, but to her amazement they did not move: they looked constrained and ill-at-ease.

"What is the matter?" she asked.

"Nothing, Mama."

"Don't you want to kiss your mother good morning?"

There was no answer. Feeling both disappointed and irritated, Eléonore dismissed them curtly, and fell again to thinking of Stanislas, far away on the high seas.

For several days after this Eléonore was puzzled by a succession of little things. One morning, paying calls in her coach, she suddenly caught sight of Elzéar sitting all alone in the Tuileries gardens. Rather alarmed, she got out of the coach and went up to him, and asked him what had happened to the Abbé Bernard. Elzéar looked up with a frightened expression in his eyes, and then said quickly, as if he were trying to reassure her: "He will be back in a moment, Mama, I swear. He told me to wait here for him."

"I will stay with you until he comes."

This made Elzéar looked quite alarmed, but he said nothing.

Half an hour later, when the abbé returned, he looked very put out when he saw Madame de Sabran. She said sharply:

"Are you in the habit of leaving your pupil all alone like this in a public place?"

The abbé murmured some excuse about a pressing indisposition, and Eléonore felt it would be indelicate to enquire any further, however great her annoyance.

When she got home she rang for her maid, Darnaud; she did not come. She rang again, and the woman came at last, in a great hurry, and not in the best of tempers. Eléonore asked her to bring the shirt that she had been making that morning for Elzéar, as she wanted to try it on him. Darnaud replied that she had not been able to finish it; did not Madame remember that this morning she had been obliged to go to a shop near the Tuileries and purchase that transparent green gauze ribbon for Madame's new hat?

Eléonore thought no more about it. But several days later more trifles came to vex her—the way Delphine seemed to avoid her, the sight of Elzéar's red eyes and his refusal to say what was the matter, an unexpected absence of the abbé when Eléonore came back from paying calls earlier than she had intended, Darnaud's neglect and forgetfulness about various little things connected with the wardrobe. At length she decided not to question anyone, in case she aroused suspicions, but set herself to watch events very carefully.

One day in late November, she was just coming out of her studio and going upstairs to her bedroom to write in her daily journal to the Chevalier, when Elzéar furtively slipped out of the dining-room and ran upstairs, carrying a letter in his hand. She called him gently, and he gave a start. "Come into my room," she said in a low voice. He looked dismayed, and tried to conceal the letter. When she had brought him into her bedroom she locked the door and said:

"Give me that letter, Elzéar."

"I can't, Mama, the Abbé Bernard entrusted it to me to give to Darnaud."

"Never mind that, Elzéar, you owe obedience to me before anybody else: I am the mistress of this household. I will give the letter to Darnaud myself."

The boy turned deathly pale and started trembling. The letter fell to the floor. Eléonore picked it up, and locking Elzéar into her bedroom she went into her dressing-room and opened the letter.

It was from the Abbé Bernard to his mistress Darnaud, revealing a plot whereby they were both going to poison Elzéar in order to secure the pension which Eléonore had left to the abbé when he had completed his education; they were also planning to poison Darnaud's husband, who was valet to Monseigneur de Sabran, so that they would be free to marry.

Eléonore was so overcome with horror that she sank into a chair in a fainting condition: "Oh, if only Stanislas were here!" However, true to her Spartan training, she mastered her emotions and went to reassure Elzéar. Then, taking him downstairs with her, she slipped into her studio and rang for her butler, a trustworthy fellow who had been in her service many years. She told him in a whisper that he must go out immediately without attracting notice from the other servants, and fetch four police sergeants with handcuffs. He went at once. When he returned and she had sent Elzéar away, Eléonore showed the letter to the sergeants, and explained the circumstances of the case to them.

"It reminds one of La Voisin, doesn't it, Madame," said one of them. "A pity the woman can't be burnt for this."

Then she told the butler to fetch the abbé and Darnaud. They came in at the same time through separate doors. When Darnaud saw the sergeants she gave a terrible start, and made as if to dart out again. But the police were too quick for her: in a moment she was handcuffed. Then she yelled and screamed and abused Eléonore, saying she knew "all the fine carryings-on of this house, and that there were many things that Madame would not like to have proclaimed on the house-tops." As for the abbé, he was very quiet, which was much more terrifying. But as he left, he turned his dark face towards Eléonore and said with a sneer: "In the Bastille I shall doubtless meet Monsieur de Manville, your half-brother, whom you have swindled out of his inheritance, and I shall be able to add to his knowledge of your blameless character." The sergeant gave him a kick in the right place, and the two criminals were taken away.

On December the 4th, Darnaud went to La Force, Bernard to the Bastille. There he spent his time plotting with this reprobate half-brother, who was a son of Eléonore's terrible stepmother. After imprisonment in 1784 for forgery, de Manville had been put in the Bastille for some other very serious offence. Bernard got into touch with him, and the pair of them were going to accuse Madame de Sabran of getting her half-brother into prison in order to secure his property, and, later, of obtaining Bernard's arrest because he knew too much "about all this".

When the two would-be poisoners had gone at last, Eléonore questioned the children, and learned that the abbé had beaten and ill-treated Elzéar, and then frightened him so thoroughly that he did not dare complain. This had gone on for eight years! Also he had tried to put both children against their mother, which had accounted for their general air of constraint. She nearly fell ill with the worry of it all. Later, there was a lawsuit brought by her half-brother—which she won, however. But all the time she was haunted by fear of what her ex-tutor and her ex-maid would do when they left prison. Oh, if only the Chevalier were here to protect her. She tried to master her weariness, and turned her mind to finding a suitable husband for Delphine. She only hoped that the gossip caused by all this would not shock would-be suitors.

The following year Marie-Antoinette was thirty-two, and already the mother of four children. After the necklace scandal, she was living a very retired life at Trianon, where the houses of the miniature village had now been completed. One can picture her entertaining Eléonore and her two children on a mild February afternoon in 1787, the year of Delphine's marriage to Armand de Custine.

The Queen received them on the terrace of her little château, dressed in a toque and rich furs and carrying an enormous muff. She turned from scolding one of the page-boys and greeted

Madame de Sabran: "Ah, Comtesse, I thought it would be pleasant to walk in the *Hameau*, I want you to see my snow-drops. *Bonjour*, Delphine, Ah, and here is my little Elzéar. And has Delphine lost all her shyness? The Comte d'Artois tells me she was quite charming at Bagatelle. Madame Elizabeth will accompany the children, and then we will all come home again for a collation. You've no idea what trouble that naughty page has been giving me. Do you know, yesterday he slipped into the stables and let a wild boar out into the streets of Versailles, and every dog in the town got to know, and there was a chaotic boar-hunt in Versailles. It was all very dangerous, and so many poor people were knocked down by this avalanche of dogs. Those pages always imagine that they can be naughty with impunity."

"I'm sure he is very penitent, *Madame*." Eléonore felt sorry for the culprit, who hung his head and looked thoroughly ashamed of himself. She always rather liked the pages, for at the Royal balls they made themselves uncommonly useful, fetched stools and refreshments for everyone in spite of the big crowds around the buffet, saw that the carriages were summoned in time, and managed everything with an air of deftness and elegance mingled with a spice of youthful impertinence which would have delighted Bennozo Gozzoli.

The gardens of Petit Trianon in February! The Queen walked with a lovely, majestic movement, carrying her head high, and occasionally bringing her lorgnettes to her blue eyes, for she was short-sighted. They strolled along the winding alleys of the English garden, under the bare elms, their winter tracery so beautiful against the tender sky. In the far distance, the Temple of Love rose out of a faint blue-grey mist, encircled by its winding stream, now covered with dead leaves. The Queen stopped and picked an aconite.

"Is there anything so innocent as the first wild flower?" she said. "Do you know, this gives me more pleasure than the rarest hot-house bloom. But you must really come here again in May: yes, I think my little Trianon is at its best in May. The Baronne d'Oberkirch was in raptures when she went for a walk here very early in the morning, during the Russian visit. Oh, the delicious stroll; picture these thickets full of scented lilac, and tuneful nightingales. The air is heavy with perfumed mists and the butterflies flutter about with their golden wings in the rays of the Spring sunshine."

And so the two Mothers, whose tastes were so similar, walked and talked about the pleasures of country life, of flowers and of how to bring up children. Marie-Antoinette was the first Queen of France who had refused to hand over her babies entirely to the scores of women of the household. She tried to train the characters of the children, supervised their health, and often brought them to Trianon, so that they would benefit by the freedom from constraint and the rambling walks. Turning to Eléonore, she said: "How dreadful for Queen Marie-Leczinska when the Cardinal de Fleury sent all her little girls away for many years to the Convent of Fontevrault."

Eléonore told the Queen how she had learned dancing from *Mesdames*' dancing master who loved to repeat the anecdote of the "Blue minuet". The conversation then passed naturally to these Royal aunts. Eléonore gathered that they made life quite unbearable for the Queen. Was it to be wondered at? They were the most pampered, frustrated spinsters in the kingdom, and for all their piety, madly jealous of their beautiful Austrian relation. Even when Madame Louise left her roof-gardens and her coral parakeets to become a Carmelite, she was still, according to the Queen, "the greatest little intriguer in Europe". Eléonore reflected that a woman never really ceases to be herself, whether she is clothed in silver panniers or brown sackcloth. But as she wanted to be charitable she said:

"But, *Madame*, the Carmelite rule is full of mortifications, and it needs heroism to endure them."

"Yes, indeed," replied the Queen, "and do you know which mortification she found the hardest?"

"No, *Madame*."

"Walking downstairs without an equerry to hold her hand. Ah, well, when you consider that even in the Palace she always went everywhere in a sedan-chair."

Elzéar and Delphine were enjoying themselves in the company of Madame Elizabeth. This young sister of the King's, a real Bourbon, with a fine nose and imperious ways, was very fond of children. She showed them the Queen's theatre, with its blue velvet seats and its miniature dressing-rooms, and then the Belvedere where a gardener had just lit a brazier on the many-coloured mosaic floor, so that the wall paintings would not be injured by the damp. In there, she pointed out all the painted fantasies on the walls, a squirrel nibbling fruit, a monkey trying to catch fish in a crystal vase, a duck-hunt. It was such fun picking out the various emblems which have now, alas, faded so much with neglect. When they reached the *Hameau*, she showed them the little model dairy of the Queen: everything was elegant there, from the butter-dishes and plates of the finest porcelain decorated with the initials M.A. to the dairy woman herself, who was dressed in the great white muslin aprons which distinguished the servants of good houses, and which it became so unsafe to wear as the Revolution gathered pace.

The woman curtseyed to Madame Elizabeth, who told her that she must come to Montreuil and meet her rival in butter-making. This girl, declared the princess, made the most delicious butter, and she had a fresh pot every morning for her breakfast. Madame Elizabeth who was the fairy godmother of the little village of Montreuil, distributed her special milk every day to ailing children, and kept a dispensary for the sick at her door.

Then they all talked with the little families in the thatched cottages of the model village around the lake. These people cultivated gardens and ploughed fields, pruned trees and brought donkeys to the mill. The scene was picturesque and animated. There was a gardener going to work with a spade on his shoulder, a pretty girl looking for eggs near the bushes, and then feeding the ducks on the pond. The Queen knew each family individually, and was greatly interested in the lives of these simple people so far removed from herself. She had a kind word for everyone. "Look," she said, pointing laughingly to the bailiff, "I had to scold him last year, for he used to hide eggs under the bushes, to give me the pleasure of finding them. I assured him I disliked artificial surprises."

Eléonore smiled, and said: "*Madame*, it is like Cleopatra, who got a diver to hook a kipper on to Antony's line one day."

After a while, the sun sank behind the cottages, the West flushed rosy-red against the black branches; heralds of Spring, blackbirds and thrushes sang Vespers with joyous abandon. Picking snowdrops as they walked, the members of the party all went back for a collation at Petit Trianon. Is there not a superstition that to bring snowdrops into the house means Death? Who was to know that Madame Sophie, the Queen's youngest baby girl, was to die in the June of that year at the age of eleven months, foreshadowing by her death some of the griefs which were to fall on the unhappy Queen with each succeeding month?

They had cups of hot vanilla chocolate with whipped cream on top, very Viennese, and as the Queen sat by her work-table, doing some embroidery—for she was never idle—she begged Madame Elizabeth to read an extract on Trianon from the poem "On Gardens", by Eléonore's Latin tutor, the Abbé Delille:

"O, you who fear Love's power,
Flee away, flee away! Love is the life-giving spirit
  of these lovely haunts;
In this delicious little valley,
Love is in the very air you breathe.
The gentle twilight of these narrow paths,
These mossy seats, this solitary cavern,

These perfumed thickets full of mystery,—
All speak of Love, all breathe of pleasure
Under the lilacs, whose drooping branches
Temper the heat of noon-day.
From a little hill-top, a hidden spring
Falls in a cascade and disappears amid the flowers.

I draw near; what do I see? On the yielding grass
The scattered flowers from a bouquet,
And, still untouched by the wind's breath,
Two initials interlaced in the sand."

As Madame Elizabeth read, the Queen dropped her tambour frame and gazed sadly out of the window into the dusk. Was she dreaming of one, whose Christian name began with the same initial as her own? He, too, had loved these haunts, once upon a time. As she thought of his loyal devotion, and of his face grave beyond his years, her eyes filled with tears.

As Eléonore pictured the "solitary cavern" of the poem, she thought of a morning in May, and of the cavern in the woods of Anizy well-nigh six years ago, to which her beloved one had led her.

A faint sigh escaped her. The Queen dabbed her eyes with a little handkerchief and quickly took up her needle and silks. Recalling that the Abbé Delille was a friend of Madame de Sabran's and of the Chevalier's, she enquired kindly: "And what is the charming Chevalier de Boufflers going to bring back from Senegal this time?"

Eléonore was startled. "Can she read my thoughts, I wonder?"

Elzéar interrupted the game of Solitaire he was playing with the Queen's older children, and coming up to her, he said: "*Madame*, *I* know, for he told me! He is going to bring back a little negress for the Maréchale de Beauvau, a hen for my uncle the Bishop, and an ostrich for the Duc de Nivernais. There will be some little monkeys for Monsieur de Poix, a green parrot with a red head for me, and for your Majesty a parakeet whom he is *specially* training to talk Senegalese and French with equal fluency, and this parrot will say: 'Where is the Queen? I want to see her. Here she is! Ah, isn't she beautiful. I want to see her always, always!'"

CHAPTER XXIII

JOURNALS AND LETTERS OF THE LOVERS

I

EXTRACTS from the *Journal* of the Comtesse de Sabran during the first journey of the Chevalier de Boufflers to Senegal. (The first entry is February 15th, 1785.)

June 16, 1786.

I dreamt of you last night, my dear husband; you were in a good temper, which does not happen often with you in my dreams. . . . We'd hardly been alone together for a moment when a crowd of importunates, those accursed importunates, who, as you well know, in happier times put me on the rack, came in by all the doors; then you disappeared like a flash of lightning, and I woke up.

[On June 16th, 1786, Eléonore went to a fête at Bagatelle given by the Comte d'Artois, and at the end there were illuminations in the style of Trianon which were a wonderful success.] The weather was very mild and the night almost as beautiful as one of your nights in Senegal. In that charming Paradise, I imagined myself transported to the Elysian fields, and I felt my soul take flight by degrees and free itself imperceptibly from this wretched husk which causes it so much suffering. The sight of that beautiful azure vault where so many worlds, so many suns were shining, made me appear so small in my own eyes, that, steeped in admiration and a sense of unworthiness, I said within myself: what am I in this vast universe, and what right have I to complain when nothing in it works according to my wishes. . . .

You are no doubt surprised, and with good reason, that in the midst of so many pleasures and distractions, I had the leisure to make such wise and profound reflections; but you know me, and you know how easily I can cut myself off from a crowd of people, however large, to give myself up to silence, to shed the painful necessity of listening and answering.

June 19, 1786.

Here at last I am alone with my own company, or rather, alone with my friend; my house is filled with memories of him; my room, my garden, my library, my pavilion, all recall moments which were very sad and very sweet. . . .

Adieu. I did not know what it was to love when I gave you my heart; if I had really known, I would have resisted so dangerous an emotion till death.

June 23, 1786.

I spent part of the day alone, like a wandering shade in my garden. By ingrained force of habit which an absence of eight months has not yet been able to destroy, every moment, I thought I heard your footsteps following me, and your voice called me as in the old days, when you came towards me looking glad.

June 28.

Va. I feel towards you as I did on the first day. Only death can separate soul and body. You are my soul: I cannot exist without you or without loving you more than anyone in the whole world.

August 17.

(She has just heard the news of his return.) I feel within myself something like a storm which plays havoc with all my thoughts; I am like a woman who is blind and deaf; I tremble in all my limbs. . . .

II

Extracts from Madame de Sabran's *Journal* during the Chevalier's second voyage to Senegal.

January 22nd, 1787.

Death is in my heart to-day, in the place of love. I spent my day in a kind of agony, and I don't think I ever remember being so sad, not even at the moment of our farewells. I would have given all I possess so that I could be freed from this horrible life.

May 7.

I left Anizy without regret; my heart was oppressed there by a thousand painful memories which hurt me a great deal. I was put into a room next door to the one which you occupied, which only vexed me still more. I have completely given up my old suite; the bishop has taken possession of it, as he thinks it more convenient, and he has already had it arranged in a very agreeable manner; he will give up his room to me, which I like much more because it will remind me less of you, and it is gayer and drier.

May 8.

(Concerning Time) I feel with every passing day the work of his treacherous hand on my mind as on everything else; I look at things in a different way, *everything tires me, nothing moves;* it is the reverse side of the medal. I'm afraid my temper will become morose ("*chagrine*"). Often I do violence to myself in order not to show most people the disgust with which they inspire me, and not to censure everything I meet.

May 15.

Here I am in Saint-Amand in the prettiest little house in the world, and in the wildest scenery. Nothing but fields full of bright flowers, little cottages scattered about, refreshing to the eye, and all the company you meet is composed of pretty little sheep and young shepherds, more picturesque than our modern shepherds, crowned with lilac, eating large slices of very black bread covered with very white cheese, or else singing in chorus the naïve charms of their shepherdesses. Knowing my taste for pastoral life, for fields, for repose, you can imagine how all that enchants me; it has all made me feel light-hearted again. I've been walking all day, and at the moment I'm just out of my bath; it is midnight; for, unlike others, *I prefer to bathe at this hour rather than in the morning* because of my children, whom I should lose sight of for too long. The bath, like the rest, reflects the simplicity of the place; it is a wretched barrel sunk in the earth, but covered with a very clean sheet; a little cloth-covered bed of which the curtains have only half the ordinary width; and small faggots of brushwood which crackle and give a brilliant little flame which resembles your wit in its happy moments.

May 19, 1787.

I went day-dreaming all the afternoon in a little wood enamelled with flowers. Never before had the weather been so beautiful, nor the nightingale so amorous; he nearly deafened me with his singing. Guess if you can of whom I was dreaming, and name yourself if you dare, and you won't be mistaken. It is the first time, perhaps, since your sin, that is to say since your desertion, that I let myself go without too much difficulty, to this perfidious sweetness; but the opportunity was so unique, the trees so green, the solitude so agreeable, I found that only you were missing to make it completely after my own heart. *You*, then; I mustn't say that any longer; it is your idea only, (not yourself that I shall see) for I am no longer allowed to hope that we shall ever find ourselves again as in the old days, both of us alone, walking through the woods, climbing up the rocks either on foot or on horseback, laughing, singing, free from all cares, from all plans, thinking only of the present, regretting only the day which was going too quickly, longing only for the morrow, and, with mutual consent, forgetting the universe. This cruel ambition which possesses you at present, which is the enemy of all real joy, of all delicate feelings, of peace, of happiness, of repose, etc. will not leave you until death. You have sacrificed me to it; you will sacrifice yourself to it, and, for the first time, you will be *constant*—through this fatal law by which man only clings feverishly to the thing which tortures him. . . .

May 29, 1787.

This afternoon, an officer visited me, well burnt, well roasted, coming straight from Senegal, to bring me three birds from you, and a pipe which unfortunately he broke on the way, and of which only a few bits remain, hardly worthy of appearing even in my wretched little cabinet. . . .

That gentleman confirmed what you told me about your health. We talked a lot about you, and to prolong the pleasure, I begged him to stay to dinner. He seemed delighted to be in this country, and thinks of nothing else but of how he can remain here as long as possible, which gave me a good opinion of him.

July 5.

[A cousin of the Dauphin of Cochin China came to visit Eléonore, and when she attempted to greet him with a kiss he backed with great dignity, as if gravely affronted. He was seven years old, wore flowing golden robes, and had been to visit the Queen.] "That miserable hideosity from Cochin China, after leaving the table, went to open the cage-door of my little birds from Senegal. They had put them near the window to give them some air. They didn't have to be told twice; directly they saw the open door, they took flight: only two, and they were the most beautiful ones, the big partridge with the red collar and a little one with the doe's breast and black wings. But listen to this example of constancy, of which you surely would not be capable. There was in the cage a little *cordon bleu* which remained in spite of the bad example of his companions. That one will be my favourite for ever . . .

. . . You always give me presents so unwillingly, you experience such regrets at giving to me what would give pleasure to others, that I would rather do without and not cause you that little annoyance."

III

Delphine's Wedding, and a walking Tour as recounted in Eléonore's Journal.

Just then, after interminable negotiations, the marriage contract of Eléonore's daughter with Armand de Custine was being signed at Versailles. So she took her two children for a picnic to Meudon, to celebrate. After that, they all went to Anizy to prepare for the wedding.

July 31, 1787.

The wedding day of my daughter. . . .

. . . Just as he (the bridegroom) was leaving Paris, he was seized with such an appalling toothache that he thought he ought not to leave without having the bad tooth out; otherwise he would have had it against his wife on their wedding day, for love, in spite of all its power, cannot overcome pain. [The dentist tore away a piece of his jaw with the tooth.] . . . He arrives in this state with his sorry-looking family. . . . I offer them breakfast, they only needed rest, they all go to bed, and I go to my room to recover from this unpleasant surprise. . . . My poor Delphine was in no better state, fear had given her the shivers. All night I had put her in my bed to warm her up, and we hadn't slept a wink. Without instructing her exactly about the new state that she was going to embrace, I had sought to dispose her in such a way as to avoid a shock which is inevitable when one is taken unawares. She was doubly agitated, embarrassed, and the news of the arrival disconcerted her completely. We spent three hours in this disagreeable condition, crouching on our bed, without thinking of getting up. In the end, a look at our clock got us up, the wedding was due for one o'clock, it was already eleven; we had to get her up to dress, to adorn her beautifully in order to appear to greater advantage in the eyes of her future husband. . . . Everything was ready at one o'clock, and in great state and the gloomiest silence we reached the bishop's chapel,—I, holding my daughter by the hand, followed by my young son-in-law and his father. Never has my heart beat so violently as at the moment when I left her on the *prie-dieu*, where she was to say that famous "yes" which, once uttered, can be unsaid no more, however much one may sometimes wish it. My own "yes" made less impression on me, and yet what a difference! I was marrying an infirm old man of whom I was to be less the wife than the sick-nurse, and she a young man full of charm and goodness. But in those days I little realized the consequences; everything seemed good to me, equally good; as I loved nothing, everything seemed to me worthy of love, and I felt for my good old husband the same feeling as for my father and my grandfather—a very tender feeling that at that time satisfied my heart. Time has undeceived me now, and, moreover, I believe no longer in happiness. And so through all the Mass I shed a flood of tears. I do not know what people must have thought of me, but I was too overcome to control myself. My Delphine did not weep, but her little face grew longer, and her husband didn't look very sure of himself, either. The bishop preached a sermon full of reason and feeling, which touched everyone. Elzéar held the canopy, and, as he was too small, he was put up on a chair of the chapel, and looked like one of the little angels in the Annunciation of the Virgin.

The ceremony was over, Monsieur de Custine, the father, took possession of my daughter and I of his son, and we went out in the same order and with the same solemnity with which we had come. We went to the drawing-room, where a very good lunch awaited us. . . .

After lunch we walked down into the garden, and as we arrived there a troop of shepherds and shepherdesses, headed by the bailiff, came to compliment the married couple, and each one sang his little couplet as in the *Amoureux de quinze ans*,—it was very touching. After that, we danced quite informally, like simple folk, and the village fiddlers played. I opened the Ball with Monsieur de Custine, the father, and my children, and never, I assure you, have I felt so nimble or danced with such zest. The songs and dancing lasted all day—it was enough to make one die of laughing. Some of the songs were rather original, particularly the carpenter's, who, no doubt, is a descendant of the famous Adam. He had used a ream of paper to make what he called the "brouillard"[1] and it was four pages long—we thought we should never get to the end of it. He stood on a chair so that we should hear him better, which made the fête look exactly like Tenier's pictures. When we were tired of dancing we played at *pharaon*; the men made a bank, which amused us till supper-time—that is to say, till eight o'clock. The bishop gave a splendid feast, with his usual magnificence. It lasted a long time; then we played *pharaon* again; but afterwards came, *le vrai quart d'heure de Rabelais*. I assure you that when I had to lead the bride to bed, I trembled, and was as embarrassed as she was—old though I am. One day, by my chimney corner, I will tell you about this little scene, to make you laugh, for I was obliged to prompt the father, so that he in turn should prompt his son, and never in my life have I felt so foolish—I believe I shall be quite red to-morrow.

Aug. 1.

It is eight o'clock in the morning; everybody is asleep in the château except myself, and I am dying with impatience to have news of my poor Psyche; I hope that, like her, she was more frightened than hurt, and I can think only of her embarrassment

[1] He meant, "brouillon"=rough copy. Brouillard=fog.

which will be extreme, when she will appear before all the eyes fixed on her. . . .

[*Later.*] *Eh bien*, my friend, my little nest is doing wonderfully well. Love is not as unkind as one thinks; it is a pretty little monster which does not bite or scratch, and my Delphine, except for a modest blush which enhances the brilliance of her charms, seems unchanged. I have only time to give you news of her and of myself, for I have a thousand and one things to see to.

Aug. 2.

[About a fête given by the Bishop of Laon at Barthois, in honour of the wedding.] I have never in my life seen anything more agreeable. Monsieur le Clerc had illuminated all that charming Elysium with covered lanterns as at Trianon, which glowed so gently and created such delicate shadows, that the water, the trees, the people, all appeared ethereal. The moon also wished to join in the fête, although she had not been invited; but her silvery and uncertain glow, far from obscuring her, lent her added charms, and she was reflected in all her fullness in the immense expanse of water which you know. She would have filled the most heedless with dreams and softened the most hardened heart. Music, songs; a crowd of very gay, contented peasants followed us about everywhere, and scattered all over the place, so that it was a sight for sore eyes. At the bottom of the wood, in the most solitary spot, was a little cabin, a house both humble and chaste; curiosity spurred us to look at it, and we found Philemon and Baucis, bent by the weight of years, and supporting each other as they came towards us. . . .

[Then Eléonore refers to herself as "thy widow".]. . . .

Her heart was breaking as she realized that she could never taste that happiness, the only happiness for which she had been born, and that, instead, she was condemned by you to live a thousand leagues away from you, with nothing to alleviate that terrible destiny.

Aug. 4.

I am very anxious this morning; my little woman had a temperature. I think it was only caused by shock; in spite of that I'm upset because she has never been ill; her young husband is quite downcast, and looks so guilty that I feel very much tempted to scold him; but I daren't, for he would have the right to ask me why I was interfering.

Aug. 5.

I spent all day yesterday, and all night by my daughter's side; she had rather a high temperature, pains in the back and a very bad headache. [Eléonore was afraid of smallpox.]

Aug. 7.

I can't resist describing to you the fête which Elzéar and I gave to-day to the young couple—the funniest, the most original, the most ridiculous. It was a version of the marriage of Gamache. The bishop wanted to give a dinner to all his peasants, and we snatched this opportunity which suited our subject perfectly. In the garden in front of the château, tables were set, abundantly supplied with legs of mutton, pâtés, young turkeys, etc. The little Peinier girl and her brother took the parts of bride and bridegroom. They came followed by an enormous crowd, to the sounds of a violin leading the way; then they sat down to table; whilst they were there, troups of shepherdesses came out of the wood, to sing several bad couplets which we had composed, Elzéar and I, in honour of the bride; and from another side appeared a troop of shepherds who had come to pay their compliments to the bridegroom. They all sat down to table, and it was a pleasure to see them eat.

[Then Eléonore describes the appearance of two peasants disguised as Don Quixote and Sancho Panza, and how the latter fell off his donkey, which made everybody die of laughing. After various frolics and a huge feast, the whole company was taken in donkey-carts to Pinon for an outdoor ball.]

How you would have contributed to the pleasure of that little fête by your wit and your gaiety. What pretty couplets you would have composed instead of all our silly nonsense, and how your poor widow could have been happy and contented. . . .

Aug. 13.

[After returning to the bridal pair from a short absence.]

I found my two little turtle doves billing and cooing in the prettiest manner imaginable. I assure you they had no need of me at all; however, they were charmed to see me again, for they love me dearly.

Aug. 23, 1787.

You will think me mad if I tell you that I've never been so happy as I am since I came here, but happy beyond any words. For the first time I see realized all the day-dreams on happiness that I'd had all my life. A good mother of a family (Madame de Pouilly) surrounded by eight children whom she had fed herself, all plump, fat, and as fresh as can be, with nothing to do but think about them and about a husband she loves tenderly *and who never leaves her*. They pass their days quietly alone, are sufficient unto themselves without fearing that importunates, malicious people and *mistresses* come to disturb so gentle a union: solitude, trust and love shelter them from those fearful scourges. They've loved one another for twenty years. . . .

We went to have lunch at a little farm which is three quarters of a league from the château. We found a very clean farmer's wife, good, plump, well-fed children, a nice fresh room for us to rest in, and a good lunch of milk, cream, butter, cheese *pâtés* and ham. . . . Heat never bothers me, it is the cold which I detest. . . . I have just dined as well as I have breakfasted. And at five o'clock Madame Pouilly and I set out to dance with our children till nine o'clock in the evening, . . . dancing as if we were fifteen: never had I felt so light and so gay. That kind and charming woman cannot get over her surprise at finding me so different from what she had imagined, for she thought I would be a "fine lady from Paris", very overdressed, full of grand airs and pretentions. Mutual confidence is so well established between us, that she confessed to me how much she dreaded me before our meeting. We've only been together for twenty-four hours, and I like her so much that I felt as greatly at my ease with her as if I had always known her.

. . . I don't know what's coming over me, I find it harder than ever to leave you; it's really ridiculous after ten years of love, four years of marriage, and two years of absence. [Written in 1787, this is the only passage which gives us a clue of the year when Eléonore became Boufflers's mistress. The exact date, May 2, is mentioned in another letter.]

Sept. 2. (St. Maurice).

[She writes from an inn near the Vosges mountains at seven o'clock at night. She, Delphine and Armand are all going to bed early, so as to rise at one in the morning and climb a mountain in time to see the dawn from the top.] You know that in this kind of expedition I seem to be endowed with unusual strength, and especially when it's a case of losing myself on the heights, and of getting away for several moments from this wicked little earth, where so many things make me sad!

Sept. 3, 1787.

(Here, Eléonore describes the wonderful walk in the Vosges. She speaks of "the soul of nature" in a manner prophetic of Wordsworth.)

. . . The moon shone with her gentlest radiance, among numberless stars full of sparkling fires. The silence of the night, broken only by the sound of waters falling from rocks, and the light breeze which gently stirred the pine leaves, that uncertain light which lit the sleeping world and revealed to us precipices or laughing mountain heights and the roofs of chalets at intervals filled my soul with a calm that I have never experienced before. . . . I felt in myself something better which raised me up and made me a part of this whole creation—the soul of nature. . . .

At about three o'clock in the morning we reached the summit . . . my two little lovers sat next to each other, and so near, so near, in the shelter of love, that they warmed each other easily; but I, poor widow, I shivered in my little corner, and I reached such a pitch of suffering that, not being able to bear it any more, I busied myself by picking dry branches and cutting all the bushes to try and light a fire with them, which gave me a lot of trouble. In the end I succeeded, and it was perfect enjoyment.

All this time, the lovely dawn was heralding the appearance of the sun for our pleasure and sowing his path with topazes and rubies; in the midst of these the morning star was shining. Gradually the sun appeared before us like a globe of fire. And in a few moments sprang out a fiery glow of light, so dazzling that the eye could no longer gaze at it, and before which I was tempted to bow down in admiration. What brilliance! What majesty!

(Then she describes how they drank milk in a mountain chalet, and ate fresh butter and excellent cheese.) It was then that I thought of you; how you would have done honour to this frugal meal and filled your poor wife with joy. I could almost hear you, and see you laughing with those great guffaws which I loved so much, and saying in one instant a thousand pretty things, the one more "piquante" than the last, inspired by the mountain air, the liberty and simplicity of the place.

(Then she walked home with her son-in-law, climbing up perilous goat paths. When they got back to the inn she had been twenty-four hours afoot, and all on a little milk and cheese.)

Oct. 29 (Anizy).

The bishop left this morning for Paris. He was all for my staying here several days with my children, and that gives me great pleasure, for now we are entirely free. We began by walking more than a league this morning, across woods and fields, my two sons were leaping about like two roebucks, they jumped over ditches and brooks, competing with each other, but their success made them lose their bearings and they finished up by causing us to lose our way, and getting very muddy, which as you well know, often happens in the neighbourhood of Anizy. . . . Oh, why am I not there any longer, or why can't I have the happiness of being drenched in your tears and dying in your arms.

Nov. 7.

Oh, vanity of vanities, all is vanity, save loving you and serving you. Solomon goes one better than that; but you are my God, I know no other. If I had suffered for another the thousandth part of what I have suffered for you, I would be assured of Paradise with the palm of martyrdom. No doubt I've made a bad choice, for I have given my allegiance to a master who is casual, capricious, who cannot see in the depths of my heart all the tenderness I feel for him, nor can he measure it by his own, and whose reward is to abandon me to all my weakness at the moment when I most need support and consolation. . . . My folly is such that I would prefer the griefs you cause me to all the pleasures which one could taste in this world and the next.

Nov. 11.

I spent the day walking with my children, in a push cart or on foot, in the neighbourhood of that little château where we walked once by moonlight and which resembles a fairy castle. How you loved me then, and what patience you had for my fears on horseback, my caprices and my follies. With so much care and kindness, joined with so much charm, how could I fail to love you boundlessly?

Nov. 12.

(How she receives his letters.) I gaze at my treasure and hardly dare to touch it. I examine the address, I look at each one of the letters to know if you were in a hurry as you wrote it, and what you were thinking of; I come to the seal, and I see that you did not use mine nor my device; that hurts me rather, I tremble, I hardly dare to break the seal; . . . my heart thumps and I end by giving way, in case some importunate person might come to deprive me of appeasing my curiosity. Once the packet is opened, I begin by the last letter, as the date is the most recent. I imagine I'm reading, but I daren't read, I am so troubled; my eyes fill with tears, and the packet on my knees is all wet. Each page is kissed separately; but I read them with the same fear and the same precautions with which one would touch a razor. . . . It takes me twenty-four hours to know what they contain . . . and when I see you downcast and suffering, I turn over the page very quickly to see if you are the same on the next page.

Nov. 19.

(Again Eléonore indulges in a day dream of rustic happiness.) Can't you see me, on my threshold, singing, turning my spinning-wheel, with a very white little cap, in a very short little skirt, in a very clean little room, where you could be received like a king each time you had the fancy of coming to visit your poor widow.

(Boufflers returned to France the following month, at the end of December, and the lovers were re-united on New Year's Day of 1788. He had come back for good. One is glad that he was not away at this troublous time, on the eve of the Revolution. It is easy to picture her joyous welcome of him, and her delight that he would not be leaving her again.)

CHAPTER XXIV

THE LAST PARTY AT THE CHÂTEAU OF SAINT-OUEN AND A PROPHETIC CHANGE IN THE FASHIONS

JUST before his arrival from Africa, Boufflers wrote the following letter to his sister, Madame de Boisgelin (who incidentally hated Eléonore, and who, during those first awful months of silence had tantalized her by flourishing his letters in her face).

"Listen, my Boisgelin; I arrive Tuesday evening in the vessel of a corsair who was shipwrecked and saved only himself. I know that I have in Paris neither shirt, nor powder, nor pomade, nor carriage, nor horses, nor money, nor credit. Arrange that I may find everything I shall need; borrow two or three shirts with lace ruffles. I think I have some coats so I shall not need your dresses—all the rest will get on as best it can. . . ."

A yellow parrot that he had destined for Eléonore died on the homeward journey; so when he was with her at last on New Year's day, 1788, he told her, laughingly, that he had nothing to bring her but a husband.

Alas, even this was not so. He might just as well have remained in France all that time, instead of inflicting those cruel months of separation on the woman he loved. He was still penniless. How could he have amassed riches, when he was always restoring slaves to freedom by paying for them out of his own pocket? He blamed Eléonore for having inspired him with these humanitarian principles. However, she resigned herself to the inevitable.

A horrible fortune-teller whom she had consulted in his absence, told Eléonore that she would eventually marry him and bear him a lovely child. Otherwise it all seemed rather hopeless. The years were flying by. Delphine was married, and already expecting her first child. Eléonore was now thirty-eight, the Chevalier forty-nine. And so the hated life of subterfuge was resumed, with its few stolen meetings, its constant need for Stoic self-command and reserve when the lovers happened to meet in society. Boufflers became the rage of fashionable country houses directly he returned; all the drawing-rooms were disputing the privilege of entertaining him, of listening to him, so bronzed and manly, as he spoke of the people of Africa and of his detestation of the slave-trade. At that time, Boufflers, in common with many nobles of his day, was being swept away by generous humanitarian ideals. He seemed gradually to leave the old life of pleasure behind him and live in the hope of seeing the dawn of a new social era.

Amidst all the flux and surging up of misguided enthusiasms, there was still a strong côterie of the disciplined and reasonable. It is difficult to convey this atmosphere of exquisite courtesy in a vanished century: it was greatly made up of a belief that there was an exact correspondence between elegance of manners and nobility of thoughts. It was fostered by a Spartan training through which men and women learned the secret of living in outward harmony with their fellow-beings, masking their boredoms and dislikes by smiles, suppressing any desire to become a centre of attention, bringing out the social gifts of others by making them feel at their best, never monopolising the conversation, but deftly keeping the shuttlecock in movement by imperceptible touches, knowing, by a turn of the head, by a raised eyebrow, by a slight movement of a fan, how to dismiss a subject or suppress unsuitable curiosity or indiscretion. And, above all, gaiety, *joie de vivre*, originality. . . .

In the summer of 1787, their friend the old Duc de Nivernais gave a great party at Saint-Ouen in honour of Prince Henry of Prussia. Eléonore and Boufflers went to it. Talleyrand's famous phrase about the eighteenth century has so often been misquoted. What he really said was: "He who has not lived in the eighteenth century, has never known the *pleasure* of living." The last glimpses of this pleasure were to be seen at Saint-Ouen that day. This party was one of the last great social events of the century, and it had the feverish brilliance that attends decline. The Duc de Nivernais was a Mancini, with all the exquisitely refined tastes of an Italian. His palate was so keen that he could distinguish the right leg of a chicken from the left, and his manners so perfect that Lord Chesterfield held him up as a pattern to his son. (Since he had lived in London as ambassador to England, the Duc de Nivernais had always maintained pleasant relations with England. Horace Walpole, for one, was delighted with his translation of his Essay on Gardens). He was old, now, but in his day had acted on the Pompadour's private stage. His hobbies were designing gardens, amateur theatricals, Latin verse and polite conversation. He was devoted to Boufflers, with whom he had arguments about "the gentlest art", during which the Chevalier used to lose his temper furiously, and go out banging the door. Boufflers sent him sheep from his own estate to put in the park at Saint-Ouen, and a friend, looking at them one day, said: "Goodness, and to think that not one of these rascals is *tender!*"

It was to the Duc's care that Boufflers confided Eléonore during his absence in Africa. In that miniature society where everybody was connected, either by blood or by marriage, the Duc de Nivernais' son-in-law, the Duc de Cossé-Brissac, achieved unhappy notoriety, by being one of the last lovers of Madame du Barry. He was torn to pieces by the Versailles mob in September, 1792; some street boys cut off his mutilated head and took it on a pike to nearby Louveciennes where the du Barry lived. They rolled it into the drawing-room through the French window on the ground floor.[1]

A most humane landowner, the Duc would have shuddered, on that summer day in 1787, had he guessed what was in store, not only for his own son-in-law, but for so many of his guests!

The Duc had invited all kinds of interesting people to meet Prince Henry of Prussia,—important members of the Academy, generals, ministers, famous artists, painters, sculptors and musicians and some of the most charming women of the Court. The guests were seated at four different tables in such a way that the laws of precedence were kept. Cross-eyed Prince Henry of Prussia sat next to Madame Vigée Lebrun, and raved to her in his German accent, about Eléonore's "grandeur of soul", and vowed that he would have replicas of her portrait distributed all over Paris—an embarrassing attention.

After the meal, which was, as usual, at two o'clock, everybody went to take the air on the magnificent terrace of the château overlooking the Seine; there etiquette disappeared and individual groups were formed. One can picture Boufflers walking with Eléonore and the bride Delphine, whose reputation for beauty was beginning to turn all heads. Perhaps they went to that wood which the Duc had filled with birds, enclosing them with a wire so fine as to be almost invisible, so that they had all the illusion of freedom. Freedom! That word went straight to peoples' heads in those days ("Man is born free, and is everywhere in chains"). Boufflers was not exempt from the general fever, and he talked excitedly to Eléonore about ballooning and revolutions. Unfortunately he believed too blindly in the innate goodness of the human race. As she listened to him weaving

[1] In 1905, the skull was found buried in the garden.

all manner of Utopias, Eléonore, who was always moderate and full of common sense and a strange clairvoyance, smiled a little sadly, and knew that one day he was doomed to be bitterly disappointed. It was beginning to be rumoured that the King wanted to summon the States General. Boufflers thought that this would surely inaugurate an era of freedom. Eléonore told him quietly that the Duc de Nivernais felt it was premature and fraught with dangers—"as unwise as putting a loaded gun in the hands of a child". She added: "To begin with, the system of representation was unfair."

But there was no restraining Boufflers, either in his new passion for ballooning or his fancy for revolutions. She had just told him that some peasants had attacked a balloon in a field with pitchforks, as they thought it was the work of the Devil. "And rightly so, I think. What a terrible world it would be if men began disporting themselves in mid-air."

A welcome change occurred when they met the two aged beauties of the Court of Louis XV—the same diverting old ladies who had come to Eléonore's famous supper party ten years ago.

"Ah, *ma chère*, did you ever see anything so fast as Mademoiselle Biheron over there: her petticoat and bodice are of different colours, and she has discarded her panniers and her pouf!"

"Well, what can you expect with these modern women: she studies anatomy in a little room with glass cases full of corpses!"

"*Quelle horreur*. I always said that a violent change of fashion went with change of morals. A woman's shyness about the sciences must be almost as tender as about the vices. Look at her, I'm sure she will come to a bad end with her *chemises à l'anglaise* and her robes *à la Jean-Jacques Rousseau*.

Boufflers laughed, and said: "But, *Madame*, surely those names are prettier than calling colours fleas' stomachs, Paris mud and dandies' intestines, as we did ten years ago?"

Madame took no notice, but, adjusting her antiquated *fontange*, continued to declaim against the modern woman. "Believe me, this habit of wearing *négligés* in public can come to *no* good. Now in *my* young days, if you wanted to lose your virtue, the passion had to be fairly serious: you were obliged to think twice about it, for your lover had to break down the triple ramparts of panniers, complicated head-dress and whale-bone bodice. No indulging in passing fancies: the damage to be repaired would be too great."

They all laughed, and Boufflers reflected, silently, on whether that had been the case in his own varied experience.

They all came out of the wood and turned into an alley of heliotrope, in the garden overlooking the Seine. *Madame's* little nigger, in his turban of saffron silk, opened a green parasol over her head. Armand plucked a striped clove-pink and tucked it into Delphine's bodice: they smiled into one another's eyes. Eléonore looked up at Boufflers with that expression which bespoke delicate health and a certain appealing melancholy imbued with infinite tenderness.[1] He caught her glance, and with his customary care to shield their love from the eyes of the world, he told her—as the conversation still ran on clothes—that his great-aunt de Luxembourg had asked him to write a sarcastic poem against this fashionable craze which women had for wearing aprons: she was going to send it to her grand-daughter, with a sackcloth apron trimmed with priceless lace. "Apparently my aunt disapproves of this new passion for white, and for *négligés*, it makes women less beautiful and more dangerous, to look as if they were just awaking in the morning."

Said Armand: "And it's so bad for our own brocade weavers, this habit of buying English lawns and poplins."

"We have the Queen to blame for that," said *Madame* acidly.

At this point Elzéar, who was as devoted to Marie-Antoinette as ever, exclaimed bitterly:

"Whatever Her Majesty does, we always find something to criticize: she sets a fashion in simplicity, and we accuse her of ruining trade: she orders a brocade ball-dress and we cry out that she is impoverishing the country by her extravagance."

And so till dusk, they walked with groups of their friends, gossiping and arguing, curtseying and bowing to left and right, fanning themselves and seeking the shade of the elm walk when the heat grew intense. In France new fashions always indicate a change in ideas or some new infatuation: as Eléonore glanced round at the clothes of the men she knew, she gave a little sigh of dismayed apprehension: there were more black coats than ever, fewer embroidered waistcoats, no wigs and much less powder on the hair, lace jabots were simpler, steel buckles were replacing diamonds on shoes, and there were very few of those high, red heels and large ostrich plumes which were *de rigueur* at Court. How horrified her older friends would have been, had they guessed that, in another two years, a man might call on them in their own drawing-rooms, without white silk hose, tricorne and sword.

These ladies might have died at the idea of men smoking in their presence. In the clothes of men, particularly, the growing seriousness of ideas and the influence of England was becoming apparent. Even with the women one got the impression that they, too, were being bitten by this new craze for freedom. Their heels were lower and they walked faster. And oh! how they

[1] That is her expression in the miniature of the Pierpont Morgan collection.

argued about politics. Freedom! Freedom! Where would it all end?

Numerous guests had come from Paris during the afternoon, and at nightfall they returned to the house after walking in the wonderful gardens; they found the reception-rooms glowing in the light of hundreds of candles, a theatre and an orchestra all prepared, and a concert in which the famous Mademoiselle de Saint-Huberty, from the Opéra, appeared. Then came the acting of a proverb called "One swallow does not make a Summer", composed by the Duc de Nivernais and the Chevalier de Boufflers. This was a sentimental piece in which Lise, a young girl, the daughter of a nobleman, is saved from marrying a rich old man whom she does not love; by the liberality of a Prince—a subtle compliment to Prince Henry—she is enabled to marry Colin, whom she loves. "Oh, Mama!" exclaims Lise, "if only all Princes were like that." "Well," replies her mother, "one swallow does not make a Summer."

After the play a magnificent supper was served, the park was illuminated, right down to the Seine, which was covered with little boats holding coloured lanterns; it was a magical sight. At last, when it was time to go home, all the carriages, followed by lackeys carrying torches and lights, went slowly round the lovely park before taking the road back to Paris.

This was the last fête held at Saint-Ouen before the Revolution.

Ah, brilliant young men of old-time France who knew pleasure, the arts, love and the exploits of war; young men whose faces had an air of hilarity now lost for ever: if you had foreseen!

And you, O delicate porcelain beauties versed in the delights of conversation, of exquisite letter-writing, of love, of generous enthusiasms for new ideas, of splendid entertainment, of dancing; O beauties whose little smiling faces had an expression of roguery and finesse which has never since been equalled: if you had dreamed! Already the shadow of a Danton can be seen lurking at the gate, Danton seething with envy, who was to cry out while the people of Paris were starving: "Well, at last our time has come to enjoy life! Delicate food, exquisite wines, stuffs of silk and gold, women one dreams of, all this is the prize of acquired power." (Such was the "incorruptible virtue" of a "true democrat"!) Surely on that cloudless day, Boufflers, in his generous enthusiasm for ideal Democracy and his fancy for revolutions, had not reckoned with men of that stamp, or with a "Friend of the people" like Marat whom Garat described as "a man whose face, covered with a bronzed yellow, gave him the appearance of having come out of a bloody cavern of cannibals as from the red-hot soil of hell, that by his convulsive, brusque and jerky walk one recognized as an assassin . . . who wished to annihilate the human race".

Farewell, procession of carriages from Saint-Ouen rumbling slowly back to Paris by torchlight. Farewell: soon it will be tumbrils, not carriages, and your lackeys, instead of powdered wigs, shall wear the scarlet Phrygian cap of galley-slaves stuck with the tricolore cockade. Your lackeys will be your jailers.

CHAPTER XXV

"FAREWELL, ALL CHARM OF LIVING"

"It was vanity that made the Revolution; liberty was only the pretext . . ."

NAPOLEON.

MADAME DE SABRAN foresaw a great deal of the tragedy ahead. It was from any participation in all this horror that she wanted to save her lover. Like many of his noble contemporaries, in that May of 1789 Boufflers believed with pathetic hopefulness in the natural goodness of the average man, and that the meeting of the States-General was to inaugurate a new era of prosperity for all.

Boufflers had gone to Nancy, as he wanted to represent the nobility of Lorraine at the States-General. In April, 1789, we find him writing in high spirits to his sister, Madame de Boisgelin: "At last, my dear child, they have elected me. . . . Good-bye, my dear girl; I love you from end to end, and that is a long way, even without your coiffure."

Eléonore looked forward to the opening day with foreboding. She wrote to him: "Let Versailles and the good city of Paris beware! There have been certain mutterings the last few days which seemed like the precursors of great events."

The nobles still saw the funny side of it; a pity the *Tiers Etats* didn't view it all with such humour. The Marquis de Créquy wrote:

The vine-dresser, arrayed like a ruffian,
Will visit the Cabinet Minister, or even Mama.
He'll come without taking off his clogs;
Long live the States-General!
And soon the fishwife will be seated
At the table of the Marchioness,
There she'll see her mackerel again;
Long live the States-General!

Since early dawn on May 4th, the streets of Versailles had been crowded by people who wanted to see the great procession of the States-General from the Church of Notre Dame to the hall of the Assembly. It had drizzled all night. Many people had slept under porches. A place on a balcony overlooking the route was almost impossible to get. Even the roofs were covered with onlookers. Eléonore, no doubt, came to watch. The sun appeared at last and lit up all the rich tapestries which had been hung on the balconies. Towards ten o'clock there was a stir in the crowd: all the King's household appeared—the squires, the pages on horseback and the falconers with bird on wrist came before the King's great ceremonial carriage. Cries of "Long live the King" as he went by. Then the Queen's carriage. And a great silence. Not a single cheer. She passed by with her head held high—how they hated the proud way she carried her head and the disdainful Hapsburg lip! Between rows of Swiss guards and French soldiers, they went to assemble first at the Church of Notre Dame. Then they all came out again, walking in two parallel lines, holding lighted tapers. First, the *Tiers Etats*, or representatives of the people, dressed in black with a white cravat and a small three-cornered hat. Only one Breton peasant had kept his peasant costume. Monsieur de Mirabeau, with his insolent ugliness, was greeted with loud cheers.

Then the Nobility came, and the cheers ceased: Boufflers was amongst them, representing the nobles of Lorraine, the land of his youth. By order of the Master of Ceremonies, the nobles had gold braiding on their black coats, and carried their large turned-up hats *à la Henri IV*, covered with white feathers, such as they wore at the Queen's balls. They, too, held lighted candles.

Boufflers was then fifty-one years of age; in his time he had been a seminarist, a novelist, a writer of epigrams, a Latin scholar, a brilliant actor in *Figaro*, a soldier in the cause of liberty, a humanitarian Governor of Senegal and a distinguished member of the French Academy. Gone was the writer of light and rather licentious verses, the young man who had vowed "eternal passions for a fortnight". In his place was a man with heart afire with true patriotism, loyalty to his King, and an earnest desire to improve the conditions of the people. The portrait of him at the end of his life shows the sad but unembittered face of a man who had gone through many searching experiences. His eyes seem to say: "Yes, I've seen through all that." But on that May morning he did not know that he was on the brink of the most searing, the most disillusioning experience of his whole life, an era of three years after which he would exclaim: "All has failed me, except love." But Eléonore knew this. She gazed down at her lover with his unaccustomed look of gravity, and perhaps met his quick glance. Was her heart filled with love, or was she very sad at that moment? This street which leads from the Church of Notre Dame to the Assembly is haunted by these ghosts of the fourth of May.

Only one deputy of the Nobility was cheered: the short-necked, pimply Duc d'Orléans: he had refused to walk with the royal family.

Then came the clergy—the bishops separated from the Abbés by the musicians of the royal band. Under a dais came the Archbishop of Paris bearing the Most Holy Sacrament. This was probably one of the last great religious processions: (the Prince de Ligne has said that God, as the first aristocrat, was the first to be dethroned).

Then the King, on foot this time, in his cloth-of-gold mantle, undistinguished, ill-at-ease, yet benevolent-looking, his lofty character obscured by a clumsy bearing. After him, the Queen in white satin glistening with gold, followed by the princesses and ladies of the Court. She was looking tragically unhappy. Her heart was with her little boy, the Dauphin, seriously ill, who had only another month to live. When she passed the balcony where he was lying on some cushions, she looked up and her eyes smiled. Then she went on, and all her contemporaries noticed her "great air of sadness". Not a cheer for her. How she must have felt the dumb hostility, she who as a young Queen of twenty had been mobbed by adoring Parisian crowds wherever she went, and who then had found it difficult to restrain her tears of emotion! "I was happy when you loved me," she said at the end.

Suddenly, as she passed, a group of Paris women raised the insulting cry: "Long live the Duc d'Orléans." The implication was so pointed, the sound so raucous with hate towards her, that it was almost a death-cry. Struck to the heart, she turned pale, stopped walking and seemed to be tottering: the princesses had to support her before she regained enough strength to complete this terrible journey.

On the route, from the balcony where she was watching the procession, Madame de Staël turned to Madame de Montmorin and said: "Ah, *Madame*, how I rejoice to see this day!"

Madame de Montmorin replied: "*Madame*, you are wrong to rejoice, for all this will result in great disasters, both for France and for us."

A cold shiver ran through Madame de Staël. She was to remember this, one terrible September day not so far distant.

On June 23rd, the King left the Assembly with the nobles and the clergy, after saying at the conclusion of his speech: "Gentlemen, you have just heard the formal embodiment of my views. It is an expression of my keen desire to do something for the common good. If by any ill chance . . . you fail to support me in this high endeavour, I shall by myself do what is best for my people." In other words, he would be the benevolent despot, like Frederick the Great and Catherine of Russia.

Mirabeau and the *Tiers Etats* put a sinister interpretation on this speech, and remained behind in the hall to discuss it. After a while, the slim young master of Ceremonies, the Marquis de Dreux-Brézé (who had married Delphine's sister-in-law) came to request them to retire in their turn. Mirabeau said melodramatically, with his eyes rolling: "Go back and tell your master that we are here by the power of the people, and nothing but the bayonet will drive us hence." Then they all rushed to the covered-in tennis court and made the famous oath not to disperse till they had given a constitution to France.

At this point, Eléonore and Boufflers nearly had their second serious quarrel. After this insult to the King, she begged him to leave the Assembly altogether. He answered harshly. Then she wrote to him, appealing to his regard for his honour and his reputation: "In the name, then, of our first friendship, in the name of your best interests and your peace of mind consult only your conscience and remember the blood that flows in your veins." But he remained obdurate, and rightly so, for it would not have furthered the King's cause to leave, just because the Assembly promised to be what Eléonore called "Hell in miniature". A man must find things out for himself: Eléonore just had to possess her soul in patience and not exasperate her lover by referring to this again.

On the night of July 12th Paris was in a ferment. Camille Desmoulins was making wild speeches near the Palais-Royal: "The beast is caught in the trap, let's do him in! . . . Never will a richer prey have been offered to conquerors! Forty thousand palaces, private houses, châteaux, two-fifths of the goods of France will be the price of its worth. They who think they're the conquerors will be conquered in their turn, the nation will be purged!" While the Chevalier was debating at Versailles, Eléonore sat alone in her great house of the Faubourg Saint-Honoré and trembled for the fate of her son, Elzéar. On the street side of the house there were hordes of rioters who, having pillaged the wine-shops, were shrieking and cursing and singing all the way down. Some were rolling on the pavement and vomiting; others clutching scythes and pikes and banging at the doors of the great noblemen's houses and then yelling raucously and whooping. It was a terrifying sound. Eléonore had given orders that the great door into her courtyard was to be stoutly barricaded and the shutters bolted. She sent Elzéar to bed in a room on the other side overlooking the garden and the Champs Elysées. But even here things were not much better. Furies with matted hair and blood-shot eyes rushed past by torch-light, with sprigs of the Palais-Royal chestnut trees in their caps—symbol of Liberty. Eléonore peeped through a window, and then drew away in horror: it was the first time she had seen the dregs of the populace let loose in this manner.

She went to bed at last, trembling in case they broke into her garden through the grille. And all night long, as she lay awake, she heard horses galloping, guns firing, the roll of drums, the shrieking of the people, and, above it all, the ominous knell of the tocsin.

The next morning she took her jewels and hid them on her person, gave the household in charge of her butler, packed a small case of necessities and then wrote a practically illegible letter to the Chevalier. How dreadful that he was ten miles away at Versailles, and she had to leave him without saying good-bye:

"The 13th of July: Monday; eleven o'clock.

"The tumult increases in such a way and the news is so alarming that I must put off no longer and go. But go without news of you! I can hardly bear it. If it were not for Elzéar I would stay, at whatever risk or peril to myself, until I knew that you were out of danger. I fear your wretched Assembly. I am afraid of some treachery. Try to keep yourself from harm—it would be my death-blow. . . . Rage and licence are at their height. Good-bye. Think of your poor wife who is a thousand times more anxious on your account than on her own, and who, in the midst of so many dangers, feels but one regret—that of going away from you. I am so distressed that I can hardly hold my pen."

And she left for Plombières.

The next day the Bastille fell, and the Revolution began in earnest.

The Bastille had been the prison for conspirators, forgers, writers of obscene books and seditious pamphlets. By the time that Louis XVI came to the throne,—this Louis who abolished torture—the damp, dark, dungeons had fallen into complete disuse, all the rooms had windows, fireplaces and good furniture. The menus of these "guests of the King" included truffles, asparagus, Burgundy and moka coffee, and the food was beautifully served. De Renneville admitted that "certain people had themselves imprisoned there in order to enjoy good cheer without expense". It seems altogether too good a spot for the Abbé Bernard, Elzéar's murderous tutor. The interior of the Bastille on visiting day, with its ladies in elegant panniers, has been sketched by the ethereal Fragonard, but the exterior of this gloomy armed fortress of the fourteenth century had played tricks on the popular imagination. On July 14th the hired German mercenaries and hooligans of the mob knew nothing of the conditions inside, and when they stormed it and released a handful of dangerous prisoners, they thought they were striking a blow at a symbol of tyranny, and furthering the cause of freedom.

When an emissary woke the King to tell him that his state prison had fallen, His Majesty said, "So it's a revolt?". The reply was: "Sire, it's a revolution."

After that, the demons of Hell seemed to be unleashed in the provinces. Eléonore told the Chevalier of all kinds of incidents near Plombières, and of how some English visitors got a hundred peasants to accompany their coach. Arthur Young, travelling in France at the time, tells us that in July, at the inn where he was staying, he found a *seigneur* and his family who had escaped from their flaming château, half-naked, in the night, "and this family valued and esteemed by their neighbours, with many virtues to command the love of the poor, and no oppressions to provoke their enmity".

The effect of all this on the nobles of the Assembly was petrifying. At eight o'clock of the evening of August 4th, at the National Assembly, the Vicomte de Noailles, known as "John Lackland", sprang from his seat, and, amidst wild enthusiasm, demanded the abandonment of privileges. Then followed what Mirabeau contemptuously called an orgy, in which the nobility and clergy vied with each other in renouncing all kinds of feudal privileges. Someone rises to protest against the "silencing of frog-croaking"—the duty imposed on the peasants of keeping the frogs quiet during the lying-in of the *seigneur's* wife. Another cries, "I propose the suppression of pigeon-cots", and "the Assembly unanimously proscribes the entire race of pigeons". Rabbit warrens fell under the same ban, amidst renewed applause. "It was delirious, it was a drunken frenzy." The members embraced one another in a passion of abnegation, during that all-night sitting, and sobbed with joy that the day of deliverance had dawned at last. At eight o'clock in the morning they flocked to the chapel to sing a Te Deum of thanksgiving.

One can imagine the disgust of the fastidious and moderate Chevalier de Boufflers. He knew that the people would not be touched by so much generosity, but jeer at the lack of dignity and the fear of themselves that lurked behind it.

For a moment, Boufflers seemed almost overcome with nausea.

He wrote three days later to Eléonore: "I must get out of this." Then he day-dreamed. Should they both go away together to a farm-house in the Vosges?

> Let us forget with Paris
> Luxury, elegance and gilded ways.
> Even if Art is prized by us
> She cannot compete with Nature,
> And there is naught to compare to a dwelling
> Where you live in love's company.

Her response was immediate: "Your plan of solitude goes to my head, and that little hermitage where, beyond the reach of all intruders I shall live for you alone! What happiness it will be to serve you, to see you eat the food I have prepared, to clothe you in the linen I have woven, to make you rest in a bed that I shall enjoy making well! What are riches compared to that simplicity which enables us to enjoy every feeling of the heart and all true pleasures of the soul? In order to be happy, what need has one of excessive luxury, of differences of rank and vain honours? . . . For this equality with which they delude us, this level they think to obtain by cutting off heads, is only a chimera. Nature does not admit of it, still less does pride. Man will always be vain and ambitious . . .

"What an amazing Revolution! I cannot grow accustomed to it, and often I rub my eyes and think that this is only a bad dream, a dreadful nightmare that day will dispel . . .

"Come quickly, my friend, finish making all your sacrifices, give up everything down to your shirt. With me you will have need of nothing . . .

"What happy days we may still spend together! Believe me, if happiness is to be found on earth, it is in solitude that we must seek it. It will be found in our little house together with love. Yes, love! For, grandmother though I am, it burns my very soul. I feel it thrilling through my veins, quickening the beating of my heart, stimulating my imagination, bringing you vividly before my mind, whenever sleep gives me any rest. . . . What matter if old age comes to freeze my senses? It is my soul that loves you. My love will be immortal, like my soul. It is in God that I shall love you. . . . We shall find each other again at twenty, and sacrifice ourselves again to love."

Alas, she was doomed to disappointment. Boufflers recovered from this attack of pessimism and made a speech to the Academy: "We know, as the Greeks knew, that there is no true existence without liberty, without which no one is a man, for law without liberty is not freedom." Alas, high-minded and generous himself, he thought others would share his views. October 6th was soon to bring him further disillusionment. When the royal family was brought back from Versailles to Paris by the mob, Eléonore was in Switzerland. Some of the events of that day were related to her by the Comte de Tressan, the old-time admirer of Boufflers' mother at Lunéville. She heard how the Queen, whom she had known and loved, whose Coronation she had attended, and who had been so gracious to her own children, this Queen had been "treated as the worst of criminals". And she concludes: "I believe that the party of Orléans was at the back of this multitude." Boufflers, who was at Versailles at the time, with the Assembly, was a witness of all this. But neither of them knew till many years later, the more intimate, the more poignant scenes of this last farewell of the royal family to Versailles.

It is strange to think of Boufflers being in Versailles on those two memorable days. Many years later, he and Eléonore would hear, from scattered eye-witnesses, of that last afternoon spent by the Queen at the waterfall of Petit Trianon, gazing at the yellowed Autumn leaves which slowed up the course of the stream. Her sad reverie was harshly broken by the valet bringing the message that she was to return to the Palace at once, as the mob was at the gate. French *émigrés* heard of the terrible hours spent in deliberation at the Palace, then of the attempt on the Queen's life at dawn by a band of women and armed men disguised as women who had found a gate unlocked, as if by pre-meditation; the headlong rush towards her apartments of dishevelled, mud-stained harridans, clutching scythes, pikes and knives tied to broomsticks, yowling obscenities as they surged on; the guards massacred; the Queen sharply awakened from sleep and fleeing to the King's apartment through a small side door.

Later in the morning the crowds thronging the courtyards clamoured for the appearance of the Queen, alone on the balcony of the Palace. Perhaps Boufflers saw her standing there in the little yellow-striped wrapper hastily thrown over her night-attire, looking so queenly that a breathless silence fell on the crowd, followed by wild outbursts of applause.

At one o'clock in the afternoon the royal family set out on that dreadful seven-hour journey to Paris. As they passed down the Avenue de Paris, did Marie-Antoinette turn her head and glance back in the direction of far-away Petit Trianon which she would never see again?

By early afternoon, the Palace was empty. No more would the mirrors in the Galerie des Glaces reflect those tossing seas of plumes above the little powdered heads, those swan necks adorned with diamonds, those faces with their varied, delicate and subtle expressions immortalized by La Tour. . . . And vanished for ever the liveried page-boys, equerries and officers in the brightly-coloured uniforms of the *Ancien Régime*. Gone the valets carrying sedan-chairs or leading goats to be milked in the royal nurseries. The last of the troops of hawkers and beggars had shuffled off wretchedly. Silence. . . .

But hush! In the distance, a delicious sound of harps and flutes. . . . It was Louis XV's great clock chiming the hour. To-day, the date on it says: "October 31st, 1789." After this fatal month the clock-winder came no more.

CHAPTER XXVI

FAREWELL TO PARIS

When Eléonore was told of the events of that day by the Comte de Tressan, one of the incidents which she found pathetic above all others, was that the little Dauphin, on the drive to Paris, kept putting his head out of the window and crying: "Mercy for Mama."

The Chevalier, of course, had been at Versailles at that time. He had seen the women break into the hall of the Assembly and dance on the platform of the President, and he had watched the great exodus. From that moment on, Boufflers, whose whole career had been ruined by Louis XVI's dislike of men who wrote verses and epigrams (for he had crossed him off a list for military promotions), now proclaimed his loyalty to the monarchy in three fine speeches to the Académie.

In the midst of the storm, the lovers sought refuge in their love for one another. He wrote to her: "*Mon Dieu, ma fille!* How far we are from the time when, driven by Maitre Jacquot,[1] of dirty memory, we rushed about Germany! When will those happy days return?"

Eléonore replied: "Indeed, you must possess great merit to have inspired me with such a feeling as I have for you—I, who cared only for independence, who felt every tie to be unbearable, I whose untamed nature and careless spirit led me to live apart from the world. . . . Ah! but the only good of life, the only reasonable occupation is to love and to be loved."

They still quarrelled. If he failed to write to her, she said: "I shall bid you an eternal farewell." To which he replied: "How could I be vexed with you, dear love—with you, who are

[1] A coachman of his.

dearer to my heart than my heart itself; with you, who even in your mad rages always love me as if you could not do otherwise? . . . Return then, once more, to the friendly affection that becomes you so well, dear love, and in times so sad and stormy as these, add not your suspicions, your anger and your vexations to those I feel for all other good people."

Later, Eléonore wrote from Nidervillers, the home of Général de Custine, to announce the birth of Delphine's second son Astolphe [Her first boy, Gaston, was now five years old and "a furious democrat". He died from small-pox in 1792.] ". . . I must tell you that my expectant mother has just given birth to a very pretty little boy, whom I received in my apron, as the old wives say, and whom I kissed heartily after he had made his toilet. This event made a great stir in the village." She then describes how, to the sound of the cannon, a hundred and fifty peasants came to lead her to church for the baptism: "A fearful wind that seemed to conspire against us, carried away our hats, blew my skirts about, and sent into my eyes and ears all the fire and smoke of the most imposing artillery in the world. . . . A *commère babillarde* was at my side. This is the custom and the title given to the woman employed to throw sweets to all the little children. . . . The silvery voices of the bells rang out, while the parish 'serpent', the organ, the hautbois and the horn, all vied with each other in making the loudest din, and the curé and the schoolmaster baptized my poor godson so thoroughly and with so much salt and water that he vomited, unhappy one! on all the bystanders, and caught a cold in one eye, which makes him blind in it for the moment. . . .

"I was so touched by the kind-heartedness of these poor peasants at a time when so many others only take up arms in order to burn down châteaux and murder their *seigneurs*, that I had all the difficulty in the world to keep from crying. I gave them my last crown piece—so much does goodness of heart appeal to me. May he be for ever held in execration in the memory of man who first thought of destroying this natural relationship between poverty and wealth, between weakness and strength, and kindly interchange of gratitude and benefit."

The following year, on June 19th, 1790, in another bid for popularity, the Assembly abolished all titles, orders of knighthood, liveries and armorial bearings. Eléonore wrote mockingly to Boufflers: "So you are now Monsieur Boufflers. . . . As for me, you must call me Eléonore Sabran, so as to avoid confusion with the Marquise de Sabran." Later, he wrote to her in the press of work: ". . . I could not help seeing your lovely form, your tender, touching look, your beautiful eyes always ready to shed gentle tears of feeling—in a word it was you. Just as if you had been there, as if I had heard you speaking, as if I had held you in my arms." And again: "One thing is certain, that is, that you can only be happy with me, and I can only be happy with you."

In the Autumn of 1790 there seemed to be a lull in the storm, and Eléonore returned to Paris. So there are no letters for a time. We only know that Paris streets looked very animated that winter, with their tricolore fashions and lampshade hats. But it was no longer the Paris that Eléonore had loved. Politics were discussed in the *salons* all the time, and women became termagants in discussion, and unbearably unsociable. Alone the woman in the provinces was still content to be womanly, and it is refreshing to read of the adoring aristocratic husband who bought a "Liberty hat" for his wife in her château in the country. [He writes to his "*chère petite amie*" that "as the gum-ribbons spoil in the rain, I've made them put on it a pretty golden *bourdalou* with fringes, which is more beautiful and more solid". She replied: "Really, you are a charming man. . . . Thy little wife who loves thee to distraction."]

However, in the Spring of 1791 things took an unpleasant turn again. The Royal Family, pining for a little air and peace, were forcibly prevented from going to Saint-Cloud. Mirabeau, dying, exclaimed: "I am so disgusted at the thought that I have only helped towards a vast demolition." At this time, Monseigneur de Sabran, who had so often entertained Eléonore and her children at Anizy, was the King's almoner. (One can picture him saying Mass at the Tuileries, for the royal household.) The King ordered him to leave the country in case of insult. The bishop urged Eléonore to come too. And indeed, at that very moment, she had good cause to feel uneasy. The Abbé Bernard was now at large, and he had written a pamphlet full of veiled threats: "Shudder! We have in our hands the letter that this Bernard wrote to his mistress, and which you intercepted." No one could afford enemies at a time like this. Eléonore was offered a refuge by the Comtesse Stahrenberg, in Austria, and by Mrs. Buller, in England, who said: "All that I have is yours." Unfortunately for England, she decided to accept the invitation of Prince Henry of Prussia at Rheinsberg, in his magnificent castle north-west of Berlin. Every day saw some new departure. Coaches packed with luggage rumbled and bounded along the roads, booed by the yokels in villages, sometimes waylaid by thieves. Madame Vigée Lebrun had already left on October 6th, 1789, the night that the royal family came to Paris. The King's two remaining old spinster aunts, rouged and toqued, had fled to Italy: after uneasy wanderings, they settled at Trieste and died there. They had sown their own little packet of mischief, and were now disappearing before the whirlwind. And they left behind them their musical instruments, books of devotion, parakeets, downy sofas, Court trains, sedan chairs, wonderful *chefs*, ladies-in-waiting and the classical statues in their gardens of Bellevue to which they had attached fig-leaves.

At dawn in the streets of old Paris, the night watchman used to call out:

"Awake, O people now asleep.
Pray God for all departed souls."

On May 14th, Eléonore had bidden farewell to the Chevalier, to her daughter and her son-in-law, Armand. As she woke, very early on the morning of May 15th, did she sense that she was never to see Armand again? Did she know that this was the last night in her blue bedroom, in this house where she had spent so many happy hours with her lover? She went to the window and looked out on to the green lawns of her garden. Over the chestnut trees of the Champs-Elysées, in the direction of the Tuileries Palace where her Queen was now a virtual prisoner, the May dawn was breaking. Again and again, Eléonore's thoughts flew to Stanislas. Would she ever see him again? What agony to tear oneself away! But she must hurry: she and Elzéar must set out before the populace of Paris was astir in the streets. They went in a small, plain travelling carriage, so as not to attract attention. Very quietly dressed and veiled, she slipped through the great *porte cochère* of her house, and, not daring to look behind her, she got into the carriage with Elzéar. The door was shut and they started off at once. The postilions were in a bad temper.

"*Sacrés aristocrates*," they kept muttering.

Paris! Paris! Paris! When she returned, many years later, everything would have changed, even the street-names. There, in the quiet place Louis Quinze (now Place de la Concorde), the guillotine would soon be seen on a high scaffold, and the sharp steel blade mowing down, not only the bearers of illustrious names, but many simple people. [The Madame Loison, who kept a marionette show in the Champs-Elysées and whom Elzéar and Delphine must often have seen, was to be a victim. She was accused of making her Polichinelle too aristocratic.] Eléonore saw vague forms hurrying to Mass. Many churches were now without priests, since most of them had loyally refused to take the civil oath.

"Awake, O people now asleep.
Pray God for all departed souls."

Pray for those about to die.

As she gazed through the carriage window, Eléonore bade farewell in spirit to all the scenes of her childhood: the Rue des Vieilles-Audriettes, the Convent of the Conception where she had lost Zina; then the church where she had been married to the Comte de Sabran, the house where she had learnt her ceremonial curtsey before her presentation to Louis XV—so many years ago now. Then that house in the Rue de Varennes, dear almost beyond all others, where she had first met Stanislas at the Maréchale de Luxembourg's. No, there was *his* house, which was dearer still, for there they had met in secret for over eight years now. When would that intolerable succession of partings have an end, and she be with him always?

. . . . .

She wrote to him from Brussels: "The thought of you torments me. . . . Think sometimes of our solitude together. Only death can put an obstacle in the way of so sweet a prospect, and I hope that my fate, cruel as it is, will grant me the consolation of dying in your arms. Good-bye, too dear friend." And again: "Since I left you I live only in the past."

When finally she arrived at Rheinsberg, Prince Henry, thinking that she would come in a large travelling coach, like so many of the *émigrés* of the day, met her with eight magnificent horses. And so, when he harnessed them all to her small carriage, it went off at one bound! Prince Henry tore madly after them through the dust.

Once arrived at the Castle, the Prince showed himself as hospitable as ever. He had a little *salon* containing busts of the four French people he admired the most, and the Comtesse de Sabran was one of them. In their correspondence, Eléonore and the Chevalier continued to quarrel as before. He complained that her letters were "short, infrequent and stupid". She says: "You are colder, drier and more tiresome than politics themselves." But then, with her great art of keeping him amused, she described a charming old man who had fallen in love with her and whom she calls "your rival". Boufflers was fascinated, and wrote her his most adoring letter.

"You only are you, dear love, and yet you are not, for one moment is never like another, and all are charming. . . . I like to praise you to-day, my wife, another time, if you wish it, I will laugh at you; but to-day I am so in love with you, so enraptured by you, so proud of you, so touched at your letter, that it would take very little to make me throw myself at your feet. . . ."

It was in June of that year, while Eléonore was on her way to Rheinsberg, that the Royal Family attempted to escape. There is no mention of this in the letters of the lovers, because the posts were now scrutinized. This event was the crowning misfortune which sealed the doom of the monarchy, and resulted, eventually, in their imprisonment in the Tower of the Temple. The story of the escape is one of the most distressing in French history.

In September, 1791, Louis XVI presented himself before the Constituent Assembly to swear allegiance to the new constitution. At his first words all the Assembly insolently sat down. A lesser man would have found the ready sarcasm to cut these ill-bred hooligans, but Louis XVI completely lacked the ability to defend himself: he had carried the Christian offering of the other cheek to such a pitch that he violated Nature's law of self-defence. When he got back to the Tuileries he said to the Queen: "Ah, *Madame*! All is lost!"

At four o'clock that same evening Boufflers left the Assembly for the last time. He had shed his last illusion about the inherent goodness of man. And then, moderate men like himself, "gentlemen democrats," were hated by both extremes. With a wry smile, he recalled that he had once said: "I have always had a fancy for revolutions." What a bitter awakening. So Eléonore had been right all along. He decided to leave everything, and go to her. He wrote to her: "Everything has failed me except Love." In December of that year, after various delays and disappointments, he was re-united to her again under the hospitable roof of Prince Henry of Prussia.

END OF PART IV

Part V

TILL DEATH

CHAPTER XXVII

A CONSIDERED VIEW OF THE FRENCH REVOLUTION

Whenever one passes Carlyle's house in Chelsea, one sees the dwelling of an unscrupulous historian who misused historical documents, and purposely led the English to believe that the French Revolution was a rising of the people against the tyranny of oppressors. Greater nonsense was never written. It is more than possible that all the bloodshed would have been avoided if only Louis XVI had begun by guillotining his seditious kinsman, Philippe Duc d'Orléans and his gang. Then he should have seen to it that the working classes were more fairly represented in the National Assembly, instead of being grossly outnumbered by the middle-class lawyers and ambitious, envious nobodies whose careers depended on stirring up class hatred and pandering to mobs craving for excitement. Also, instead of being so squeamish about firing on mobs, he should—like Napoleon some years later—have aimed a cannon on a rowdy crowd and killed a few hundreds in order to save thousands. But continual emotional excitement caused by mob-rule had given Louis that form of nervous collapse in which a man cannot decide on any course of action. (Madame Campan says that his face was pallid above his violet coat.) France could have been saved by a democratic ruler who was temporarily a benevolent despot, and who kept order by just force. Also the nobles should have realized the danger, taken up arms like Englishmen during the Civil War, and organized themselves into an aggressive body, with its own propaganda and its own demands.

Owing greatly to the writings of Dickens and Carlyle, the English have been greatly misled about the Revolution, they do not realize that the whole bloody machine was set in motion by Philippe d'Orléans: he hated Marie-Antoinette because she had repulsed his amorous advances, and begged the King to exile him to England. Being a man who could never forgive an injury, and immensely ambitious, he conceived a plan of posing as "the friend of the people" so that they would do his dirty work for him, and, by killing off the King and Queen, make him ruler of France. He was helped by his vast wealth and his bevy of diabolically clever organizers, chief of whom was Laclos, author of *Les Liaisons Dangereuses* which I have described before. Orléans' mother had been a German; he was also descended from a daughter of Madame de Montespan and Louis XIV. His name was synonymous with debauchery. In his Paris house of the Palais-Royal, he continued the tradition of orgies for which that palace had long been famous; he threw girls stark naked into his park of Monceau, girls whom he had collected from the lowest quarters of Paris. As well as Laclos, he employed Madame de la Motte, of Necklace fame, newly escaped from prison, and bribed her heavily to write scurrilous pamphlets against the Queen, also a notorious Belgian courtesan Théroigne de Méricourt, who eventually led the march of the "women" to Versailles, and an Italian called Rotondo, who assassinated the Queen's great friend, the Princesse de Lamballe; it was Rotondo's wife,[1] a kitchenmaid, who gutted her mistress in the street. All through those months, when Paris was crowded with representatives from all over the country, the Duc kept the people near the Palais Royal in a perpetual ferment by providing fireworks at his own expense, and getting mob agitators to stir them up by speeches at street corners. Liberty! Equality! He never believed in either, and in his heart he secretly despised the vile masses whom he was using to further his own ends.

It has been proved by several reliable witnesses that Philippe d'Orléans was seen strutting about Versailles on the morning of October 6th, when the King and Queen were forced back to Paris, and it was probably he who showed the murderous, howling mob their way to the Queen's bedroom, at dawn that day.

The French Revolution was not an uprising of the people at all. The ordinary common workman was too decent a fellow to want to take part in this carnage, therefore the paid agitators of the Duc used the scum of the population when they wanted to form a mob—the malcontents, the drunkards, the galley-slaves, criminals, pickpockets and unemployable. Paris was full of them: it was the most dangerous city in the world from this point of view. The large district of the Faubourg Saint-Antoine round the Bastille was composed of tenement dwellings of men working in tanneries and glass factories, and it is noticeable that when human beings are herded together in flats instead of houses they are more talkative, more likely to be in a ferment and meet together at the pub and at street corners. When the massacre of the nobles actually did start, the assassins were made drunk beforehand, and the liquor must have been drugged, for they became unnaturally frenzied, and kept calling for more wine, as if unable to quench a burning thirst. Ordinary reliable workmen committed deeds of atrocious cruelty which would have

[1] Found by N.H.W. in the Record Office.

horrified them had they been in their right minds. Many went mad as a result of the drug. These methods were characteristic of those employed by Orléans. Eléonore, with her usual good sense and her gift of clairvoyance, saw the part played by the Duc d'Orléans and said so in a letter to Boufflers . . . "It is Monsieur le Duc d'Orléans who is making the Revolution . . . his levity has hitherto saved him from suspicion; no one thought his proceedings were worth watching . . . he had his object. This object is to make himself, before long, master of the kingdom."

It was the money of the Duc d'Orléans which bought up all the reserves of grain after a bad winter; it was his agitators who incited the mob to seize some of the grain, in order to drown and burn it, and so cause an unnecessary famine. Alas, he was the millionaire of the Revolution. It was his money that bribed brigands to commit deeds which no decent citizen would have done. Madame Vigée Lebrun records that on the morning of the capture of the Bastille she overheard two men talking. One said to the other: "Do you want to earn ten francs? Come and make a row with us, you have only got to cry 'Down with this one! Down with that one!' Ten francs are worth earning." The other one answered: "But shall we receive no blows?" "Go to," said the first man, "it is we who are to deal the blows!"

It was the Duc's money which bribed a whole horde of courtesans to seduce the King's guards from their allegiance and gradually corrupt the army. When, at last, the women marched to Versailles "to ask for bread", many, many of the women were really men in disguise, most of them had forgotten to take off their trousers under their skirts, and they were seen by several people. That was a clever move of the Duc's: knowing the King's softness of heart, he felt sure that he would never give the order to fire on a crowd of women, and so he placed them in the forefront of his mob as a protection to the rest. How it infuriated the proud, imperious Marie-Antoinette, this seeming inability of the King's to defend himself—often a sign of degeneracy. (Eléonore herself deplores the fact that "the clergy is without ambition and the *nobility without energy*".)

It was the paid agents of the Duc who flooded the countryside with forged orders to the peasants "from the King" to burn down the castles of the nobles. This destruction was not the spontaneous work of the people at all, but resulted from mistaken loyalty to the King: they had been told that the nobles did not agree with their King's plans for reform. (In one notable instance, however, were they checkmated: the monks of Cluny and their devoted peasants defended themselves stoutly with stones from the windows, and finally seized the malefactors and brought them to the Royal prisons.)

Romantic writers and inaccurate historians have always said it was the fishwives, or ladies of the markets, who fetched the King and Queen from Versailles. This is a slander on the fishwives, who formed a respectable though outspoken body of women, devoted to the Royal family, and who used to come to Versailles in their black silk and diamonds bringing bouquets of flowers to congratulate them on ceremonial occasions. The women who formed the nucleus of that crowd on the fatal October 5th and 6th were mistresses of men like Laclos, and of deserters from the French guards. They broke into shops, workrooms and private houses on the way, to force cooks and seamstresses to swell the tide. Many barefoot women were bribed. One laundress said, indignantly, that she had been approached by one "woman" whom she recognized as a noble of the Palais Royal whose valet she washed for.

The second great intrigue of the French Revolution was that of Frederick the Great of Prussia. When Louis XVI, then a Dauphin, cemented an alliance between Austria and France in 1770 by marrying Marie-Antoinette, an Austrian princess, Frederick saw this as a direct threat to his own ambitions. He sent his ambassadors to Paris with secret instructions to make trouble between France and Austria if they could. One ambassador, his own brother, the Prince Henry of Prussia who was so great an admirer of Eléonore's, was sent with the same purpose, but he reported that the Queen still hated everything Prussian.

It was then becoming the fashion in French society to dislike everything Austrian and to nickname Marie-Antoinette "the Austrian woman". This was started by the King's aunts at Bellevue. They veered towards the Prussians. How short-sighted: if only they could have foreseen the wars with Prussia, beginning at the end of the century, and then culminating in the great wars of 1870, 1914 and 1939, they would have realized who were their real enemies. The policy of Prussia had always been to take advantage of the internal troubles of other nations.

And then, one must probe under all this talk of heavy taxation grinding down the lives of the poor. Feudal dues, etc., sprang less from intentional tyranny than from an obsolete system that demanded readjustment. Many of the dues were not enforced at all, though they sound bad enough in the pages of history books. At the time of the Revolution the power of the *seigneurs* over the persons of the vassals existed in law but not in fact. (Does not the law of England allow that a man may beat his wife with any weapon no thicker than his thumb? But has this yet brought about a state of ferment in our women?) Were the French people really unhappy? Too often have we had the opinions of the pessimistic Arthur Young flung at our faces. What about another Englishman, Dr. Rigby, travelling in France in the summer of 1789? Travelling between Calais and Lille, after commenting on the extraordinary fertility of the land, far surpassing that of England, he says:

"The general appearance of the people is different from what I expected; they are strong and well made. We saw many agreeable scenes as we passed along in the evening before we came to Lisle: little parties sitting at their doors, some of the men smoking, some playing at cards in the open air, and others spinning cotton. Everything we see bears the marks of industry, and *all the people look happy*. We have indeed seen few signs of opulence in individuals, for we do not see so many gentlemen's seats as in England, but then *we have seen few of the lower classes in rags, idleness and misery*. What strange prejudices we are apt to take regarding foreigners! . . ."

And after the Revolution? Mrs. Richard Trench, who travelled through France in 1802, writes:

"Breteuil, July 8. Where is the gaiety we have heard of from our infancy as the distinguishing characteristic of this nation? Where is the original of Sterne's picture of the French Sunday? I have seen to-day no cessation of toil, no intermixture of devotion and repose and pleasure. I have seen no dance, I have heard no song. But I have seen the pale labourer bending over the plentiful fields, of which he does not seem (if one may judge by his looks) ever to have enjoyed the produce; I have seen groups of men, women and children working under the influence of the burning sun . . . and others giving to toil the hours destined to repose, even so late as ten o'clock at night."

Sometimes when I read the romantic nonsense that is written about the Revolution, I feel inclined to echo the words of a Frenchman to Dr. Moore: "Damn liberty, I abhor its very name." "Let us examine a list of the victims of the guillotine during the existence of the Revolutionary Tribunal—that is to say between March 10th, 1793, and May, 1795. The number for Paris was two thousand eight hundred. Out of all these victims only about four hundred and eighty-five were nobles, two hundred and five were ecclesiastics—almost entirely obscure and humble priests. Thus eliminating the nobility and clergy, we find that two thousand one hundred and ten people of the middle and working classes perished. Among these two thousand one hundred and ten people were one hundred and six domestic servants, forty-eight artists, authors, architects, thirty-two doctors and dentists, thirty-one barbers and hairdressers, twenty-three working women, one hundred and thirty workmen, and so on. (Besides these are the curious items of a rat-catcher, a poacher, a chimney-sweep, several old-clothes sellers, and pathetic victims such as "Ostalier, good poor man and gardener, and Dorival, a hermit weaver".) In the provinces the proportion of victims taken from "the people" was, of course, far higher. Arsène Houssaye says that out of eleven thousand four hundred and seventy only six hundred and thirty-nine were nobles.[1]

And the Comte de Breteuil, who perished in spite of thirty villages appealing for his release? Did he die by the will of the people?

One can only account for so many of the victims being so obscure, by realising that the day for private vengeance had come. Any of your enemies, even your own servants, could denounce you to the Revolutionary Tribunal. There is the notable instance of the cook who got home very late on her day out. She had gone to watch the guillotining, and had not returned "after the second head". When her mistress remonstrated, the cook just went off and denounced her to the Tribunal!

Some of the obscure victims were so pathetic. There was the little seamstress of seventeen known as "*la petite Nicholle*", too poor even to afford a bedstead, and when they sought her in her attic on the seventh floor, they found her lying on a straw mattress laid upon the boards. Though assured of her innocence, they condemned her to death because she had taken food to an actress called Grandmaison. Equally heartrending is the picture of the poor peasant woman from Poitou who was suckling her babe when the moment came to be driven off to the place of execution, and who shrieked and cried out when they tore the child away from her breast. Women just risen from child-bed were taken tottering to the guillotine. Some poor women died from fright on the way, and they guillotined the corpses. Or again there is the eighty-year-old Abbé de Fénelon, adored by the poor of Paris, particularly by the little Savoyard chimney-sweeps, who made their way into the hall during his trial, crying out that he was their father, and imploring mercy for him and sobbing.

Too much unjust blame has been thrown on the nobles themselves. And they were not as rich as all that. Of two thousand noble families, only about two hundred to three hundred really had any money. Arthur Young glibly reproaches them for absenteeism from their estates: he forgets that changing economic and social conditions had made it impossible for many of them to live on in their crumbling châteaux. Owing to the changes in coinage since the Middle Ages, feudal dues had fallen so much in value as to be useless. The country nobleman was not allowed to sell his estate, or to go in for trade; and if he married into the

[1] Mrs. Webster compiled these figures.

rich middle-classes he was snubbed by all his neighbours and accused of blotting his 'scutcheon. So they flocked to the attics of Versailles in the hope of securing some good post, leading a dog's life meanwhile. Courtly smiles on top, gnawing anxiety underneath, and a desperate attempt to grab at any military or diplomatic post that was going—for that was their only means of livelihood. And in spite of this, all over the kingdom, scores of impoverished gentry stuck to their posts. There was a natural affinity between them and the peasants: they had been brought up together on the same estates, baptized in the same font, they kept the same Church feasts and holidays by singing and dancing together in the grounds of the château, suffered the same reverses in their farming plans by hail or drought. It was a very healthy thing for the state, this sympathy between two great sections of the population. The squires always went to village weddings and danced with the bride; when wolf and bear hunting began, the *curé* announced this on Sunday after the sermon, and the village lads would arrive gaily, armed with guns to watch in the spots arranged for by their squire. When the nobles unwisely gave up their hunting and shooting monopolies, the roads became unsafe, with every untrained village lad popping off guns in all directions. Arthur Young nearly came to an untimely end in this way.

Happy days which will come no more! The tenants were sometimes godparents of the numerous offspring of their landlords, they flocked to him for advice, or to ask him to settle their legal disputes. There was an old country gentleman who was never known to be sober, who used to settle the most acrimonious quarrels in his own original way: he invited the parties to dinner at his château and gave them plenty to drink, and then, when tempers were mellowed, self-interest in abeyance and hearts softened, he would pronounce his final legal verdict. If anybody interrupted, he would call: "Another glass of wine for *Monsieur*."

And then, of course, there was the dispensary cupboard at the château, kept by the squire's wife. Traditional experience over many centuries had made her very good at healing sores, and of course she had inherited from her mother and grandmother all kinds of secret herbal recipes for lotions, elixirs, juleps and infusions. They were distributed from her great wardrobe on Sundays after Mass. How much more personal than any government controlled system!

Many gentry helped to make their tenants industrious and rich. One in Provence planted olive-trees all over wild ground, setting the example himself in all weathers; another turned his orangery into a silk manufactory, after having planted mulberries on his estates.

Yes, they were a great loss to the nation. It was they who begot vast quantities of fine soldiers for the wars. They were renowned for their large families—like one Du Plessis de la Haye-Gille who had seventeen children by his first wife and sixteen by his second. And another had twenty-six by one wife alone. [Incidentally, there should be a monument to these unnoticed women whose sufferings helped to found a nation.] To help men like these, Louis XIV had made an edict giving a thousand *livres* to gentry who had ten children, and two thousand to those who had twelve. And these young men grew up and fought like lions for the King; it was of the hard-working, hardy, poor, energetic sons of country gentry that the Italians said, that they went to death as if they would resurrect on the morrow, so recklessly brave were they.

Poor they were, too. One historian places the lot of a good peasant labourer well above "the little squire, lord of a dilapidated grange, who hardly has enough to feed his wife and children". In fact there were some well-born lords who had to give up shooting, their only pleasure, because they could not afford a gun. Some of them went to market like peasants, basket on one arm, sword dangling at their side, to sell the produce of their farmyard and kitchen garden. And many were the country gentlemen who ate in their huge kitchens, at a round table apart from the household, and then spent the evening by the great kitchen hearth.

There is no denying that Democracy, true Democracy is a fine thing, and there was a welling-up of something great in many men of that day. But, alas, that evil men seized the reins and plunged the country into an abyss from which it has not yet wholly emerged, even to-day.

In order to be quite fair, it must be admitted that two excellent things resulted from the Revolution. First, impoverished men of noble birth were able to earn their living without losing caste: there need be no more young men like Boufflers, victimized into false situations by penury. Secondly, people were looked upon as individuals, instead of just members of a family—notably in the case of women who in the past had been forced to be nuns if they lacked dowries. True, conventual life was much pleasanter then, than now: it was more like a social club, for women who were all in the same ill predicament. But the evils, although hidden, were none the less real, and it was very necessary that books like *La Religieuse*, of Diderot's, should expose the Lesbian cancer. One cannot forcibly incarcerate a great section of the female population without the social organism festering somewhere, and eventually stinking. And it is very important that Catholic historians should *not* suppress the Truth because of their fear of scandalizing Protestants.

In the eighteenth century, when there was a complaint against the richer nobles, it was often found to be because they had handed out the collecting of rents to men of the people who were cruel and rapacious. Matters were eased when they investigated the matters themselves. And when the nobles did take to looking after their tenants and peasants personally, they showed that they were imbued with all the generous ideas of humanity of their class. After watching men like Boufflers in Senegal, one can imagine that he would have been an excellent landlord if only he'd had the chance. The Duc de Nivernais was beloved on his estates, the Princesse de Lamballe was called "the good angel" on hers—to take but two examples.

The nobility is more fitted by tradition and by experience over long centuries to look after the peasants, than the men of the middle class. It was nobles like Boufflers who formed themselves into a Society of Royalist Democrats, fired with enthusiasm for true liberty, while it was a worm like Robespierre who, while preaching on the doctrine of equality, destroyed it in his electioneering speeches, when he played on the baser passions of the mob, notably envy and said: "Too long have the rich been the sole possessors of happiness. It is time that their possessions should pass into other hands. . . . Everything will be changed, for masters will become servants, and you will be served in your turn."

Is this equality? liberty? fraternity? The reality of the situation was pointed out by the Vicomte de Ségur when he said that the only principle of the times was "get out of that place, so that I can get into it".

J. M. Thompson, in his *French Revolution*, says that the inexperienced reader becomes an historian from the moment that he uses his common sense and asks himself "Is it likely that people would behave as they are said to have done?" In this case the disciples of Carlyle and Co. would find it very difficult to account for the enormous wealth of human feeling which was always being displayed by these very masses who were supposed to be struggling against tyranny. The answer surely is that the great mass of the people did not feel oppressed at all. And they were glad when their so-called oppressors escaped death. For example, every single acquittal was hailed with acclamations by the mob assembled around the prisons, often with rapturous applause. The Royalist Weber found it hard to extricate himself from the embraces of the harridans outside his prison. Also, to the fury of the demagogues, the people themselves so often remained furiously aristocratic. "Nowhere," said Taine, "are there so many suspects as among the people; the shop, the farm and the workshops contain more aristocrats than the presbytery or the château . . . the butchers and bakers are of an insufferable aristocracy." A shop-keeper said he heard some women of the people in his shop saying that morning that they did not wish to be called citizenesses any longer: "They say they spit on the Republic."

Monsieur Lenôtre asks who, at the last moment of the Queen's life, "were the Royalists who risked their lives to rescue the Queen? A shoe-black, a pastry-cook, three hairdressers, a pork butcher, several charwomen, two masons, an old-clothes seller, a lemonade seller, a wine merchant, a locksmith and a tobacconist. Four of these heroic people paid for their devotion with their heads."

It has often been pointed out how the notorious leaders of the Revolution had been, in their early days, embittered and frustrated in some way, and were therefore jealous of the class above them. This is even more true of the women. The so-called great woman of the Revolution, Madame Roland who, by her mocking incited the members of the Assembly to fury, when they were inclining to the view that the King really had benevolent intentions, this Madame Roland was a desperately conceited, envious, spiteful little nobody who had never recovered from being invited in early life, by an old lady of the Court, to spend a week at Versailles; and after watching all the ritual of the Court, felt she hated them all so much "that she did not know what to do with her hatred". She detested Marie-Antoinette, and loved to gloat over the recital of the petty humiliations inflicted on her.

It is also noteworthy that four of the great criminals of the Revolution were not French at all: Marat and Laclos had Spanish blood in their veins. The assassin, Rotondo, was an Italian, and the crazy harlot, Théroigne de Méricourt, was a Belgian.

Mrs. Webster has described Marat:

"Under five feet high, with a monstrous head, the broken nose of the degenerate, a skin of yellowed parchment, the aspect of 'the Friend of the People' was more than hideous, it was supernatural. His portrait in the Carnavelet Museum is not the portrait of a human being, but of an 'elemental', a materialization of pure evil emanating from the realms of outer darkness."

"Physically," says one who knew him, "Marat had a burning and haggard eye, like a hyena; like a hyena his glance was always anxious and in motion; his movements were short, rapid and jerky; a continued mobility gave to his muscles and his features a convulsive contraction, which even affected his way of walking—he did not walk, he hopped."

Dr. Moore says: "Marat is a little man of a cadaverous complexion, and a countenance exceedingly expressive of his disposition; to a painter of massacres Marat's head would be invaluable. Such heads are rare in this country (England), yet they are sometimes to be met with at the Old Bailey."

A follower of Marat was the Marquis de Sade, a moral maniac, to whom we owe the adjective "sadistic", a devil whose atrocities perpetrated against poor women of the people in no way debarred him from an honoured place in the ranks of democracy. He demanded that Reason and Virtue be worshipped in churches in place of the "Jewish slave" and "the adulterous woman, the courtesan of Galilee".

Indeed, they all wanted to destroy religion; they seemed to be in league with the powers of darkness. There was already a first whiff of sulphur in the passion for necromancers which was rife on the eve of the Revolution.

The Cardinal de Rohan, of Necklace fame, had dealings with magicians like Cagliostro. When one reads of the frightful profanity that was inaugurated during the reign of Terror, the worship, yes, the actual worship of Marat. ("Oh, Sacred Heart of Marat, have mercy on us"), one is convinced that these men were possessed by the Devil, inflamed with hatred against all spiritual influences which worked for good in the world, and that they became indeed the vehicles for the ruined Spirits whose cause they had made their own.

And like the Gadarene swine, they became victims of the destruction they had themselves engendered. At length, one after the other, all the terrorists found their way to the scaffold, each betraying the other. Robespierre came with his broken jaw bound with filthy linen; the executioner ripped it off, his face fell apart, and he gave a roar like a lion at bay which sent shivers through the crowd. The most blood-stained of them all, Fouquier-Tinville was followed all the way to the scaffold by a woman who clung to the back of the cart, and screamed at him: "Give me back my husband. Give me back my husband." And then, at length, the instigator of it all, Philippe Duc d'Orléans himself, amid the derisive howls from the mob: "You voted for the death of your kinsman," and again, "Scoundrel, it is you who are the cause of all our ills!" "It was you who had the Princesse de Lamballe assassinated." However, he had fortified himself with champagne before taking this last journey across Paris. Like all demagogues, now the game was up he could afford to sneer at the *canaille*, the vile mob. And so he who had stirred the dregs of the populace of Paris, bribed hordes of brigands in the countrysides to burn the châteaux, voted for the death of the King, and started in motion this hideous avalanche which every passing day had gathered force and momentum and volume, he himself was hurled at last into the bottomless abyss.

CHAPTER XXVIII

SCENES OF THE FRENCH REVOLUTION

WHILE Boufflers and Madame de Sabran were exiled, they received news of the horrors in France from friends who escaped. After listening to the tale of their country's destruction, and of the fall of a most exquisite civilization, they were never the same again.

What were these scenes, brought so vividly to their imaginations by eye-witnesses? It is no good asking Carlyle!

Unfortunately for the interests of truth, Carlyle has set the tone in England for far too much romantic nonsense written on the French Revolution. His oratorical declamations have blurred the outlines of many vignettes. However, if true scholarship is rooted in a certain delicacy and fastidiousness of taste, what can one expect from a man who blew his nose into his woollen gloves?

Great precision of outline is the key-note of the original documents which describe revolutionary scenes. With the help of these memoirs, it is necessary to make an excursion into Paris itself, so that the sounds, the sights, the very smells may come back to one.

At the outbreak of the Revolution, when Paris was filling with deputies from all over the country, what were the manners of these "democratic" gentlemen who modelled themselves on the ancients and spoke so often of "their virtue, their incorruptible soul and their sensibility"? Manners! The Théâtre Français was obliged to put up the following notice in the theatre: "Sirs, you are requested to take off your bonnets and not to commit nuisances in the boxes."

The city wished to provide prostitutes for the hordes of men, new to Paris, who were seeking amusement—those same crowds of deputies who flocked to see the sights of Petit-Trianon and made it so unbearable that the Royal Family went away for a time. The police were too occupied elsewhere to track down prostitution, and it grew with alarming rapidity. At the windows of the Rue St. Honoré and the Palais-Royal and its neighbourhood, "ladies" were watching the crowds below and making signs. "Walking-out sisters", as they were called, were oozing out of everywhere, from furnished rooms in attics, in basements, in the back-rooms of shops, or even from dormitories kept by horrible matrons around the Palais-Royal. In these slept together women aged from twelve to forty, *grisettes* on strike from the workrooms, little apprentices who had quarrelled with their dressmakers, flower-girls, all waiting their turn to satisfy the lusts of so-called democrats.

By 1790 this army began to divide into three classes. A publisher who had a flair for business, discreetly launched a useful little booklet of names, addresses, prices and other information. It was sold in locked boxes to excite curiosity, and gave the particular attraction of each *belle*, and the minimum fee required. "If you are economical, go to Victorine whose favours you will gain with six *livres* and a bowl of punch. Same tariff *chez* la Paysanne, number 132, but you are warned that this demoiselle sleeps all night."

Prostitution had its own set of aristocrats—"femmes du monde"—living in luxury on the second floor of the Palais-Royal, where the ceilings were low but the views delightful. These had charming manners and varied talents, such as playing the piano, singing and dancing, and some of them were even accomplished housewives. Their method was to make arrangements with one, two, three or even four strangers, and be attached exclusively to them, visiting the theatres and the surrounding countryside with them. Beware if they enticed the man to play *biribi* or *trente et un*, for then the provincial dullard would be trapped and plucked like a trussed chicken.

Unusual amusement was promised to those visiting a certain *boutique* in the Rue St. Honoré, for there could be found pseudo-nuns who claimed to have escaped from their convents without even having had time to throw on a few clothes, and who told their clients heartrending stories of forced vows. So this is how these idealists of 1790, who made such fine speeches about the dignity of man and the regeneration of the human race, spent their leisure.

In the Spring of 1792 a terrible new element made its appearance in Paris—the band of ruffians who, from the tattered garments they wore that did duty as breeches, became known as the *sans-culottes*. These young boys were like hooligans in any great city; they inspired such terror everywhere that at the mere sight of them, peaceable inhabitants would fly, trembling, into their homes, and barricade the doors. Two to three hundred of them invaded the gardens of the Tuileries and stirred up popular feeling against the Queen, and insulted her under her windows.

Is it surprising that the Royal Family attempted to flee to Varennes the following June? When they were caught and forcibly brought back, their doom was only a matter of days.

The sack of the Tuileries Palace took place on the following 10th of August. The members of the Royal Family were obliged to flee, and were later imprisoned in the Temple. The King, with his usual imbecile inability to protect himself, had given a written order to his Swiss Guards not to fire on the mob if they attacked the Palace. The rabble, hearing of this, surged through and started massacring them. Some fled through the gardens. Young Napoleon, who passed through the Tuileries gardens at that moment, declared, at the end of his life, that none of his battlefields had given him the idea of so many corpses as in the Tuileries gardens on this August morning, strewn with the bodies of the Swiss Guards. (In order to picture the scene accurately it is, of course, necessary to see the Palace without the modern Rue de Rivoli running alongside.)

The crowd, emboldened by success, swelled into a mighty torrent. With nothing to stop them, they broke into the Palace and surged up the main staircase, making straight for the Queen's bedroom. There, a mad rage for destruction seized them. Furniture was flung from the windows, the great mirrors in which "Medicis-Antoinette had studied the hypocritical airs she showed in public" flew into a thousand fragments; treasures of art, clocks, pictures, porcelain, silver, jewels were pillaged and destroyed. Women of the town rushed to her vast cupboards and started putting on her hats. Then they all tried on the gowns. The floor was strewn with odd things like loose piano-keys, and tatters of the Queen's pink petticoats. One woman threw herself into her bed and shrieked out: "There's somebody under the mattress." They tore it off, and found a Swiss guard there trembling, whom they murdered with yells of glee and diabolical laughter. After this, they took the mattresses and hurled them out of the windows, and the gardens were thick with floating feathers.

In the meantime the men had gone down to the royal cellars, in which were stored ten thousand bottles of wines and liqueurs. They started popping corks and drinking indiscriminately from the bottles. No less than two hundred died of the effects. While some were vomiting or lying in a helpless stupor on the cellar floors, others bore supplies to their comrades upstairs and outside. Soon the gardens and the courtyards of the château were a sea of broken glass. Before long, the insurgents were in a state of complete dementia. Shrieking, whooping, breaking bottles and mirrors as they went, they streamed down to the kitchens where the servants—who thought themselves safe—were continuing their work. Every man, from the *chef* to the meanest scullion, perished. It has been said that "the cooks' heads fell into the saucepans where they were preparing the viands". A petrified under-cook who had not had time to escape, was thrust into a copper and exposed to the heat of the furnace. Then the assassins turned their attentions to the food, to that last meal which the Royal Family never ate. "One carries off chickens on a spit," says Mercier, "another a turbot; that one a carp from the Rhine as large as himself . . . A murderer played the violin beside the corpses; and thieves, with their pockets full of gold, hanged other thieves on the banisters." Hordes of *sans-culottes* then searched the Palace from the topmost attic down to the remotest cellar, to ferret out anyone left in hiding. If they found any Swiss guard moaning in his death-throes, they finished him off.

Then dreadful mutilations of the dead took place, with young women presiding. It was hard to tell whether it was blood or wine that streamed in great red rivulets along the polished parquet floors. "Cutlets of Swiss" were grilled before the fires and eaten, and a hireling of the Duc d'Orléans drank a glass of blood.

Outside could be seen the dead bodies of the Swiss, with gloating women perched on them like vultures. A girl of eighteen was seen plunging a sabre into the corpses. A weird sound filled the air: it was the *Dies Irae* (Day of Wrath and Doom) played on the chapel organ by a young Savoyard.

The corpses were left about till they began to stink, then they were hastily and inadequately buried in the cellars. After a day or two, a man passing in a street near the Tuileries had to cover his head with his coat, so nauseating were the whiffs blowing from the Palace in those hot August days. Madame Vigée Lebrun said that pregnant women went about the streets yellow with fear. And yet, even as they were burying the Swiss, people stopped to read the notice near by: "Madame Broquin *continues* to sell her flesh-coloured pomatum for dyeing the hair."

So much for the humanity and fraternity fostered by a so-called democratic system founded on mob rule. Now for the integrity of the leaders when it came to dealing with the wealth of their victims when it fell into their hands. Nothing illustrates this so vividly as the little story of what happened to Madame du Barry's jewels at her château of Louvecienne—it reads like a miniature detective tale of the reign of Terror.

Louvecienne (*louve ancienne*) was a peaceful hamlet of a hundred and twenty-four fires, clustering round its church. The village was composed of gardens and orchards, and was enclosed by groves of tall chestnut trees where the peasants danced on

Summer evenings. The noble arches of Marly aqueduct give this picturesque landscape the Italian aspect of a piece of scenery by Hubert Robert. Old inhabitants of eighty years ago still remembered having seen the du Barry on the steps of the house teasing two white monkeys which jumped about after her handkerchief. Herself one of the people and beloved by the peasants for her generosity, the du Barry, now fifty years old, thought herself safe, far away from the Revolution in this little retreat. True, she sometimes got an unpleasant glimpse of it, as on the morning of October 6th, 1789, when she saw some of the Queen's wounded guard seeking for shelter under her roof after having dragged themselves through hedge and over ditch from Versailles. As all her former friends had emigrated, she sometimes sighed as she looked round at her empty dining-room, immortalized in Moreau's perfect engraving of a supper party, and thought how deserted it looked now. But the bronzes chiselled by the peerless Gouthière were still a dream. "Tiresome," thought she. "I haven't paid his bill yet, and he keeps asking." (Gouthière died in great poverty with the bill unpaid.)

She continued to go up to Paris sometimes for a night, to see her lover, the Duc de Cossé-Brissac.

There was a man staying at the village inn called Greive, who appeared to be interested in the du Barry, and used to enquire about her from the innkeeper. He was always watching the road. When her jewels were stolen and the comtesse went to England to try to retrieve them, he became the oracle of the whole village, and talked about the "flight" of the comtesse.

Greive was a revolutionary government official, and when the du Barry returned to Louvecienne, he sent soldiers to the house to arrest her. She attempted to flee, but was overtaken at the bottom of the park. She shrieked as the soldiers placed their rough hands on her—this woman of the people, who had cheered the last days of a king whose example of moral turpitude set such an example to the whole of Paris and eventually spread a canker of rottenness throughout the kingdom. A man who chanced to be passing along the road at the time heard her sobs as the carriage passed through the gates, and they were enough to melt a heart of stone.

In prison, in the hope that she would be spared, she confessed where she had hidden all her remaining treasures—in ponds, under trees, in cellars, in all kinds of strange places. Long after the Revolution fragments of this mighty wreck were still to be found in the villagers' homes.

But that is just where Greive did not want them to be: he questioned all the peasants, and effected a wholesale surrender of the property by force of threats. Even in the waters of Marly watches were found. By this search for buried treasure the village was brought to ruin: lust for gold was its undoing.

And what of the stolen jewels, the famous diamonds which Greive was commissioned to find? They were never found! And no regular confiscation of the other treasures took place, no honestly conducted sale. The reason of this is simple: they were stolen by Greive himself. He had watched until he saw her coach going off to Paris for the night; then he bribed some ruffians to steal up to her young scarlet-clad porter, who acted as sentinel outside the château gates, and lure him away to a wine-shop and make him dead drunk. The rest was easy, in spite of her staff of twelve servants.

All her servants were imprisoned, too. Knowing that they could only regain their freedom by denouncing their employer, they consented to do so. Zamor, the plumed and bejewelled nigger-boy, who had lived in the lap of luxury and owed everything to the du Barry, called her "a Bacchante crowned with ivy and roses".

Before following the du Barry to the guillotine, one might try to form a reasonably clear picture of what this journey to the guillotine was: for the usual accounts of it have been excessively vague.

At first, the Grand Guignol processions of tumbrils full of victims caused a great sensation, completely novel as they were. It is not surprising that the cook on her day off should have lingered for such a free show. True, it blocked the traffic and paralysed trade for the time being, but it was worth it. It was preceded by the rolling of drums and the raucous singing of revolutionary songs. One of these has the sound of bones being rattled on tin cans by devils let loose from Hell:

He will obtain a cure
My *guingueraingou*,
He will obtain a cure
By praying devoutly
To the holy Guillotinette
My *guingeraingette*.

I would buy heads
If I had the means,
At fêtes I would carry
One in each hand.
Long live the Guillotine
Which looks so nice
And cuts off so well
The heads of these dogs!

My fine aristocrats
Into Samson's sack
Let us spit!

To this cacophony were added the cries of the news-vendors: "Here is the list of the winners of the lottery of the most holy Guillotine." Every window would be filled with onlookers, every doorway and balcony packed.

Suddenly the cry would go up: "They're coming. Look. Here they are." Then a flood of imprecations, beginning like a snarl and ending in fierce shrieks, and more revolutionary songs, with the cart now coming in sight. It is difficult for us to realize how terrifying is the roar of a huge, angry crowd, increasing steadily in volume. Hate is a terrible thing. It is Hate which makes Hell so murky. And their eyes, glittering; and sometimes they would spit. . . .

The victims were sitting with their hands tightly bound behind them, with their hair cut short above the neck line. A disappointing spectacle on the whole, because all these people, with the single exception of the du Barry, remained calm and carried themselves proudly. They had been called away at recreation-time in the prison, usually about six in the evening, and they left quietly, as if not wanting to disturb a game of cards in some drawing-room of the old days. The Duc de Biron had called for oysters and white wine. He ordered another glass for his executioner, and said: "Take this wine. You must need it in your trade." The public prosecutor, Fouquier-Tinville, used to watch the departure of the victims from a window and cackle with unholy glee.

No emotion showed in the faces of the aristocrats, unless perhaps a slight touch of contempt, a glance of supercilious and faintly-amused interest, as if to say: "*Dieu*, what a commotion!"; a little curl of the lip and quiver of the nostril, as if to say: "*Dieu*, what a smell!" But nothing more. Their composure infuriated the revolutionaries to such a degree that there was serious talk of having them bled by a leech before leaving prison, so that their nerve might go. One old courtier put rouge on his cheeks so that the crowd might not think him pale from fear. When Delphine saw him in prison by candlelight, the night before her husband's execution, the sight was so totally unexpected—this old man in his swansdown-edged dressing-gown, his night-cap and his rouge—that she started to laugh, and she and Armand had violent hysterics. (They were still so young.)

On the way to execution, woe betide the victim who met an old enemy, for she would have to endure jeers and obscene insults shouted at her all the way, like the duchess whose fine carriages had excited the envy of the working women in her district, so that when they saw her in a cart, riding with her back to the horse, they cried out, shaking their fists and spitting: "Ah, ha, different sort of carriage this time, isn't it, my beauty!"

On the scaffold, ingrained courtliness would show itself, even at the hour of death. Marie-Antoinette, treading on Samson's foot, says: "I beg your pardon." All the courtiers dying before Madame Elizabeth bow low to her as their turn comes, and all the ladies curtsey to her and kiss her. The sixteen Carmelite nuns of Compiègne ask the blessing of their prioress and her "permission" to die.

Once a very young man on the way to the guillotine called out: "Is there anyone here who will go to number 16 Rue de la Vieille-Draperie?" "Yes, I will go," answers a voice in the crowd. "Thank you, my boy; go and tell my wife and children that I die loving them, and that they must console each other."

Sometimes the victims searched the sea of faces for a priest who would give them Absolution as they passed. The Abbé Carrichon, a non-juring priest, gave Absolution to the Noailles family. He had arranged that they should recognize him by his red waistcoat and his dark blue coat.

Madame Vigée Lebrun says that this courage made their doom more certain. "The imagination of the people is not vivid enough to make them realize unfamiliar suffering. It is easier to excite their pity than their imagination." (But a priest, an eye-witness, said of the whole spectacle that it had a hateful fascination. It was impossible, he said, not to look.) This fortitude of the victims did not stand them in good stead in the long run. When Madame du Barry's shrieks were heard, many onlookers fled from the scene, and closed their doors, uttering cries of horror. The Terror might have been shortened if they had all done that: it would have lacerated the nerves of the onlookers to shreds. Instead, they were numbed by a surfeit of emotion, or simply bored because the victims were so quiet. "After a while," says Marie-Victoire Bonnard, a little seamstress, "carts passed and we worked on, hardly lifting our heads as they went by."

At last, the place of execution is reached. You could tell it with your eyes shut, by the stench of blood. The hole dug under the scaffold to receive the blood is quickly filled, and the exhalations poison the air. The neighbours are always complaining, as they are afraid of plague, and the guillotine is moved to different quarters of Paris.

The women are indifferent to losing their lives, but to the very last they feel that any affront to their modesty is worse than death, and this is the only thing that loosens their tongues.

Madame Elizabeth, whose neckerchief had become unpinned, whispered to the assistant: "In the name of your mother, *Monsieur*, cover me." It was the same with Charlotte Corday. Poor Marie-Antoinette had already drunk her fill of this kind of humiliation before she left the prison, where, worn-out by haemorrhage, she was obliged to change her linen under the peering eyes of the jailer who refused to look the other way.

The last one to be guillotined has the worst time. He sees his companions having their hands unbound, their coats taken off: then quickly, deftly, with graceful movements, the executioners' assistants in red short-sleeved overalls, holding a red rose in their mouths, lays him face downwards on a plank; there is the noise of a wooden halter falling to keep the neck steady, then Samson takes the rope and lets the slanting knife fall. The head drops into a basket and the body is thrust in after it.

Was death as painless as it was made out to be? They said of Madame du Barry that "the knife cut badly into her fat neck." Some French surgeons at the beginning of the last century declared it an excruciating form of death.

After the last victim had gone there was a roll of drums, the Marseillaise was sung, and the crowd dispersed. Those who had been to an execution could be recognized from the bloody footsteps they left behind for a long way in the street.

Then, dusk falling on the deserted square, the cart with the bodies would make its way slowly to some mysterious burial ground, escorted by the grave diggers and a police sergeant.

And then more Grand Guignol. At first the executioners had been allowed to keep the clothes of their victims. Later they were given to the poor, to prisoners, and to the sick in the hospitals. At the edge of the gaping trench, three-quarters of which was filled by the previous batches of bodies covered in quicklime, the officials stripped the headless corpses and flung them naked on top of those of the day before. How terrible to think that, till the snarling of the Trump of Doom, you might be lying near your worst enemy! No privacy, even in the grave.

Wood fires were kept burning: thyme, sage and juniper were thrown on them. Then the coats, jackets, women's dresses, shoes, boots, capes and shirts were sorted into different heaps, of which a clerk made an inventory. The blood-stiffened finery was sent to the river before being distributed. [Ah, Seine!]

The officials had wardrobes containing treasures found hidden on the victims, never given up during the frequent searchings. A knife would be secreted in a garter, a packet of love-letters tied with a hair-ribbon in a bodice. What pathetic relics—a censer chain, a sack containing twenty-five *fleur-de-lys*, a figure of Christ in silver, a pine box containing a pair of bracelets with men's portraits mounted in gold and surmounted with diamonds, a chalice and paten, rings, tobacco boxes, a linen *fichu* embroidered with *fleur-de-lys*, a broken tortoise-shell box containing a picture of a woman and child.

After the Queen's death, they found in her cell: "A box of powder, a swansdown powder-puff and a tin of pomatum, and, amongst other garments, fifteen chemises of fine linen, richly trimmed with lace and twenty-eight cambric handkerchiefs." The Queen's underlinen and dresses were taken to the Salpêtrière and were kept for a long time by the one to whom they were given. A soldier had picked up and restored to the Conciergerie the shabby black silk shoe, full of holes, which slipped off her foot as she mounted the scaffold. It was exhibited in 1865 at the Musée des Souvenirs, and I have seen a drawing of it.

[How pitiful are some of the relics of the Revolution, and what strange things happened to them. After Versailles was abandoned by the monarchy, the great coverlet from Louis XIV's bed disappeared. Many years later there died in Versailles a mysterious woman living alone in great squalor, and when she was laid out they found that in fact she was a man, and that he was in possession of the king's bedspread. At the great auction at the Palace which lasted over a year, it would have been interesting to trace the journeyings of some of these mute witnesses of the last days of splendour. By the strangest of coincidences the chairs of Madame Elizabeth were bought by the modern owner of Montreuil, and he never knew what they were until he turned them over one day and found written underneath: "Garde-meuble de Madame Elizabeth." One wonders, too, what was the ultimate fate of all those precious vestments and reliquaries stolen from churches and worn in sacrilegious processions in the streets. They may still lie forgotten in some attic.]

Here is an account of the du Barry's death given by an eyewitness: "On arriving at the Pont-au-Change I found that a fairly large crowd had assembled. I had no need to ask the reason, for an explanation was soon forthcoming. I heard piercing screams in the distance, and immediately saw the death-cart . . . leaving the courtyard of the Palais de Justice. In this, as it slowly approached the place where I stood, I saw a woman whose face, attitude and gestures expressed the deepest despair. Now deep red, now deadly pale, struggling in the hands of the executioner and his assistants, who had difficulty in keeping her on her seat, uttering those *terrible cries* which I have just mentioned, she alternately appealed for their pity and for that of the onlookers. It was Madame du Barry being taken to the scaffold. . . .

"Entirely clothed in white, like Madame Elizabeth, who a few weeks before had passed along the same route, her most beautiful hair formed a contrast similar to that presented by a pall thrown over a coffin. Her hair at the back was cut level with the nape of her neck, as is usual in the case of those who are being led to execution; but that in front fell every moment over her forehead, owing to her wild movements, and hid part of her face. 'In heaven's name, my friends, save me!' she cried, in the midst of sobs and tears. 'In heaven's name, save me. I have never done harm to anyone. Save me!' No one had the courage to insult her. *It all created a great impression. People were stupefied by her piercing cries.* Force was used to attach her to the plank. 'Pardon! pardon! *Monsieur le bourreau!* Give me a moment more, mister executioner, just a moment . . .' And then all was over."

What a contrast here to the way the priests met their butchers at the Carmes prison. Some of them had been reading their Breviaries, and the Commissioner was so struck by the expression on their faces that, when it was all over, he said: "It beats me; I don't understand it at all. . . . Those priests went to their death as cheerfully as if they were going to a wedding."

And yet they had spent a terrible day and night in anticipation, for they could hear the piercing screams of other victims being killed with swords—*not by the people, however*, but by bands of hired ruffians. St. Méard says their chief concern was to know what position they should adopt in order to die less painfully and more quickly, and after sending their comrades to watch at the windows, they decided not to protect their heads with their hands, else hands and arms only fell before the bodies.

In prison the well-bred were still true to the traditions of their caste, even though they were waiting every evening for their name to be read out on the death roll. In Saint-Lazare, when domestic tasks were done, the inmates became people of the world again, calling on their neighbours, paying their respects to those of higher rank, observing the laws of etiquette just as scrupulously as if they had been at Versailles. It is at Saint-Lazare that Hubert Robert painted charming little landscapes on plates with the prison stamp on them.

At the Conciergerie, where the women had a fountain in their courtyard and could therefore wash clothes, they wore three different *toilettes* each day, just as at Court. "They appeared in the morning in a coquettish *néglig*é, the parts of which were adjusted so neatly and gracefully that the general effect did not give the least indication that they had passed the night on a pallet, or more frequently on fetid straw. At midday they dressed with care, and their hair was becomingly arranged. Their manners, even, were different from those of the morning—more distinguised and imbued with a kind of dignity. In the evening they changed again into *déshabillé*."

A number of these women, particularly if they had no money, spent their nights surrounded by rats and other vermin, in a vitiated atmosphere. There were not enough beds, and some took it in turn to remain standing, in order not to be stifled by having to lie on top of one another. At the Carmes prison, Delphine shared a room with the future Empress Joséphine, whose wails and tears made everyone blush for her.

In the great prison of the Château de Chantilly, those who were rich enough could have things arranged to their advantage—strangely enough, in the midst of all the egalitarian boasting. They paid and received calls, played cards, balloon, chess; went for picnics, enjoyed tea-parties and music. Some asked an old fortune-teller to predict for them, and sometimes they would turn pale at what she told them. The young people met in the courtyard, or acted Proverbs, and there were some charming flirtations. All the customs and even the ridicules of high society reappeared with these people who were going to die any day. Dresses were fastidiously cared for, and some of the women decked their heads with flowers, plumes and ribbons, while others had frizzed, curled, powdered wigs.

Money was the key that unlocked most doors. The Comtesse de Böhn, in her account of the prisons of 1793, says that the soldiers on guard were usually former lackeys, who now came into rooms without knocking, threatening and swearing at their ex-employers. The chief *concierge* at Chantilly was a well-known bandit, who had been dismissed from the Duc de Beauvais' for theft. She describes how, returning to Paris—still as prisoners, of course—no *concierge* of any prison would admit them, because they looked too poor to make any handsome payment! At last, after searching far into the night, they were thrown into a certain prison. At two o'clock in the morning the *concierge*, arrayed in a white piqué dressing-gown and with a *madras* artistically arranged round his head, poked his lantern under their eyes and said: "There, my beauties, don't worry, you'll spend the night here; they deceived me, you seem well-born women—I recognize them when I see them."

Those in the know would pass on the trick of how to bribe the soldiers so that when precious possessions were handed over, something, at least, could be kept back. The soldiers would be vexed if things were surrendered too easily. They liked to be bribed in kind, with liqueurs or clothes; and there was one who coveted a great green curtain, which he put on, and, as it made him look like a barrel, all the prisoners laughed.

The Government seemed to provide nothing for these prisoners. They were put into rooms, after a long fast, in the dark, with no fire, no bed and no water. The warder of their part of the prison, an old coachman of the Duc de Nivernais, appeared on the scene, swearing hard and demanding twenty *sous* for oil for a lamp. When he heard that the ladies were friends of his old master he changed completely and said: "Why didn't you say so before?"

But even money would not command medical attendance. At Chantilly a lady died of measles without having been able to see a doctor. Someone else had a stillborn child, and it was left with the mother for twenty-four hours before being taken away. Another woman (wife of a doctor) who drank half a bottle of brandy per day—as many women did—threw herself out of the window, was picked up alive in a broken condition and left to die alone.

People in England at the time of the Revolution imagined that the whole of Paris was a scene of carnage. Nothing could be farther from the truth. One of the extraordinary things about the city was the complete ignorance of one district about another, typified in the unconcern of housewives going on with their marketing while the massacring was taking place at the Tuileries near by. During the September massacres at the Carmes, there could be wholesale murder of priests and nothing known of it in the local taverns. The propaganda of the Duc d'Orléans had been so clever that the working class felt little emotion: they had been hoodwinked into believing that the victims were the enemies of the nation and deserved their fate. They were even afraid lest the aristocrats should escape from prison and murder them. The whole thing was looked upon as a work of justice, and they went about their daily tasks as usual. Only after the execution of Louis XVI does an eyewitness say that everybody walked slowly and people hardly dared to look at one another. Women were sad and life took on a drab air, for everybody wore darker clothes.

Pitt and Burke, who pictured Parisians covered in rags and blood, would have been surprised had they seen, hardly three days after the 10th August, the cheerful crowds in the Tuileries gardens—at the very time that they were burying the massacred Swiss guards. And the Champs-Elysées were still full of charming women riding in elegant phaetons. This can only be explained by the extreme insularity of the Parisians. Paris was, as it still is, composed of many little townships, each having its own particular trade. The inhabitants hardly ever crossed their frontiers. They met at each other's doorsteps, and gossiped on Sundays at the nearest tavern. They intermarried, and were occupied together in the same trade. They were not in the least interested in the neighbouring district.

Amid the fearful bloodshed of the Terror, nothing seems to have stirred the women of Paris so deeply as the question of butter—"butter of which they make a god!" says Daubun. Thus the Committee of Public Safety describes as one of the chief dangers of the capital "the crowds waiting for butter, which are more numerous and more turbulent than ever". It is one of the tragi-comedies of human life that in the midst of cataclysms, nothing is so real to us as a shoe that pinches our own foot.

The housewives, after being promised an era of plenty by the demagogues, began to have a hard time of it in earnest by the year 1793. The food situation was then very serious. There was a shortage of sugar and soap at the end of February, of bread at the end of May and June. There were queues outside bakers' shops from midnight till eleven the next morning, and if the stock were exhausted it was no good shouting, or the shopkeeper threw a pail of water over you from above. Butchers slipped pigs' trotters into your allowance of meat, and said: "Be damned to you!" if you complained. Timid housewives would not dare to protest against shopkeepers who charged above the official maximum price. Then in the winter of 1793–4 no candles, because there were no cattle, and therefore no fat; and no wood for fires. People had to go to bed at dusk, and there was an epidemic of bronchitis and chilblains. And, of course, unemployment was rising by leaps and bounds, as one luxury trade after another collapsed. It is sad to see all the craftsmen of the great Parisian industries losing their skill—painters of Sèvres china, weavers of carpets and tapestries, cabinet-makers, goldsmiths and jewellers, makers of snuff-boxes and of fans, engravers who had learnt their art from their fathers and grandfathers before them, tailors and dressmakers. Even Marat himself said that in twenty years there would not be found in Paris a single man who could make a decent pair of shoes.

However, in the midst of all this, the humble, apparently insignificant little lives of many *bourgeois* families continued just as ever. Precious details are given to us in the *Journal of a Governess*. The author draws for us an entrancing vignette of a family—mother, daughter and son—living in a house of the

Rue St. Marc. They also owned a tiny cottage amongst the vines of Auteuil, near the property of the artist, Hubert Robert. In the great heat of the summer of 1793, six days after Marat had been murdered in his slipper-bath by Charlotte Corday, the boulevards were crowded with people taking the air. It is strange to think of the many small householders going on with their usual occupations in that stifling heat, while a young woman, coming by coach from the provinces, takes a room at a hotel, unpacks her clothes and slips out to buy a carving knife. Little people, the hour of deliverance is near! A descendant of the great Corneille, a beautiful and heroic French girl cast in the mould of Joan of Arc, (and who, it appears, was not approved of at her convent school) is going to assassinate the monster, and thus paralyse the hand which is still signing death-warrants.

On January 21st, 1794, this *bourgeois* family of the Rue St. Marc had apparently forgotten that this was the first anniversary of the king's death and, in spite of the food shortage, they gave a dinner party to three of their friends. What a menu! including, amongst other things, *raie au beurre noire*, fried soles and a dessert of cheese, apples, pears, plum jam and *raisiné*, (grape and pear jam), all of this being accompanied by a wonderful Malaga wine and brought to a climax by cherries in brandy. The conversation turned on the prevailing clothes shortage, when one of them said they had seen in a second-hand shop of the Rue du Bac a grand dress for twenty-two *livres*. It could be cut up into corsets, gaiters, petticoats and slippers! After many bargainings, it was duly bought. Alas, the dressmaker could do nothing with it, as the material had perished. Perhaps it was the Court gown of some great lady of Versailles, stolen by her maid and sold to a second-hand shop of the Rue du Bac!

The family went a great deal to the theatre. No doubt they saw the play, produced shortly after the execution of Louis XVI, in which Pope Pius VI threw his tiara at the head of Catherine II, who replied by smashing the pontifical cross with a blow of her sceptre, while the King of Spain lost his cardboard nose. Thérèse, the cook of the household, seems to have been a dear creature. When she took the little girl Ziguette to the Louvre she wore a dress of blue satin with big pleats and a shawl "*gorge de pigeon*". When the whole family went for a Spring picnic to Auteuil they took a cab to the city barrier, and then Thérèse ran races in the field with Ziguette, before unpacking a huge hamper stuffed with an enormous *pâté*, salad, gingerbread, brandy, fish, apples, cheese, and coffee.

How curious is the calm of this family, living so near the Tuileries and the Palais-Royal, within ear-shot of howling mobs and firing guns. They took each day as it came, and preserved a good humour, which in itself was a form of courage.

A little Parisian seamstress, Marie-Victoire Bonnard, who had come on the roof of her father's stage coach to become an apprentice to a *lingère* near the Rue St. Honoré, wrote some memoirs which also throw light on this everyday life that simple people continued to live amid the carnage. She was sent on errands by her mistress, always taking care to put the red, white and blue cockade on her hat—the girls in the workroom all shared the same one, and it was dangerous to go out without it. During the September massacre of priests, she was coming back from the Faubourg St. Honoré when she met some butchers' carts full of carcases of calves. Seeing that the passers-by gazed at them with horror, she looked more closely and stifled a cry: a human arm was sticking out here, a leg there, blood was oozing out on the pavement. The cart stopped. The macabre monster who was driving it—a thin, pale man with a pointed nose—cried out: "You see this rascally priest in the heap?" He made a body sit up, but it was still warm and limp, and it flopped down. He slapped the dead priest's face and shouted out: "I had a lot of trouble to kill the *scélérat* (the villain). And high time, too, for he had some false paper money in his pocket."

Marie-Victoire later on went to another *lingère*, Mme Rataud, in the Rue des Petits-Champs, who was certainly not a patriot. One day Marie-Victoire was mystified because Mme Rataud told her not to come for supper at her table, as she usually did. She stayed in the workroom while a delicious smell of fried chicken pervaded the house. After a while, a tall, good-looking man passed quickly through the workroom into the back of the shop, hiding his face in a handkerchief. He stayed there for four hours. She writes: "This accursed chicken made me resentful for a long time afterwards." The stranger was none other than the Marquis de Ségur: Mme Rataud had been a servant of his in the good old days. One wonders how many other devoted retainers provided their one-time masters with a decent meal in those troubled times. Isolated instances of devotion from servants to their employers run like a thread of gold in this dark, blood-stained arras of the Revolution, from the *bonne*, Marguerite, who assisted the Marquise de la Tour du Pin through her numerous confinements and was a kind of watch-dog to the whole family, down to Delphine's Nanny, Nanette, who looked after Astolphe de Custine during all the months that his mother was in prison, and nearly got lynched by a crowd for sticking up for General de Custine. She met street criers calling out atrocious insults against "the traitor Custine", so elbowing her way through the mob, she started shouting: "What do you dare to say against General de Custine? All lies, I tell you. I was born at his home and brought up by him, so I know him better than you do. He is my master and he is worth all of you put together, do you hear?"

And in face of numberless testimonies like these, Carlyle would still have us believe that it was a people's revolution.

CHAPTER XXIX

ELÉONORE RECEIVES A PROPOSAL

"Come into my arms," said Prince Henry to Boufflers when he arrived in Germany at last. And so it was as his guest that he and Eléonore spent the years 1791–1797, years of which we have almost no record.[1] The news which reached them from France was growing more and more sinister. In January, 1793, Louis XVI was guillotined; Marie-Antoinette followed him to the scaffold on October 16th. Like *émigrés* all over Europe who had been loyal to the monarchy, Eléonore and Boufflers went into mourning, and heard a Mass for the repose of their souls. The Prussians invaded France, and the revolutionaries made this an excuse for the Terror. The year 1794 was particularly terrible for Eléonore, for in January Delphine's husband, Armand, was guillotined, in spite of her heroic efforts to save him, and in February, Delphine herself was imprisoned at the Prison des Carmes, in company with Joséphine de Beauharnais who was later to become Napoleon's first wife and Empress. The Revolutionary Tribunal sat from March, 1793, till May, 1795. Boufflers' sister was guillotined, and many other friends and relations. Delphine was released in July, 1794, with the fall of Robespierre. In 1797 the estates and houses of exiles were confiscated by the French Government and became national property.

1797. Nearly twenty years since Boufflers and Eléonore had first met. He was now fifty-nine, she forty-eight. Though the loss of so many of their loved ones in France had naturally left its indelible mark, they were always young in mind and manner. In fact, when Boufflers was an old man someone said of him that he was "still quite young". The Chevalier had suffered from bad attacks of depression. At first, in the drawing-rooms

[1] M. Gaston Maugras intended to publish some letters in his possession, relative to that period.

of Prince Henry, his conversation had been as brilliant as ever. But as he spoke so fast, and his ideas were like shooting stars, German society did not understand a word he said. When his witty sallies were greeted in silence, he thought he'd become a bore, and this worried him a great deal. Also, like every true Frenchman abroad, he endured moments of unbearable home-sickness. It needed all Eléonore's great tenderness and gentleness, born of her long understanding, to make him smile at all. How sorry she felt for him: he had always roamed freely all over Europe, and done what he liked. And even if he'd been poor, at least he'd had some revenues. Now he was an exile, a man of immense physical and intellectual energy, with no future, no scope or profession, and, above all, no money. Without clinging to him, or revealing her secret delight that at last after all those years, he was constantly with her, Eléonore tried to distract and amuse him by little things.

One August, she decided to take him to a little farm called Merkatz, which Prince Henry of Prussia had given them on his estates. She would get him to help her to pick cherries and make jam! We have a delightful letter which Boufflers sent afterwards to the Prince on the first of September. Speaking of the cherries, he says:

". . . our proud victor exercises cruelties on her prisoners unparalleled in any wars; to soil herself with their blood, to wrench out their hearts, and, what am I saying, to cut off their tails, those are the atrocities I saw her perpetrate, and which I still blush to have seconded. Then, after having plunged our hands, red with carnage, into the tranquil waters of Merkatz, we take a meal, more simple, more frugal and therefore more heroic than all meals of Homeric heroes. Without giving us time to eat our fill, she gives an order, and . . . in a trice they bring wood, they ply the bellows, they light the ovens, they hang up the hot-pots, and already billows are a-bubbling against the sides of the cauldron, when the goddess, who always tempers her fiercest cruelties, orders that sugar be brought. She plunges it into the boiling water and presides over the concoction, for she alone knows the exact degree of boiling required. . . .

"From time to time I suggested that the completing of the work be left to a faithful servant-girl, and my advice was always repelled with the same indignation. . . .

"Our steeds, who'd been waiting for more than four hours, bored with the long delay, dazzled with a little light, and goaded by the love of oats and the stable, were not easy to mount, and appeared disposed to outrun our desires. To prevent them from bolting, I walked on foot by the side of the ambling nag of the beauteous jam-maker, like the prime minister of Ahasuerus and Mordecai.

"All of a sudden, my horse, who was following, led by hand, escapes; the groom chases him. That set the bad example, and all our cavalcade was in a frenzy. Even Isabelle (that's the name of the ambling nag) rears two or three times; the horsewoman sits as firm as a rock, but after the danger is past she fears still greater mishaps, and wants to dismount. Well, as her wishes are no doubt written in the heavens in starry letters, my objections are vain. She dismounts, and, after crossing some sands, where she feared the fate of Cambyses, she reaches Rheinsberg, where a good supper, and above all the kind note of Monseigneur, make her forget all the fatigues of that memorable day."

What a charming picture! It is a change to see the Chevalier having to give in a little to Eléonore's caprices for a while, after all the years of trouble he had caused her by his elusiveness and his roving ways, his ambitions and his independence. And yet, it is easy to see that he adored her more than ever. This unsuspected feminine talent for jam-making no doubt filled him with admiration. And so he did as he was told, and helped her to stone the cherries and stir the pot.

After two years spent at Merkatz, jealous tongues had caused a misunderstanding between Boufflers and the Prince, and Boufflers detected a little coolness in his manner. Just then, the King of Prussia offered Boufflers an estate in Poland called Wimislov. He decided to accept it, and start a colony for French exiles there.

One day, in the Spring of 1797, Boufflers, looking for Eléonore, found her in the garden, walking in the cherry-orchard at Merkatz. She was holding a letter in her hands, and her face was radiant with happiness. He hurried to her and asked her what it was. She suddenly looked confused, blushed and said: "You will know, all in good time." But he persisted. "Don't be coy. Tell me at once what is in that letter."

Eléonore ran away into a mossy alley hedged with yew. She was as nimble and light-footed as ever, "like a little chamois". Vastly intrigued, and determined not to be rebuffed in this way, Stanislas, for all his sixty years, ran after her. He only managed to catch her because she was laughing so hard that she had to stop to get her breath. He seized hold of both her wrists and said: "Now, tell me at once, what is in this letter which is causing you such extraordinary happiness, and making you forget that you are a grandmother!"

She dropped the letter and throwing her arms around his neck, she cried: "Ah, my child, such good news, such wonderful news. This is the happiest day of my life. At last I'm as poor as you! I've just heard from France that the State has confiscated my house and all my property because I emigrated."

The Chevalier gave a gasp of amazement, then, suddenly, he understood. And he lost his head completely. He gave an enormous cry of joy which resounded all over the garden and, seizing her in his arms, he clasped her to his heart and covered her face with kisses.

This went on for some time, because they were both so happy and they didn't know what to say. Sometimes they held each other at arm's length, laughed into one another's eyes, and then fell to kissing again. At last she said: "Say it, say it quickly."

"What?"

"You know, the thing that it's unlucky for me to say *yet*."

He whispered in her ear: "Madame de Boufflers. Do you like the sound of it, eh, Comtesse de Sabran?"

"Yes, I adore it."

"Oh, you lovely creature. You are fairer than love itself."

After a while they went for a walk in the cherry-orchard. At a turn in the alley, suddenly glancing down at her, he saw that her eyes had filled with tears. "What is it, *cher amour?*"

"Ah, my child, I don't need to tell you."

He did indeed know, alas. She had always longed to have a son of his, and now it was too late. Boufflers, not knowing how to comfort her, knelt down at her feet, and leant his head against her breast. At this moment he became aware for the first time, of the suffering he had inflicted on her since they had first met. Any other woman with less sweetness of character, could have turned on him many a time and accused him, with truth, of ruining her life. But though she had suffered deeply, she had never reproached him. Realizing all this, and overwhelmed by the depth and constancy of her devotion, he said nothing, but remained very silent, with his head resting against her heart.

After a while, her tears ceased; looking down at his white hair, she bent to kiss his brow, furrowed with so many cares, and said: "But you are my child. Nothing can take *this* child away from me. Oh, I have always spoilt you so."

"We will spend the rest of our lives spoiling each other," he whispered. "You have always been right. I should have listened to you long ago. Will you really marry me and come and live with me at Wimislov? Then you will be like Aline, and your kingdom will be my heart. Nature will heal our griefs. Together we will find balm in the murmurs of field and wood, and in the music of one another's souls. Ah, my dearest love, it is strange that, like Aline's lover, I should wait till the end of my days before I learnt to be wise."

Almost immediately, Boufflers started for Wimislov to prepare for her arrival, and from Breslau he wrote her this enchanting letter—surely the most original proposal of marriage a woman has ever had! ["*Mais viens donc vite que je t'épouse, petite paresseuse, car cela devrait être fait depuis longtemps.*"]

"But come then quickly, so that I may marry you, little lazy one, for that should have happened long ago. You cannot imagine, my dear girl, or rather, I hope you can feel of your own accord instead of imagining, how greatly I am longing for this event. I can picture us two doing something serious together for the first time in our lives. You will be embarrassed without being *gauche*, as for me, I will content myself to be *gauche* without being embarrassed; well, anyway we shall manage, like so many others who have not been killed off by it. What flusters me most, though, is my wedding suit, because my chest has not yet arrived, for it was too difficult to go up-stream on the flooded river, but in the meantime I hope it will be possible to fix things up, and, in any case, if the bride appears before the chest, I won't be the one to complain.

"Here, you are the object of general admiration, they can't imagine how a woman, whom they all suppose must be accustomed to, and even dependent on, all the refinements and all the elegancies of France, should make up her mind to lie down on a heap of straw with an aged Job in the depths of Poland. . . .

"Do you know, I am quite cross with you, I've had no letter from you, and I shall be away for eight or ten days, during which time, if you have written to me, your letters will have to wait for me, and I assure you, whatever fun you may poke at me, all this is very tiresome for a newly-engaged man."

Again, on his way to Wimislov, he wrote to her in rhyme: "You complain of me, I complain of you; so we're quits; when I can, I will quickly seek my haven between your sheets in your arms; and Love, hand in hand with Hymen, will flee away no more."

His letters during this time are very tender:

"Your letter reeks of all the *chiffons* of balls, weddings, parties, plays, etc., in the midst of which it was written, and according to the famous adage: 'Tell me the company you keep and I'll tell you who you are,' your letter is nothing but a *chiffon*. However, that title of husband which you give me, that confession of your faults which you make to me, your assurance that you love me, that need you feel of Wimislov and therefore of me, all that touches me profoundly and gives to your little *chiffon* a price which . . . all the great ones of the century would never have been able to give to all their credit notes. Besides, that pretty comparison of the little bird who'd lost all his feathers, who on his wobbly little branch begins to sing again at the first ray of sunshine, and closes his poor little beak and hides it in his little half-naked breast at the approach of a storm, that charming miniature of your misfortunes, of your griefs, of your hopes and of your fears, have become imprinted in my imagination and endears you still further to my heart. . . ."

"I have not yet spoken to you of the thing which you speak to me about so prettily, poor little dear wife. After you have touched that chord, who would dare to say anything? It would be like singing after a nightingale, or playing the lyre after the god of music. But if words fail me, I have, none the less, a heart which is in tune with yours and responds to it."

"I've again done something silly, my poor child. I lost my temper yesterday with that damned Meissel; I called him a scoundrel several times, and here he is on the point of bringing an action against me at Petrikau. . . . Defend your husband, not because you are his wife, but because you have always been his most intimate confidante." [Then he says he is beginning to work quite seriously at the lecture he is hoping to deliver that summer at the Academy of Berlin, on literature and the difference between the author and the man of letters.]

"What else shall I say to thee, good little wife? That I love you with all my heart? It is a subject which should have been exhausted long ago, if it were not inexhaustible. One would sooner be sick of living than of loving you, and of breathing than of telling you so. . . ."

"My plan is to abdicate all authority over my person, and confide it to a little queen I know, who will dispose of it according to her pleasure. Farewell, my dear little wife; if you can read this you will be cleverer than I am, for I do not know which is the worst—the pen, the ink, or the paper. No matter, none of the three will refuse to convey that I love you, and that I kiss you with all my heart."

The estate to which Boufflers hoped to bring back his bride, surpassed all his dreams:

"I am here at the prettiest, or rather, the most beautiful place in the world. The Oder flows at the foot of the garden, and from my room I can see four or five big vessels pass every hour. . . . The views are perfectly arranged, and the scenery as varied as can be expected in a plain. . . . All goes fairly well here, except for the new garden, which, but for a few trees, gives no sign of life. . . . The geese, turkeys and pigs will be plentiful; we will also have ducks. If you happen to lay hands on some money, it will be very necessary to start a sheep-fold. . . . After that we'll have a brewery, and if possible a windmill. . . . The house progresses slowly; just now they are plastering your little room. If things go on at the same rate we may be ready by Pentecost, or, like poor Marlborough, *à la Trinité!*"

June, 1797, exactly twenty years since they had met, Stanislas, Chevalier de Boufflers, and Eléonore, Comtesse de Sabran, were married in Breslau by the Bishop, Prince of Hohenlohe. Elzéar, then twenty-three years old, accompanied them. In those days one was not allowed to receive the Sacrament of Marriage without first having secured a "*billet de confession*" from a priest. It was probably thirty-six years since Boufflers had been to Communion, the last time being at Saint-Sulpice, and it was sixteen years since Eléonore had been a practising Catholic. In the meantime she seems to have lost her Christian faith to a great extent, and almost become a Deist. But it is not fantastic to suppose that the religion of their childhood, the Faith of so many generations of Catholic ancestors, acted as a powerful pulley at this great moment of their lives, and brought them joy and consolation. So many aristocratic exiles clung to their Faith as their one remaining link with their country and their loved ones. When the *émigrés*, bereft of their possessions, flooded back to France at the beginning of the nineteenth century, it was the ruined bearers of ancient names who crowded the churches for Mass in the Faubourg Saint-Germain, dressed in the shabbiest of clothes, while the *nouveaux-riches* around Napoleon stayed away.[1] For all his levity, did the Chevalier heave a great sigh of relief after unburdening himself of the sins of thirty-six years? And Eléonore loved him better than ever for giving her the peace of a clear conscience after so many years of conflict. Although, strictly speaking, Boufflers, in making Eléonore his mistress, had lived in grievous sin, it is doubtful whether he would ever have purged the sensuality and egoism of his nature had he not loved her and been loved by her. Years before he had said to her: "You are my chief means for laying hold on perfection." The story of their love is only another instance of God writing on crooked lines. Boufflers is a rare example of a man who emerges from a wild past without being irretrievably smirched. And yet he always remained his gay self, he did not turn into that worst of all horrors, the sensualist who becomes pious and thinks of the body with disgust. It was a new man who stepped out into the June sunshine on

[1] Until they were obliged to go, officially.

his wedding day, cleansed by the trials and disappointments of twenty years—very different from the libertine who in his time had only sought in women the appeasement of the senses, the gambler, the spendthrift whose footsteps were dogged by creditors, the flirt who betrayed Eléonore with provincial belles.

He had said himself: "I'd rather be a good devil than a bad saint." If strenuousness of endeavour, if longing for the welfare of humanity, and if keeping strictly to his own code of honour make up a man, give me such a human being any day, rather than the one whose passport to salvation is stamped aright with the correct ecclesiastical seals. The Chevalier is the living witness of the ennobling power of a great love on a turbulent nature.

Again, there is practically no record of their years at Wimislov. With his usual energy and boundless high spirits, Boufflers started to organize the colony for French exiles. Eléonore, who had known how he'd suffered from the enforced inaction of the last six years, was glad to see him completely engrossed in a scheme which needed all his powers of organization.

Alas, it was foredoomed to failure, and it was not all the fault of Boufflers' hasty temper. One can blame his confederates. Exiles uprooted from their native land are always difficult, but French aristocrats particularly so, for they love their own country so much, and have such ingrained habits that they can never acquire new ones. Being members of an intellectual race, they are too individualistic to co-operate, and possibly none of them had Boufflers' prodigious capacity for hard work. They were probably discontented and exacting, and full of petty spites and jealousies. One can imagine the women were envious of Eléonore, and misconstrued any graciousness on her part as patronage. Gradually it must have become a veritable Hell on Earth, and all hope of making it a paying concern soon disappeared. This is easily understood after reading what Monsieur Madelin has to say about French *émigrés*. "The first *émigrés* had begun by astonishing Europe; now they were busy exasperating it. People had received them fairly well—for they thought they would be rich and agreeable. But from Brussels to Turin they had paraded the terrible smile of the Frenchman abroad, and had wounded the feelings of both nations and princes. In point of fact, they were more hard up than one would have thought, and in that way had been a disappointment. In a word, by frivolities typically French, they shocked the German, Belgian and Swiss *bourgeoisie*. They were very soon detested."

1800. "The best part of being respectably married," thought Eléonore, "is that you don't have to part at dawn." And so, they would enjoy talking to one another before rising in the early morning, this bridegroom of sixty-two and bride of fifty-one, who loved each other more tenderly and more ardently with every passing year. And again and again, in the little bedroom overlooking the Oder, they found themselves talking about Paris, and both had spells of home-sickness. It was: "Do you remember this?" and "Oh, do you remember that?" followed by deep sighs, and sometimes a tear. But never, never, did Eléonore show any regret for the loss of her lovely house in the Faubourg St. Honoré, for, as she said, this loss had given her Boufflers. She looked at him in the half-light; his hair was entirely white now, and his face was worn and worldly-wise, as if he'd seen through everything in human life. It was very nearly the only face which had mattered to her at all, for the last twenty-three years. Suddenly she said: "Do you know, I think the Revolution will have done one good thing."

"Impossible! What?"

"People like yourself will not be debarred from a profession which would enable them to marry. I always felt very sorry for so many of our impecunious friends at Versailles; only Church and military appointments available for them; the middle classes keeping them out of business; they could not sell their family estates, which were often a great burden to them, and if daughters were dowerless, they had to become nuns. What an injustice! At least Napoleon will give equal chances to all. And there won't be so many girls dying of a lingering fever, dying of love. How well I recall Madame Henriette[1], when her father had forbidden her marriage with the man she loved; she simply faded away."

"Yes," said Boufflers. "I remember her corpse placed upright in the carriage, all dressed and rouged, between two maids."

"What a picture! Poor victim of parental despotism and the social system. There should be fewer of these in the new world. The young must no longer be at the mercy of the old."

"You little anarchist! Don't let Elzéar hear you talking in this vein: he calls Napoleon 'the Corsican brigand'."

"Poor Elzéar. But then, he was just a little in love with our dead Queen. He was such a little courtier, and always felt quite at home at Versailles. Oh dear, what a long time ago that seems. However unjust things were, I loved those days. I wonder what has happened to Petit Trianon. I must write and ask Delphine to find out."

"Oh, didn't you know? I meant to tell you: I heard the other day that Richard, the old gardener, hoping to save the place, suggested that the château should be turned into an

[1] A daughter of Louis XV.

inn. It seems that Russian and English visitors pay ruinous prices for the privilege of spending one night in the Queen's bedroom. The pavilion of the French garden is a café, there is a public bar in the garden and people dance there. Richard also managed to rescue the orange-trees."

Eléonore was absorbed in thought: she was recalling those night-fêtes in the gardens when trees and guests had looked so ethereal in the strange, concealed lighting.[1] The alleys were covered with rose-coloured sand, very fine and soft, and even the earth in the flower-beds was blue-grey. It pained her to think of this garden of love, desecrated by the rough crowds, with their vulgar curiosity, frightening away the ghosts of the courtiers in the scarlet livery and white satin waistcoats which etiquette ordained for Trianon. She recalled them playing blind-man's-buff and hide-and-seek, or walking in pairs or in trios, greeting their friends with that mannered courtliness which was the mark of the Frenchman. Alas, alas, for the times when the world was young and gay.

"Don't sigh like that, *cher amour*," said Boufflers, twining her golden hair around his wrist. "What were you thinking of?"

"Oh, the games of hide-and-seek which the Queen used to play with her friends. I suppose the populace magnified them into orgies. She was so young when she became Queen; only twenty."

"Yes, but so indiscreet for a Queen! Don't you remember the day when she was out-of-breath after dancing with Monsieur de Dillon, she said to him: 'See how my heart is beating,' and the King had to say: 'No, Madame, he'll take your word for it'."

She was silent for a while, then she said: "Oh dear, I can still picture those flower-beds in Spring, full of scented hyacinths, of narcissus and frilly tulips and daffodils. And never a dead flower or a dead leaf anywhere!"

"You've got nostalgia badly: I can see it. Oh, my God, I've got it, too, *ma fille*; I don't know what it is, but I sometimes get *overwhelmed* by an immense longing to *smell* the streets of Paris again. Just that. Yes, I know it's all changed, and our hearts would be wrung all the time, and they've even altered the old, familiar street names; but I want to go back all the same. I'm sick of this German food, too. Oh, do you remember the meal I described to you once after, after—Valenciennes?"

Eléonore pressed her face against his and laughed: "You and your large appetite! Yes, I remember it to this day: you see how I re-read your letters? . . . 'larks, plump in a way you will never be, and negligently lying on a slice of *brioche* which served instead of fried bread'."

[1] See picture by Lavreince.

"Yes, it's the bread I miss, too. I'm not surprised we French don't travel much: we are so comfortable at home. Give me my own hovel any day, rather than someone else's palace. And French bread. It would be nice if we could go back now and furnish some tiny little house where we could live together in peace. Since the auction at Versailles and the big houses, the second-hand shops are crammed with beautiful pieces of furniture, and you have such taste, you could make a miniature Paradise out of two *sous* and a piece of brocade."

Eléonore seemed lost in thought. Then she said: "My love, if you and I decide to go back one day, we will be returning to a city of shades."

CHAPTER XXX

NAPOLEON RECALLS THE EXILES

DELPHINE, alone in Paris, in the city of shades, was longing for the return of her beloved brother. They had only met once since Armand's death. Eléonore had sent her a poem which she had written for her:

> You were my joy, you were my glory,
> And all my pleasure and my happiness;
> You will never die in my memory:
> You are rooted in my heart!
>
> Rose-tree, tend your leaves,
> Forever be beautiful, forever be fresh,
> So that after the storm
> Your flowers may cheer my winter.

Delphine wrote to her mother:

"Poor dear mother, how good and sweet you are! What a pity you should be buried in the depths of Poland! You alone are cleverer than a thousand other people—you have so much charm, you write like an angel. . . ."

In November, 1799, Napoleon became First Consul. Delphine saw her chance for getting her stepfather's name crossed off from the list of *émigrés*. She called on Joséphine, who had shared the same bedroom with her at the Carmes prison, and who bore her no grudge for having flirted with her first husband.

Joséphine was then no longer in her first youth. She spent hours every morning at her *toilette*: she only appeared, afterwards, as the finished product of the bevy of maids. Napoleon himself realized how important it was to deck the cynosure of so many eyes, for he paid her fantastic debts for dress over and over again. Everything in her appearance, down to the smallest detail, was carefully thought out. The subtlest colour schemes had been artfully combined, the right trinkets chosen, and she had a gift for adding the finishing touch by those becoming *mousseline* scarves carried with such feminine gestures. She put on plenty of rouge, because Napoleon liked it. Every movement of the future Empress was a poem of languorous grace, her voice so melodious that the servants of the household used to pause on the stairs to listen to it. She had that special grace without which beauty is of little worth to a woman.

Delphine was fascinated from the moment that she was ushered into her drawing-room. Joséphine's horrible little dog, Fortuné, whom she would not turn off her bed on her wedding night, and who had bitten Napoleon on the heel, came yapping across the room at Delphine.

"Ah, Madame de Custine," said Joséphine as she glided across her salon to greet Delphine, "how nice of you to call on me. Down, Fortuné, down." (Joséphine smiled with her mouth shut, for her teeth were bad.) "I see you do not forget your friends of old times." (Joséphine, in spite of her natural indolence, always made a point of remembering names and faces, and when she became Empress she engaged a specialist to tutor her in genealogies and general knowledge.) "And how is your charming mother, the Comtesse de Boufflers?" (Joséphine prided herself on her aristocratic connections, and tried to make Napoleon realize what an asset she was to him in this way—Napoleon, whom she had nicknamed Puss-in-Boots when he had been so madly in love with her, just before his campaign in Italy.) "Come and sit down. Tell me all about your mother. I will ring for tea." (Joséphine's *patisseries* were renowned all over Paris.)

And so Delphine told her how terribly she missed her mother and how she longed to see her, and couldn't dear Madame Buonaparte do something about it?

Now Madame Buonaparte was a very good-natured woman and would do anything to help her friends. So that night, as she was getting into bed—an act she performed, according to Napoleon, with the grace she displayed in all things—she roused her husband, who had gone to bed sometime before her. "Popo," she said. No reply. "Nana," she said. (That is how the great are nicknamed by their wives in private!)

"Yes, what is it? More bills for chemises?"

"No. I've found you a wit, somebody to adorn our *entourage*."

"*Hein?*"

"You remember that distinguished Comtesse de Sabran, who was such a friend of Marie-Antoinette's, very well-connected, I assure you, and mixed with the élite of Versailles society?"

Napoleon sat up in his night-shirt. He'd lost that bleak look of an under-fed Corsican second-lieutenant and minor poet. Although thirty-one, he was now like an antique cameo of a Cæsar. He'd plumped out a little, but he was still pale, and his black hair fell in a streak across his forehead. His hands were small and beautiful, and he was rather proud of them. At the moment, he smelt of eau-de-cologne, for, like Joséphine, he also performed an intricate *toilette* for the night.

The future Emperor of the French sat up in his night-shirt and gave his wife an eagle look. Then he smiled, and his whole countenance was transformed; nothing could convey the compelling fascination of that smile. It was like a flash of lightning. In his glance, one caught a glimpse of the personal magnetism which held an immense army in thrall and exacted obedience and discipline from all his subordinates. If only Louis XVI had possessed that touch of personal genius, and if only he had ruled his wife with a rod of iron, as Napoleon eventually ruled Joséphine!

"Madame de Sabran?" he said. "Oh, but very charming, and wouldn't meddle in politics. I can't bear women who talk politics. It's not their job. She might teach some of our own generals' wives good manners." He tweaked his wife's ear (one of his more detestable habits). "Clever of you to think of her. Let's have her back. The old families are against me here; what is left of the Faubourg Saint-Germain will hate me like poison. We need people like Madame de Sabran."

A little later, when it was suggested that Boufflers' name should be crossed off the list of emigrants, Napoleon said: "True, he will make us songs." As Mrs. Webster says: "Strange coincidence! Louis XVI, because Boufflers was a versifier, had crossed him out of a list for promotion: Napoleon, for the same reason, erased him from the number of the banished."

Probably Napoleon admired this man, who had rushed off to Corsica, his own native island, in its struggle for liberty under Paoli. And then he was told of his reputation as "the most delightful madman", and heard the verses which had been written of him as a young man:

> Your travels and your witty sallies,
> Your pretty verses and your horses
> Are cited all over France;
> We all know by heart those charming trifles
> Which you throw off so negligently:

Yes, decidedly a man to have about. And Napoleon liked the part he had played of "gentleman democrat" in the National Assembly.

Boufflers did not have to be asked twice. "I would rather die of hunger in France than live in Prussia," he exclaimed. And he went up to pack his bag at once.

So, after nine years of exile, Boufflers came back to Paris, to prepare for Eléonore's home-coming. The trees were yellowing in the Champs-Elysées, and there was a sorrowful wind sighing.

What a different Paris! The Faubourg Saint-Germain, the aristocratic quarter, was rather empty, and in some streets grass was growing up between the cobble-stones. Paris was haunted by the ghosts of his old friends. Boufflers sighed as he thought of the Duc de Nivernais, the friend who had given that last party at Saint-Ouen. He had died in 1797 after his release from prison.

Eléonore's house had been given to one of Napoleon's generals, the son of a Lunéville wheelwright! He had proposed to Delphine, but been scornfully refused. No house had its rightful owner. Everywhere the antique shops seemed singularly crammed with a profusion of beautiful objects, many of which seemed strangely familiar. In one street he saw a priceless lace ball-gown which he recognized as having belonged to Marie-Antoinette: it was blowing disconsolately outside a lace-shop in the Autumn wind. He could see none of the dashing one-horse gigs driven furiously by the young dandies who had been his friends, none of the magnificent painted coaches with scarlet spokes to their wheels, and white-wigged footmen in gold-braided coats, riding outside. Several of these old coaches, in a very dilapidated state, were now used by cabbies for hire, and the meagre horses who had survived the Prussian war could hardly drag them along. Boufflers found the sight unbearable. Then, as he'd foreseen, so many of the street names had been re-baptized: for instance, Rue Monsieur-le-Prince was Rue de la Liberté; the saints, too, had all been dismissed, for they were supposed to have done as much harm as the princes. It was no longer the Rue Saint-Roch, but the Rue Roch. He passed by his old seminary of Saint-Sulpice, and remembered hearing that the cloisters had been turned into a dance-hall. Immediately after the Terror many convents and seminaries had been transformed into "dancings"; as a reaction from fear, the people had gone dancing mad. Boufflers smiled wryly: "I wonder what the Superior would have said if he'd seen half-naked Directoire women dancing in his cloisters and chapels!" Even the Novitiate of the Jesuits and the Carmelites of the Marais were vowed to Terpsichore.

In the Faubourg Saint-Germain there were the famous *bals à la Victime* to which were admitted only authentic relations of the Victims of the Terror, and they came dressed for the part, their faces waxen and a blood-red ribbon around their necks in the right place. They had been badly frightened, and they multiplied their extravagances to remind themselves that the nightmare was over. In a dance, a young man cried out to an unknown girl: "Polichinelle, they've killed my father."

The girl took out a handkerchief: "They've killed your father?"

"Yes, they've killed him." And he went on dancing and singing: "*Zig zag don don, au pas de rigaudon.*"

Boufflers tried to turn his mind away from the Revolution, but it was almost impossible. The *fleur-de-lys* of the Royal Appointment signs had been torn down over the shops which he had frequented in his young days—regimental tailors, perfumers, hatters, makers of gloves and snuff-boxes. The young men he could see walking in the street had lost all air of leisure, and they did not know how to greet each other as in the old days—with low bows and flourish of plumed hat and hand on heart. What a lot of civilized details one had taken for granted, and only began to miss when they had gone for ever. Boufflers could not imagine any of the modern young men wielding a sword in a duel, trifling with a lace-edged handkerchief, or tapping the lid of a snuff-box with their finger tips. As for the women, they seemed to have been dethroned. How strange it was to see Parisian women in those slim, high-waisted gowns, instead of panniers. As a result they all walked differently. He had heard about the plump wives of the new government officials, whose one aim was to be as pale and languorous as the beauties of the Court of Marie-Antoinette. For this purpose they gave up rouge, tried to look like Psyche in Gerard's famous picture, and begged their physicians to bleed them. They went into mourning for the Queen, and carried fans inscribed with words of devotion to the Monarchy. It was terribly *chic* to pose as an aristocrat newly-returned from exile. Alas for these socially-ambitious ladies: their birth always betrayed them sooner or later. At Republican tea-parties they began by complaining that they had the appetite of a sparrow, and after a little while succumbed to great slices of beef and large sandwiches, eaten with a devastating gentility. Then a hiccough would be their undoing, or a common phrase, like "*Pardi*". (*Fancy* that!)

The work-people in the streets were different, too; an entirely new element seemed to have filtered into the population; the quiet civility and *bonhomie* of the eighteenth century were replaced by a general air of insolence, and above all an unstable and hurried manner. The French manner was originally much more stable than the English, but the Revolution destroyed that. And there were so many women in black everywhere: no doubt the widows and mothers of thousands of young men who had swelled Napoleon's victorious armies, for during Boufflers' exile in Poland the future Emperor had been shaping his military triumphs.

What would Eléonore say to all this change? He began to doubt whether he had any right to bring her back, now that every street corner had its own sinister memory. The kitchen garden of the Benedictine nuns around the Madeleine, and the field near the "Folie Monceau", were filled with the corpses of the victims. And the erstwhile Place Louis XV, in which so many of their friends had perished under the blade of the guillotine, was within sight of Eléonore's old garden overlooking the Champs-Elysées. Boufflers stopped the cab he was in, and asked the cabby to wait a moment. In the twilight of an early Autumn evening, he went up to the great iron grille and looked at her garden, just as he had first done twenty-three years ago when Charlot de Ligne had caught him in the act. Here were the same chestnut trees. Nine times had Spring lit those pink and white candles since she had left Paris. How often had they glowed above them in the Springs of long ago, when he had made violent love to her, and she had kept him at bay for four long years. Now the path was strewn with glossy chestnuts bursting out of green cases. The chestnut trees were sinking into the smouldering fires of their Autumnal decay. Among the yellowing leaves, Boufflers could see the gummy buds which held the flowers of 1801, tight packed as poppy petals. Kings and constitutions might crumble to the dust, ancient civilizations perish, but flauntingly, unheedingly, the chestnut bud swells and bursts from its sheath, waxes and wanes; the fruit succeeds the flower, symbolic of man's destiny. As Boufflers mused on these things he knew that he had come to the Autumn of his life, and that despite the encircling melancholy, he was far, far happier than in his Spring.

He continued to gaze. Here was the same winding alley near the little pavilion where he had seen her coming towards him that June morning, under her frilly mauve parasol. How beautiful and frail she had seemed, floating towards him in her white dress! But to him, now, she was twenty-three years more dear. As he wrote to a friend later (comparing her with his mother), he said she had "the same mind, the same tastes, the same wit, the same inward equability with the same outward variety, and those innocent caprices, those unexpected traits, that indefinable charm and at the same time that incorruptible simplicity. . . ." The Chevalier leaned his head against the grille and realized that he had lost nothing, but rather gained: "All our true possessions consist in thoughts and feelings, and so in this respect every man has within him a mine more or less abundant . . ."[1] The air was moist with the smell of dead leaves and damp moss. He gazed across at the long French windows overlooking the terrace and recalled the hours he had sat for his portrait in her studio, their violent quarrels and their tender reconciliations. Then he remembered the maddening interruptions of her friends, depriving them of their precious privacy together, and again he realized that he had gained rather than lost, for now they could be all in all to one another.

He went back to his cabby and said: "Take me to Madame de Custine, Rue Martel." The man made one of those mysterious horse-noises, heard only in France, and drove across the cobbles. He was getting quite used to watching aristocratic old gentlemen of shabby but distinguished appearance, gazing outside great houses. The influx from Europe was beginning. And being a kind-hearted fellow, who himself had seen better days, he muttered: "Poor gentleman, I suppose he's lost everything."

Of his personal possessions, Boufflers had only managed to salvage a few books from the deluge, among which were a Cicero and a Dante. His engravings and papers, which he had entrusted to his sister, had, of course, disappeared when she was guillotined. His journals and his correspondence with Eléonore were safely preserved by Delphine, after they had been retrieved from under her sofa. Delphine had not emigrated, so her property was not confiscated. As she was in a position to buy herself the château of Fervaques, near Lisieux, in Normandy, one can conclude that she did all in her power to help the mother she adored.

Boufflers went to pay his respects to Napoleon and Joséphine. The first consul offered him a small pension, only just enough to provide for the necessities of life. Boufflers wrote to Eléonore and Elzéar telling them to come.

So in December, 1800, they rumbled back into Paris in a huge travelling coach. Delphine describes how she waited with the Chevalier in her house in the Rue Martel. At last she heard the jingle-jangle of bells. She went to the window and saw the coach piled high with trunks.

"Look, their carriage is a house!"

"The house of the tortoise!" said the Chevalier, who had been longing for this moment. Delphine cried: "Let us run to kiss them! We can scold them at our leisure."

At first, the Chevalier and his wife lived near Delphine, then in the Rue Verte, but eventually they settled at 114 Rue du

[1] From a letter of his.

Faubourg Saint-Honoré, quite close to her old house. She found it impossible to keep away.

When Chateaubriand saw Eléonore, three years later, he thought her charming, although "somewhat depressed by exile and privation". As for Boufflers, a contemporary said . . . "But Monsieur de Boufflers is still quite young. . . . Admit that he is amusing, his kindness and politeness are extreme. It is only people of that age whom I can care for; there are no others who are really good-hearted." Years before, when Eléonore had planned the Utopia of their old age together, she had always pictured herself looking after her Chevalier, for she was much younger than he. But the situation was reversed: it was the Chevalier who looked after her. In spite of his record of formidable colics, toothaches and migraines, he had a constitution of iron, and a wonderful fund of gaiety and resilience. Eléonore's tiny feet were now crippled with rheumatism. This must have been increased by their Paris house which had been abandoned by its former owners on account of the damp. So every year Boufflers took her to Plombières for a cure. (At the end of his life he was to be seen wheeling her round Plombières in a bath-chair, or half-carrying her up the hill for a walk.) He increased his small income by giving Latin lessons, and writing articles and verses, so after a while he was able to buy a cottage just outside Saint-Germain-en-Laye; Boufflers likened his abodes to those of the town rat and the country rat—both holes. This cottage—8 Rue Saint-Léger—was bought later on by the Carmelite Order. Do the nuns ever feel the ghostly presence of these two ardent admirers of Voltaire? In the garden the lovers planted the oak Stanislas, and the lime-tree Eléonore, and these trees were still standing fifty years ago. Perhaps they are now.

Boufflers had always envied squires on their estates, and it was a delight for him to own a piece of land. In the full flush of possession, he wrote to an old friend of his mother's, Madame Durival:

"All our domain consists in a fairly large fruit and vegetable garden, which promises much in Spring, but, according to the sad custom of Nature, contains little in Autumn. But this garden, now blessed, now cursed, feeds its owners and even gives them drink, for I have a little vineyard and a wine-press, and we have the good sense, or perhaps the folly, to think our wine the best for twenty leagues round Paris. At any rate we find there is no sweeter form of intoxication than getting drunk at our own wine barrel."

Years ago, he had written to Eléonore:

"If I am in the world when you are no longer young, I would propose that we buy a country house for the two of us, so that you might enjoy for once all the pleasures you have missed till now. You don't realize that one can have motherly feelings towards trees, towards plants, towards flowers. You don't know that a garden is a kingdom where the prince is never hated, and where he enjoys the fruits of all the good he does. Your Paris garden can give you no idea of all that happiness." He had also written to his sister, long ago: "It seems to me that nothing can prevent me from being happy in a peasant's cottage, all you need in it is the society of the being you love."

The Chevalier was one of those human beings who, in possession of a patch of ground, plant things assiduously, and are perhaps better rewarded than the rich gardener. At Malgrange, in the old days, he had designed and planted out new gardens and grown strawberries, cherries, apricots, peaches, figs and muscat grapes "with the greatest success".

How little it takes to make a human being happy!

He had said of this country cottage: "This home is happier than if it were more brilliant."

It is delicious to picture them both, living in a civilized and urbane background, preparing Latin translations together, squabbling about the right word; and he looking after her, and she utterly dependent on him, and delighting him as ever with her gifts of mind and heart. This great love of theirs had not subsided to the level of a glorified companionship: the years had simply mellowed it and given it a deeper tenderness. One can picture their simple little *salon*, opening out on to their garden. Delphine must have helped them with gifts of her own furniture. As Eléonore was a fastidious woman in spite of being a little untidy, and she was making a home with the man she loved, it is impossible to imagine their little room as other than charming, though of course very simple. In Eléonore's own dress as a young woman, the general effect had always been of studied simplicity.

There is a bloom on everything, as on possessions much loved and a little faded. On the grey stucco walls hangs the portrait, which Eléonore had painted, of herself and the two children when they were small. The long windows overlooking the Spring flower-beds are framed in crushed strawberry *toile-de-Jouy*. The garden is reflected in the mirror over an elegant little French mantelpiece decked with narrow-necked glass vases holding a few flowers plucked in their domain, flowers so tenderly watched and culled and hailed with joy when the first buds opened. One's own flowers are always individuals, first white violets, fragile anemones, some dark red gilliflowers. On the mantelpiece, too, a pair of floral china candlesticks on either side of a small round clock supported by white porcelain Cupids. A wood fire is crackling in the grate, and lighting up a bookcase full of their few remaining treasures, among which the collected works of Boufflers, jostling side by side with Cicero, Dante, and all the Latin poets. A delicate rosewood and ormolu bureau holds quills, wax, seals and sandpot, and, locked away in the drawers, those packets of their letters and journals, the sight of which is a poem in itself. By the window an old *bergère* in white-painted wood, cushioned in cherry-coloured velvet, where Eléonore can read and think, or just rest in the dusk and listen to the blackbirds calling from the apple-orchard in the Spring rain. Then Stanislas, wearing the red ribbon of the Legion of Honour, comes in holding a bottle and says: "Let's have a bottle of Château-Boufflers with our supper." Enough to turn any wilderness into a Paradise—books, wine, the woman one loves . . . and home-grown flowers and vegetables! Domestic bliss in the country together.

In spite of their poverty, they went out in society a good deal, and paid their court to Napoleon. He was crowned Emperor in December, 1804. They probably watched the Coronation by the Pope in Notre Dame, and witnessed that terrible moment when Joséphine's envious sisters-in-law, who were her train bearers, let go of her immensely heavy long Court mantle at the very moment when she was to ascend the altar steps to receive her crown from her husband's hands, and she nearly fell backwards.

Strangely enough, both Eléonore and Stanislas had a great admiration for Napoleon and a liking for Joséphine. Eléonore wrote: "I enjoy going often to see them, and showing what I feel at seeing them in the midst of the crowd that surrounds them." And what a crowd! The new society is described in a letter, unsigned, written to Eléonore by a friend.

"'Every wealthy and educated person now lives in poverty, and, under the burden of shabby clothes, preserves a show of politeness and an air of dignity, I will even say of superiority, for this attitude is not readily thrown off. Politeness, courtesy, good taste and ease of manner are now to be found only in garrets, which are the refuge of French politeness and good breeding, two qualities now regarded as ancient prejudices and ridiculed by the prosperous who cannot acquire them. The play of wit, the careful phrasing of trifles, the intellectual banter of the Court, and the sound of the gentle voices of educated women, are replaced by the coarse familiarity of the middle-classes.

"One of their greatest delights is eating, lunch parties are fashionable. I went to one of these orgies, and will try to give you an idea of what I saw and heard. They meet at midday; the deputies (their wives keep house) drink a glass of brandy before starting for the Legislative Assembly; everybody, men and women, drinks to the health of the Republic. Then they begin their lunch with tea, which is supposed to be fashionable, and finish with wines, liqueurs and an uproar unbearable to ears accustomed to the old *régime*. This lunch lasts for about two hours. Then, while waiting for dinner, they play little innocent games of kissing, slapping and tearing each other's clothes, amusements that create such an uproar as to advertise the whole district of the entertainment. At four o'clock the deputies return and dinner begins. The table is laid with dishes to the utmost extent, and in the greatest profusion. Good taste decrees that the price of each dish on the table shall be explained. The most moderate calculation brought the cost of the dinner at which I was present to two hundred and sixty thousand francs in normal value, that is to say in *assignats* [paper money].

"Dinner was over at six o'clock and we then went to the National Gardens and places such as Monceau, Tivoli, etc., which only deputies and those with them may enter. The gentlemen acted the part of fauns and the ladies nymphs. Republican jokes are extremely free, I can assure you, it is the only form of liberty left in France, and they make the most of it.

"French women have become bad characters. If a woman takes a fancy to a man she indulges her desires; to say 'my lover is amiable, honourable or clever is out of date' . . . amiable is a term no longer used, and honourable is synonymous with stupid. Cleverness consists in making money, no matter how. The younger generation are completely corrupted, and to very few people would one entrust a *louis* to get change for it. . . .

"Luxury in dress is extreme in the case of women, and is carried to the height of extravagance. . . .

. . . "It is good style to pose as an aristocrat, and regret the old *régime* while fearing a new one.

. . . "The greatest ladies walk in the mud with bundles of wares under their arms which they propose to sell for the *toilettes* of the ladies of the day."

Probably the Chevalier and Eléonore went to stay with the Emperor and Empress at the country estate of Malmaison. One wonders how they survived the boredom of those visits: the Duchesse d'Abrantès said it was like being in a gilded cage. There was a frightful lot of small talk and jealousy and gossip. Directly you left a group of women, you could be sure they would start chattering about you. These women, mostly the wives of Republican generals who had suddenly risen to fame, lacked the background and the training in self-control which made Eléonore so delightful in society. However, they were very curious to know all about Marie-Antoinette, and doubtless asked her the most ridiculous questions. Eléonore was delighted when

Napoleon turned out the money-making inn-keeper from Trianon and restored the little château to something of its former glory.

What a relief that it was no longer an inn for foreign souvenir hunters.

Napoleon recalled the *émigrés* in April, 1802, so the Chevalier and Eléonore were able to hear news of many of their old friends again. What heartrending stories some of them brought back. Those with money and friends had not fared too badly, and it is pleasant to think that many women like the Marquise de la Tour du Pin found safe harbourage for a time at Richmond. Some of the destitute were allowed a shilling a day in England, but in spite of this, Chateaubriand sucked pieces of linen dipped in water and would spend two hours in front of a food shop in winter, simply staring at dried fruit and smoked meat. And in the cruel towns of Germany—Coblentz, Hamburg, Munich—many aristocrats, at the end of their resources, begged in the streets, or plied menial trades. The Comte de Vieuville became a shoeblack and errand boy, the Marquise de la Lande held the cash desk in a café, the Comtesse de Virieu mended stockings in the open street. Others had become lemonade-sellers, hairdressers, floor-waxers, dancing-masters.

But now, in 1802, they were crowding back again. There is an old caricature of the *émigré's* return; he is absolutely in rags. But anything, anything to get back to France. Duchesses and countesses who had owned magnificent private houses at Versailles, were now only too grateful for an attic room let out to them somewhere in the town of Versailles, where they could see their old friends again and talk about bygone days. Some would tell hair-raising stories of how they had hidden during those terrible house-to-house searches in the Paris of the Terror, when the soldiers of the Revolutionary Tribunal were trying to lay hands on any aristocrat they could find. Up to this day, in some of the old houses in Paris, one can see holes in the walls of garrets, most cleverly plastered over; and behind these some wretch once hid in darkness and silence for days on end.

And now they had come back. All their possessions and houses had been confiscated; if they had entrusted anything to servants, it was almost sure to have been stolen. Delphine's servants, who betrayed her, went off with all the plate and linen. In 1802 there must have been countless tragi-comedies in the fortuitous meetings between old servants and employers, ex-ladies'-maids wearing the stolen trinkets of their haggard mistresses. (Girls preferred to starve rather than go into domestic service, the well-trained, superior professional servant of the old *régime*, with her huge, white-frilled apron was nearly extinct. Delphine herself wrote to her mother in accents of despair: "I cannot undertake to train any more servants.")

Sometimes there were strange encounters in the streets with obscure persons who once had played important roles in *la petite histoire*. One day if he were wandering near the dingy Rue Perdu, Boufflers might see a faded old nigger skulking into a malodorous house. It was Zamor! Zamor, who had jumped out of a pie at a supper party of Louis Quinze, glittering in a jewelled turban, Zamor who had betrayed the du Barry to whom he owed everything. One gleaned from local gossip that he was penniless, and hated by the neighbours for his cruel slappings of some pupils he had once taken. He died at length in great squalor, and was buried in a pauper's grave. . . .

Then at dinner, one day, at the house of the Marquise de Créquy who had professed such an admiration for Boufflers' looks, they would be sure to meet her cook, who had given to Marie-Antoinette the white cap she wore on her way to execution. Any little thing which had belonged to the Queen was treasured as a relic.

The French have a great respect for the dead, and are very ceremonious in the cult of mourning; it was agony for these *émigrés* not to know where their relations were buried after they had been guillotined. However, after a very long search, a certain old lady was put on the track of Rose, a servant girl, who, one evening, had followed, at a distance, the cart full of corpses from the guillotine, until it reached a field where the bodies were stripped and buried. This field was identified, and bought up by the *émigrés*, and the little cemetery may still be seen, through the railings of a walled enclosure at Picpus, quite unspoilt.

But no one knew exactly where Marie-Antoinette had been buried. It was not till the Restoration, when Louis XVI's brother came to the throne, that searches were made among the bodies eaten up by quicklime; after the royal martyr had been identified by a garter which a nun had knitted for her, the body was transferred to the Chapelle Expiatoire. The Chevalier did not allow Eléonore to dwell too much on the blood-stained past. She needed protection against her own over-sensitiveness, and he tried to make her skip those ten years in her memory. He had written to a friend: "Let us look back no more, dear friend, or rather, let us look back farther—over these last ten years as over a river of blood in which our imaginations would be defiled. Beyond that frightful chasm, the mind can rest; there is an Elysium. . . ."

CHAPTER XXXI

AN UNFORTUNATE TEA-PARTY

MORE exiles came back. Paris and Versailles were slowly filling again with the friends of Eléonore and Stanislas, wan, impoverished, shabby. But instead of returning to their lovely houses, they were glad to find an attic somewhere in the neighbourhood of their past glories. The first thought of many was to know where the bodies of their relations had been buried, and to search for loved ones who were reputed to be still alive.

After a little while the *émigrés* settled down to some kind of hand-to-mouth existence. Those who went back to country estates—if they had not been confiscated—found them pillaged or the furniture sold; and they were struck by the general sadness of the peasants, who certainly had not prospered in the new social era.

One can picture Eléonore giving a tea-party to some of her friends in the little house in the Rue du Faubourg Saint-Honoré one Spring afternoon in the early nineteenth century.

"Oh dear, oh dear!" exclaimed Eléonore in agitation that morning. "How unfortunate that Céleste should choose this very day to walk out on us. What shall we do? Stanislas, are you listening?"

Céleste had been the maid-of-all-work in the Boufflers' household—the typical modern maid. She insisted on calling her mistress "Citizeness", refused to wear an apron, because it indicated servitude, never answered a bell, because she thought it was undemocratic, did as little work as possible, and kept humming a disturbing song which went like this:

"I would buy heads
If I had the means,
At fêtes I would carry
One in each hand.
Long live the Guillotine
Which looks so nice,
And cuts off so well
The heads of these dogs!"

"My fine aristocrats
Into Samson's sack
Let us spit!"

Boufflers had been made President of the Academy. He heard Céleste muttering this ditty one evening when he was preparing a speech, and he went out to her and told her to stop. She had been very rude, and said: "Ha-ha! My mother was in service as a cook during the Terror. On her half-day she used to go and watch the guillotining. One day she got home late because she'd stopped to see the last head; when her mistress complained she reported her to the Tribunal, and whizz . . . off went her head."

Boufflers felt like throwing her out then and there, but he dared not, for poor Eléonore was much too delicate to manage alone, and nearly crippled with rheumatism. Not only he, but Delphine had been very anxious about her health. Her letters were full of advice to her mother: ". . . try to take the life-giving grains of Doctor Franck . . . and you must come and get fat upon our good cow's milk." And she was recommending her to take camomile for her continual headaches. The slut must remain, at any rate until after the tea-party.

Alas! When Céleste heard that there was to be entertaining, she disappeared early that morning, taking with her one or two of those new high-waisted Empire dresses and poke-bonnets from her mistress's wardrobe, and all the liqueurs provided for the guests.

However, with his usual resource, and cheerfulness, Boufflers prepared a buffet of *petits fours* and *syrop de framboise*, while Eléonore arranged posies of lilies-of-the-valley everywhere, and pushed chairs into niches.

What a tea-party! Here were men and women who had seen and heard terrible things. If they had escaped the guillotine themselves, they had watched others in prison leave their game of cards quietly in the evening when the list of victims was read out, and they had not seen them again. In many prisons they had suffered insult and ill-treatment from their jailers, some of whom had been their own footmen. Or, disguised in the Paris crowds, they had heard the terrifying roar of the mob, increasing in volume as the tumbrils went past very slowly, the load of victims holding their heads proudly and going to Death as unconcernedly as to a Court ball. During the September massacres of priests they had seen the carts returning afterwards, filled with bleeding corpses, with here and there an arm or leg sticking out. In the times of house-to-house searches, they had crouched for days in terror of their lives, behind false walls in old attics, or in the depths of cellars. Here was one who had heard the frantic shrieking of the du Barry as she was taken to the guillotine; here was another who had watched Marie-Antoinette go past, nearly unrecognizable except for the way she carried her head and the lower lip which almost spat its contempt for the jeering rabble. Yes, they had seen terrible things in France, and had endured great privations in exile. But of course all that was buried in the dark chambers of memory. True to type, they would never refer to the past, but bravely put on a bright façade and made the most of the social amenities of the present. Now as ever, they would rather die than cease to be agreeable. At four o'clock, Eléonore heard the rumbling of a splendid coach in the street; it stopped outside their house, and from it emerged the aged Marquise de Coislin, an ex-mistress of Louis Quinze, who lived to be a hundred. The coach had been a royal gift. Although very rich, she was disgustingly mean, so she had no footman. [She was so mean that she would not even give coffee to her rare guests.] Boufflers ran to open the door to her and her little dog, Lili, who spent the day with her mistress in bed. The Marquise was decked like a shrine and her skin dried up like an Egyptian Mummy. She wore a jacket of white silk bordered with pink fur, a sky-blue mantle, a black velvet hat lined with flesh pink. She threw this off, revealing a little tulle bonnet trimmed with roses.

If it had not been for her wonderful gift for mimicry and pantomime, and her caustic wit, this old lady, who was very ignorant, and could not even spell, would have been ridiculous. She looked at the *syrop de framboise* with disapproval, and muttered something to her dog about the poor Boufflers acquiring the habits of Napoleon's *parvenu* entourage, who gave beer and sweetened water at their parties. Eléonore explained that Céleste had stolen the liqueurs. The Marquise softened, and then told them how she had hidden during the Terror, disguised as a servant in a farm. She gobbled up *éclairs* noisily: she liked visiting the friends who could give her food, and thus save her unnecessary expense. She had just come from a delicious luncheon at Charlot de Ligne's daughter-in-law, whose *chef* was renowned. She told them how Madame Suard's cock in the Rue Royale had kept her awake all night, and she had written to her: "*Madame*, have your cock's head chopped off." And this upstart nobody had dared to reply: "*Madame*, I have the honour to inform you that I will not chop off my cock's head." She threw up her hands: "What dreadful times we are living in. Just look at the clothes, for example, and this fashion of women having such masses of underclothes. It stinks of the *nouveau riche*. Now in *my* time, we only had two chemises, and we only replaced them when they were worn out."

It was difficult to realize that she had once been very dangerous, had treated Louis Quinze *à la cruelle*, and had outwitted the Pompadour.

Very soon the little *salon* was crowded. Few of the dresses were fashionable, many of them betrayed the fact that they were

Louis Seize gowns with the panniers reduced and the low necks filled in. However, the most was made of family jewels and resuscitated ornaments: it was almost pathetic to see old ostrich feathers, newly crisped and curled, faded garlands of flowers, precious laces of a bygone age brought out of the lace box after twenty years. And the manners, too, were of a different era: smiles and elaborate greetings, compliments and gallantries, many of them false, to be sure, but how greatly did they contribute to "*le plaisir de vivre*". Yes, courtesy, and above all youthfulness: the people of the *dix-huitième* never grew old: that was their distinguishing trait.

Anyway, one's dear friends never grow old. One can see Charlot Prince de Ligne, thoroughly reformed in his old age, having nearly forsworn the fair sex, and, wonder of wonders, he now said his prayers and went to church very devoutly. And then, the Comte de Vaudreuil,[1] the evil genius of Marie-Antoinette, for it was he who persuaded her to act in Beaumarchais' revolutionary play: during the Revolution, he had married in England and taken to the devout practice of religion. It was almost uncanny to think that this tall, pock-marked, grave old man had been the lover of Madame de Polignac, and had acted the part of Almaviva in the miniature blue theatre of Petit Trianon. He was in correspondence with his great friend, the Comte d'Artois, in exile, and he only lived for the day when he would see him crowned King as heir to the Bourbon dynasty. Another friend had also married in England: the Abbé Delille. He did not stay for more than a moment, as his common, shrewish, money-making little wife expected him to turn out so many hundreds of verses a day, and woe betide him if he failed!

They all gossiped about their friends, making enquiries concerning the newest arrivals, and telling anything they knew about others who had disappeared for a while. Monseigneur de Sabran was still in Poland. "What happened to that delicious little Abbé Porquet, you know, he became the admirer of Mademoiselle Quinault?" asked an old friend of Lunéville days.

The Chevalier's face saddened. "Ah, my dear old tutor! I'm afraid he was so poor after the Revolution that he committed suicide rather than endure the lingering death of slow starvation. Poor little fragile Porquet. And to think he had been nicknamed 'the famished skeleton' in times past, because of his enormous appetite!"

"Why is it that the evil flourish as the green bay-tree? Here are consummate craftsmen like de Gouthière and Riesener, and artists like Fragonard, dying of hunger, while tricksters like la Bertin, our dead Queen's dressmaker, still survives, and Her

[1] He is mentioned in *An Adventure*.

Majesty's maid, that snobbish Madame Campan, has got a successful finishing school at Saint-Germain, where the Emperor's step-daughter went to be polished off."

"Much good may it do her!"

"Sh . . . Sh . . . we must be careful what we say."

The Chevalier turned to his old friend the Duchesse de Choiseul, now a frail old lady, very lost without her devoted Abbé Barthelemy, and living in great poverty. They started talking of the house-parties of Chanteloup so long ago, the crowded supper-parties where champagne flowed and all competed in witty rhyming, the hunts through the woods filled with wild strawberries. . . .

The Chevalier offered the little Duchesse a *madeleine*: "*L'estomac* is as capricious as ever. This will suit me very well. Ah, Chevalier, and to think that they have sold Chanteloup! But I still love to recall the Chinese Pagoda, dedicated to friendship, where all the names of our friends are inscribed on the walls."

In another corner of the room Eléonore was listening to an acrimonious duel between the aged Marquise de Coislin and a Russian with mystical inclinations, Madame de Krüdener. This intense person seemed to be getting on the old lady's nerves. The Marquise was still marvellously beautiful, and up to the very end of her life was wont to exclaim with a proud, dominating expression in her ironical eyes: "Yes, I saw His Majesty at my feet: he had magnificent eyes, and his language was seduction itself."[1]

Madame de Krüdener, who did not approve of this, was turning the conversation to the life of prayer, regardless that the old lady's style of interior decoration was not her own: "*Madame*, who is your interior confessor?"

The Marquise snorted: she had all the *sans-gêne* and crudity of the great ladies of the eighteenth century: "*Madame*, I do not know my interior confessor, but my confessor is in the interior of the confessional."

There was a little rustling all round, and veiled glances of amusement. Eléonore skilfully manœuvred that the Comte de Vaudreuil should come to the rescue and receive a few of the mystic's effusions, while Charlot de Ligne provided for the more earthly needs of the Marquise de Coislin and offered her his snuff-box.

The Prince de Ligne and Madame Vigée Lebrun then came to sit near Eléonore's winged arm-chair. Boufflers joined them, and exclaimed: "How strange, we compose the same little group which gossiped together in the gallery, at the ball of my great-aunt de Luxembourg!"

"Only the Prince de Croÿ and Monsieur de Caraman are missing."

[1] See *Louis XV intime et les petites maitresses*, by Comte Fleury.

The Marquise de Coislin again startled her entourage: "The Prince de Croÿ? I wish he'd confined his interests to botany: used to assist his daughters-in-law in childbed. Terrible forceps deliveries. . . . Should have stuck to strawberry growing. . . ."

The Chevalier deftly drew the conversation back to the ball of the Maréchale de Luxembourg:

"Over twenty-five years ago! It was at this ball that I met my future wife." And he bent over Eléonore's little hand and kissed it with tenderness and gallantry.

"I remember," said de Ligne. "We talked about the new gardens at Petit Trianon, and you, Madame Vigée Lebrun, were hoping to paint the Queen. Is it not extraordinary to think that this made you unpopular with the people of Paris, and you had to flee at the outbreak of the Revolution? Tell us about the Russian women you painted. Are they as beautiful as our French women?"

Gradually the guests went home, murmuring "Charming. Charming. Just like old times. We must positively keep together. We will act little plays and charades. Delightful!" The last to go was René de Chateaubriand, who had stood mootionless by the fireplace all the time in a classic pose, his hand in his waistcoat. He was disgusted because the *salon* had not centred round him, and no one had flattered him. He felt out of it. The only tangible good he had extracted from this ridiculous afternoon, was a promise from the Marquise de Coislin that she would let off to him the attic of her mansion in the Place de la Concorde, No. 4. But he rather feared her avarice . . .

"Come, *pur amour*," said Boufflers, seeing that Eléonore looked sad, "it is a beautiful May evening. We will go for a walk in the Parc Monceau. I'm so glad I've been given a key."

Soon they were strolling together in the little sandy alleys of this miniature jewel of the eighteenth century, then in the country outskirts of Paris. There the late Duc d'Orléans had built his *Folie* in 1778, after a design by Carmontelle. What fêtes he had given there (and alas what orgies)! The paths wound among the peerless green lawns, by spinneys of lilac, around tiny, one-roomed pavilions for the keepers which were little gems of architecture. In the distance, a blackbird in a chestnut tree sang full-throatedly to banks of dark amethyst clouds in the sunset. All was quiet in the peace of a Spring twilight. Husband and wife walked together without speaking, occasionally looking at one another and smiling.

Suddenly the sky became more overcast and a fine warm Spring shower began to fall. They hurried for shelter to the shade of a weeping willow tree who was dipping her finger-tips fastidiously into the little lake. Eléonore and Stanislas were completely protected there, and yet they could peep out at the ivy-twined columns of the classical ruins around the lake.[1]

Eléonore gave a shudder and clung more closely to her husband.

"What is it, my child?"

"I was just thinking of the victims buried in the field so near here. . . ."

Stanislas took hold of his wife's shoulders and looked at her intently. She returned his gaze. Her violet eyes, tired though they were by anxieties and weeping, were as fine as ever under the wide arches of the expressive, rather melancholy brows.

He said: "I knew this tea-party would upset you! Oh, why can't you learn to live in the present? I wish I could infuse you with a little of my fund of gaiety. We ought to be so happy in our Autumn together. We are so much more fortunate than anyone who came to see us this afternoon! We have each other. We have love and friendship; and those others . . . think a little! The Marquise de Coislin, living on the memory of a few nights spent with Louis Quinze before she was discarded in the heartless way he always gave his mistresses their *congé;* Delille henpecked by his wife; Madame Vigée Lebrun has lost her only daughter, and her husband has always snatched from her all the money she earned as a painter. Charlot and Vaudreuil both taking refuge in piety after having multitudes of affairs which meant nothing. By the way, you wouldn't like me to become a *dévot*, would you?"

She laughed merrily. "You couldn't if you tried. You will always be yourself. Believe me, I shall be very worried on your account, when it comes to preparing you for Death."

She put both her arms around his neck and kissed him with all the ardour of the first day. His eyes filled with tears, and he said: "I am not worried: I will humbly present my credentials to the Almighty and say: 'Sire, I would rather die than cease to be honest! I have done many evil deeds in my day, through my folly, hot blood and independence. My only plea for pardon is that I found forgiveness and indulgence in one who loved me very faithfully for over a quarter of a century.' Could He be less merciful than one of His subjects? But *Sacre Dieu*, I am becoming solemn!"

And he fell to kissing her as if he were twenty. And the sinking sun, resplendent at last after the shower, stole through the screen of yellow, grey-green willow leaves and bathed in a cloak of radiance those two ageless lovers who could forget all their sorrows and infirmities in the joy of being together at last.

[1] The columns of the Abbaye de Saint Denis had been used for this.

CHAPTER XXXII

FAREWELL

Delphine had ceased mourning for Armand long ago. Because of the unrest of the times, and because her marvellous beauty drove men wild, she was flirting with Joséphine's husband in prison quite soon after Armand's death. She is described by her son, Astolphe: ". . . Her enchanting beauty, the delicacy of her features, her perfect profile, her mourning garments, her youth, her dazzling complexion, the magic of her pale golden hair . . . her passionate yet melancholy face . . . the courtly manners . . . the matchless quality of her silvery voice . . ."

When her mother returned from exile, Delphine had fallen a victim to a hopeless passion for that monster of vanity and egoism—Chateaubriand. Delphine's infatuation was slowly to undermine her health, sap her vitality, and drive her to an early death. She had given herself to Chateaubriand, and then he had gone to Rome with another woman, and had never even written to her. Delphine was not intelligent and cultured, like her mother, and Chateaubriand was soon bored. When he came back to Paris she knew that she had ceased to exist for him. He could barely find time to write a note to her to break an appointment or answer a request for promotion for Astolphe. Consumed with grief, she retired more and more to her château at Fervaques, near Lisieux, where she had once entertained him. Eléonore and her husband went to visit her at Fervaques, and, as they could not keep a private carriage any more, they had to take the stage-coach for the first time in their lives. Eléonore was loud in her complaints about the hateful lack of privacy, but Boufflers thought the incident charming, and laughed at his wife.

When mother and daughter were together again at the château, Eléonore unpacked the purchases she was always asked to make for her daughter in Paris,—the little painted watering-can, the snuffers, the "face-cream of Madame Buonaparte" (of that unfortunate Joséphine who was now divorced). One day Eléonore brought a hat which delighted Delphine—"Little mother, your hat is charming, and suits me perfectly, you do my errands beautifully; you will tell me what I owe you, twelve *livres* isn't it?" But after the first bubbling up of excitement, Eléonore always felt the same pang of grief to see Delphine sitting very quietly for a long time, as if she were suffering in secret. She had the look of a woman waiting, waiting for someone who never came. How well Eléonore had known, long ago, the same weariness of long suspense. Did she begin to regret that during Delphine's girlhood she herself had lived only for love? She had unwittingly created that atmosphere of torment and instability which accompanies illicit passion. How many hours had she spent writing to the Chevalier and pining for him, hours she should have devoted entirely to her children? How much poisonous mistrust of their mother had the Abbé Bernard instilled into them before he was finally sent to the Bastille?

Elzéar, no less than his sister, was a cause of anxiety to her. He fell in love with Madame de Staël, so greatly disliked by Napoleon, and therefore he came to be looked on with suspicion by government officials. He used to go and stay with her and Madame Récamier in the country, and act in amateur theatricals with them. The correspondence with the charmer was intercepted, and one day in 1813 this delicate, highly-strung young man found himself in Vincennes prison, by order of the Emperor.

Eléonore was in despair. She appealed to *Petit Père*—as they called the Chevalier,—to use his influence and do all he could to get him released. This he eventually did. He looked upon Elzéar as his own son. The Chevalier, then aged seventy-seven, hurried off into the country in mid-winter to thank his benefactor. The effort following on a period of strain and anxiety, had been too much for him. When he returned to the Paris house he complained for the first time in his life of being very, very tired. In April of the following year, Napoleon was exiled for the first time. Boufflers saw the first Restoration of the Monarchy. In June of that year, Louis XVIII made the Chevalier the second administrator of the Mazarine Library. But it was too late. By then, Boufflers was a broken, wrinkled old man, scarcely able to walk, and who was fast losing his memory.

January 17th, 1815, the day before Boufflers' death, Elzéar had been reading the Latin poets aloud to him. At the line,

"My friends, just think I'm asleep!"

he looked at his stepfather, and his eyes filled with tears of remorse and misery. The Chevalier stretched out his hand and comforted him. Then he said: "That is how you must think of me." Elzéar went out of the room, and Eléonore, white-haired and very frail, came over slowly to the great bed, leaning on her stick. She was sixty-six, and her feet, which had danced so lightly with peasants on country estates and in the ballrooms of Versailles, were now completely crippled.

The Chevalier's lined face lit up with joy when he saw her, and he held out both hands to embrace her. He was still her lover, after all those years. They were so spiritually at one, that they could feel no grief: there would be no real parting. She caressed the face of her Chevalier who had mocked at fidelity all through his youth, and then spent the rest of his days in faithfulness to her. So much did he belie his past theories that a friend had called him: "Boufflers, tender and faithful husband." She whispered to him: "Yes, it has been worth while, all the sufferings I have endured for you. If I had to live my life again I would change nothing. I would prefer all the torments inflicted by you, than peace with any other, mad, mad woman that I am."

She bent to kiss his head as it rested so wearily on her breast. She recalled his words of exultation to her, that Autumn night at Anizy: "Let us love life and not fear death, for souls do not die, but live eternally!"

The night was spent in complete trust and union, watching in a chair by his side. At four o'clock the next morning, Stanislas fulfilled the dearest wish of his heart, and died in the arms of his wife. By her alone, he had "laid hold on perfection", and in her arms he went to meet immortality. If God, like Napoleon, welcomes wits to His Heavenly Court, He surely had mercy on the sins of the Chevalier de Boufflers, and admitted him to the society of His spiritual aristocrats, the constellations of the gay, the dashing, the heroic, the songsters, the generous, those who love their fellow-men and try to make them happier. And after a first flicker of surprise, Boufflers would not have been so ill at ease: a courtier of the *Ancien Régime* would feel at home anywhere, even if the Superior of Saint-Sulpice, Monsieur Couthurier, were in the vicinity and exclaiming at this unexpected appearance of his ex-seminarist!

His body was buried in Père Lachaise, in that vast cemetery which shelters the grave of Héloïse and Abélard. He was placed next to his old friend, the Abbé Delille, who had written on Trianon as the garden of love. Eléonore had these words engraved on his tomb:

"Mes amis, croyez que je dors."
("My friends, just think I'm asleep.")

1815. Five months later came Waterloo. The Allies marched up the Champs-Elysées. The *fleur-de-lys* replaced the emblems of the imperial bee on all the signs and palace decorations.

Eléonore lived on for twelve years after Boufflers' death. She came from a generation of women who knew how to welcome old age as a friend. She does not give the impression of a tragic figure. The Prince de Ligne has put all the secret of a fading woman's charm into one line:

"Love has passed that way."

The de Goncourts say: "The old woman emerges from the memoirs of the times, gently she rises from the mists of history, like the faded flower of some old pastel figure of kindness and shrewdness, smiling at the shadow of the years."

Eléonore de Boufflers had a kind of happy grace as she journeyed towards the grave, upheld by good sense and philosophy, by "*bon ton*" rather than by any religious fervour, proving, like so many women of the eighteenth century, that there is a subtle affinity between elegance of manners and nobility of soul.

So here she was, an old lady alone with her memories, sometimes touching the packets of his letters which she already knew by heart. Alone, a widow, crippled, her sight failing, her world gone, all her wealth vanished, most of her friends dead and her children causing her nothing but sorrow. Did she feel pity for herself? Madame Vigée Lebrun gives the answer. She says that Elzéar's arm "was, so to speak, fastened to his mother's, and one could re lly envy the lot of Monsieur de Sabran, for, in spite of her sufferings and her age, Madame de Boufflers was always kind, always agreeable, and preserved that charm which pleased and attracted every one. I remember once that at the end of her life, Fortense, the celebrated oculist, operated on her for cataract, and she was obliged to remain in the dark. One evening I went to see her; I found her alone without a light. I meant to stay only a moment, but the never-failing charm of her conversation, which was so piquante, so full of anecdotes that no one else could tell as she could, kept me with her for three hours. I thought, as I listened to her, undisturbed by any outside objects, that she was reading in herself, if I may so put it, and it was this magic-lantern of things and ideas that she sketched so skilfully which held my attention. I left her with much regret, for never had I found her so charming. . . ."

Two more great blows came before the end. Astolphe, her grandson, whom she had held at the baptismal font, had now grown into a dissolute young man. No doubt he lacked a father's control, and was suffering from the instability of his early childhood. In 1826 Delphine dragged herself wearily to Switzerland and died there, blighted by her passion for Chateaubriand. He mentions her laconically in his memoirs. Thus perished Eléonore's rose-tree, her rose, her glory, the baby she had welcomed so rapturously, crying out, "Thou, at least, shall know a mother's love". How she had changed, this beautiful child who acted before Queen Marie-Antoinette, the girl who had rested in her arms before her wedding day, trembling with fear, the young woman whose children were born "into her apron".

Rose tree, tend your leaves,
Forever be beautiful, forever be fresh,
So that after the storm
Your flowers may cheer my winter.

And now, without Delphine's white and gold radiance it was winter indeed. The last cord of resilience was snapped. The next year, on February 27th, 1827, when she was nearly seventy-eight years of age, Eléonore de Boufflers died. In the manner of a bygone century she had composed her own epitaph; in the French it has all the crystal precision of classical antiquity:

At last I have reached the haven
So greatly longed for.
I needed death
To rest me from life.

Boufflers had once written to her from Senegal, when he was hoping to return to her again quite soon:

"With what joy and eagerness I shall prepare for the journey! With what impatience I shall cross the seas. Once on land how I shall fly to you."

And then again:

"It is midnight, and I am going to bed, to try and sleep. Perhaps my spirit then will cross the seas and come without a word to your blue bed."

In speaking of life after death, he had written to her:

". . . Perhaps I shall be a plant and you my flower, then I shall arm myself with thorns to defend you, and shade you with my leaves to protect you; so, under whatever form you exist, you will be loved."

His love, so passionate and so tender, the love of this Chevalier who had been the charm and torment of her life, would reach out beyond the dark threshold of the grave and draw her into a glittering Eternity.

FINIS